FRESH WATER

THE ESSENCE OF LIFE

Published in China on PEFC certified paper
by Earth in Focus Editions—a division of iLCP
Printed in China through globalinkprinting.com
2011 Crystal Drive, Suite 500
Arlington VA, 22202
www.ilcp.com

Fresh Water The Essence of Life
By Russell A. Mittermeier, Tracy Farrell, Ian J. Harrison, Amy J. Upgren,
Thomas Brooks

ISBN: 978-0-9841686-2-0

10 9 8 7 6 5 4 3 2 1

Production Direction: Abbie Williams
Design: Stefan Gutermuth
Text copyright © CEMEX, 2010 / iLCP

Cover images: © 2010
Background photograph: Claudio Contreras Koob, iLCP
Top Row Left to Right: Frans Lanting, iLCP; Frans Lanting, iLCP;
Paul Nicklen/NGS Image Collection
Bottom Row Left to Right: Karen Kasmauski, National Geographic
Society; Frans Lanting, iLCP; Garth Lenz, iLCP

Opposite Page: Four Kayapo girls running across the Rio Riozinho, a tributary of the mighty Rio Xingú.
—Cristina G. Mittermeier

Following spread: Great egret (*Ardea alba*), Yucatan, Mexico—Claudio Contreras-Koob

FRESH WATER

THE ESSENCE OF LIFE

Series Editor: Cristina Goettsch Mittermeier

Russell A. Mittermeier, Tracy A. Farrell, Ian J. Harrison, Amy J. Upgren, Thomas M. Brooks

Foreword by Luc Hoffmann

CEMEX CONSERVATION BOOK SERIES

CONTENTS

IN GRATITUDE TO ARMANDO J. GARCIA SEGOVIA

It is truly a pleasure and an honor for me to write this tribute to my very good friend Armando J. Garcia, who retired this year as CEMEX Executive Vice President of Technology, Energy, and Sustainability. CEMEX's wonderful series of conservation books—of which *Fresh Water* is number 18—would not have been possible without Armando's leadership and constant support. His enduring vision was that these books would demonstrate to the world the CEMEX commitment to sustainability and biodiversity conservation.

On behalf of all those who have had the special opportunity to join Armando on his conservation journey, I want to express our sincere gratitude and respect for all he has done. Armando, as you have said so often, "we can only take care of those things we know." Thanks to you, we have been able to learn so much and to spread the word around the world. You are a true leader, a tireless champion for nature, and above all, a wonderful, loyal friend. We all wish you the best in your continuing journey.

Russell A. Mittermeier, Ph.D.
President, Conservation International
Vice President, International Union for Conservation of Nature (IUCN)

TOC: Great egret (*Ardea alba*), Yucatan, Mexico-Claudio Contreras—Koob
Opposite: A Maroon boy plays in the Coppename River. The waters of this river are born in the Wilhelmina Mountains and flow through pristine rain forest all the way into the Atlantic. Village of Asindohopo, Suriname. —Cristina G. Mittermeier

Colombia

Stream located at Chingaza National Natural Park, in Colombia. This protected area is a key freshwater ecosystem that provides 80% of the purified water that Bogotá consumes. CEMEX is proud to contribute with 2,400 hectares adjacent to this important natural park of the Colombian Protected Areas System. The area donated is part of a restored quarry and includes native forest and micro river basins that add to the Chingaza hydric system.

A LETTER FROM CEMEX

PICTURE EARTH WITHOUT WATER—would any living organisms exist? Water is essential for the delicate chemistry that makes life possible. With two-thirds of our planet's surface covered by water and the human body consisting of about 65% water, this liquid is clearly one of the key elements responsible for life on Earth. Water literally is what the subtitle of this book implies: the essence of life. It circulates through our planet just as it does through our body: transporting, dissolving, and replenishing nutrients and organic matter while carrying away waste material. Human subsistence directly depends on fresh water yet it comprises only 2.5% of the total water on Earth—and of that small proportion, only 0.3% is easily accessible in rivers, lakes, and swamps.

Fresh water is a renewable resource, yet the world's supply of clean fresh water is steadily decreasing. Freshwater ecosystems—including rivers, streams, and lakes—deliver a wide range of services for human well-being, including food and fiber, water supply, water purification and detoxification of wastes, and climate and flood regulation. An exemplary ecosystem providing these services is the Chingaza National Natural Park. This protected area provides 80% of the purified water that Bogotá, Colombia's largest city, consumes. Located on the oriental cordillera of the Tropical Andes, a hotspot recognized by Conservation International, the wetlands of Chingaza are part of the most important center of biological diversity in northern South America. Recognizing this area's importance, CEMEX is proud to have donated 2,400 hectares of land adjacent to the Natural Park to the Colombian Ministry of Environment, Household and Territorial Development. The donated area consists of native forest and micro river basins, adding to the Chingaza hydric system.

At CEMEX, we recognize that protecting healthy ecosystems ensures their continuing ability to provide essential services for human well-being and sustainable development. Water is integral to our operations. We constantly work to optimize our water consumption and to preserve the quality of water resources in the communities in which we operate. Together with scientific and NGO partners, we have designed the first phase of a global water assessment project that will establish a baseline of our global water use, impacts and develop management standards and operating guidelines for our business units. We are also involved in the WBCSD Water Working Group, which shares best practices across sectors and helps integrate water issues in strategic business planning. Our ultimate goal is to ensure that our freshwater ecosystems are protected, and that they deliver the services required for a sustainable planet.

CEMEX is honored to collaborate with such highly respected organizations and experts as Conservation International, Nature Serve, Wetlands International, and Ramsar to produce the eighteenth edition of the CEMEX Conservation Book Series, *Fresh Water: The Essence of Life*. The book highlights the growing global freshwater crisis and the freshwater biodiversity and ecosystems that are in peril, and offers solutions and actions to be implemented now and in the future.

The CEMEX Conservation Book Series is a key part of our commitment to inspire and raise awareness for the conservation of our planet's biodiversity. For almost two decades, we have teamed with leading conservation NGOs to publish this series. We express our sincere appreciation to all of the participants, and a special thanks to our publishing partner, the International League of Conservation Photographers, who continue to do a superb job.

At CEMEX, we know that natural ecosystems perform fundamental life-support services on which all civilization depends. Unless carefully planned and managed, human activities will continue to impair or even destroy valuable ecosystems. We hope that this book will inspire each of us to live in a way that ensures the continuity of vital ecosystem services for generations to come.

PREAMBLE

I have had the unique experience of floating in a pristine river from which you can confidently drink the water, knowing that you will not get ill; one that still has its full complement of plants and animals, and whose water is clear, free of chemical pollutants and human waste. In other words, a healthy freshwater ecosystem.

This is becoming a rare experience on this planet.

My fortunate experience was on the Riozinho, a tributary of the mighty Xingú River, which in turn feeds into the Amazon somewhere in the interior of Brazil, hundreds of miles before the flow reaches the Atlantic Ocean. There is something exhilarating and primeval about knowing that there are no human settlements for hundreds or even thousands of kilometers upriver from where you are—and that, therefore, the water is free of humanborne diseases, pesticides, and industrial waste. More and more, the rivers, creeks, lakes, and other bodies of fresh water around the planet are becoming more polluted, more crowded by human settlement, more eroded, silted, diverted, desiccated. We are increasingly destroying the most important life-giving resource on our planet.

I hope that this book illuminates the imperative for a larger vision to better develop, use, and protect our last precious pristine fresh waters. The text provides valuable scientific arguments and tools for governments, decision makers—and anyone who might be in need of a drink of water in the near future. The photographs stunningly illustrate the thousand ways in which fresh water touches, shapes, transforms, and ultimately supports all life on Earth.

As I floated down the Riozinho, swimming and drinking at the same time, I marveled at the fact that not so long ago it was possible to do this in many places around the world. Much has changed forever at the hands of humans and economic development, but there is still a chance to protect what's left. This book provides a blueprint for how to go about it.

Cristina G. Mittermeier
President
International League of Conservation Photographers

Opposite: Forest in monsoon-season flood at Wangi Falls, Litchfield National Park, Northern Territory, Australia. —Theo Allofs

11

FOREWORD

It is trivial to emphasize the paramount importance of water for any form of life. And for life outside the oceans, water means *fresh water.* Yet fresh water makes up only 2.5% of all water on Earth. It is therefore a critical resource. If that is so, one would think that a wealth of knowledge has been accumulated and that there should be no need for publishing a book like this.

The reality is different. The interactions of water with the living world are very complicated and vary to a great extent according to a multiplicity of factors, such as soil, declivity (downward slope), and climate—to name just a few. These interactions may be either apparent, or hidden under the surface. This means that the characteristics of many flows have been discovered very late; many within the last fifty years.

Not only is our knowledge of fresh water still poor, but we also have many problems sharing this scarce resource. This is particularly true in arid and semi-arid countries, but even in many areas with more abundant rainfall, legal and illegal extraction may seriously deplete resources. When estimating water needs, we must not only think of direct human uses (drinking, irrigation, industrial use such as manufacturing, etc.) but also of the needs for wildlife and wild vegetation, as well as for ecological services such as natural filtration and toxin removal, and influence on climate. Water sharing is difficult enough within individual communities and countries, but it becomes even more complicated *between* countries, where it sometimes results in war.

Of particular importance—and vulnerability—are wetlands, particularly the transitional zones between permanently wet and generally dry environments. They carry a large part of the planet's fresh water, but have long been neglected, considered marginal parts of the biosphere and barriers to development. Yet they offer important services such as water storage, regulation of flooding and sedimentation, and elimination of toxic materials, among many examples. In spite of their importance, wetlands have been drained over very large areas, mainly during the twentieth century, with the result that large parts of the terrestrial world are today under water stress and in poor balance with their water resources. They have lost the ecological services they need from these wetlands to reach full productivity and maintain biodiversity.

Sharing of water resources is one of the major challenges of our generation if we want to develop in harmony with the planet. It concerns all countries and needs the cooperation of all. Transboundary agreements on water between neighboring countries are rare. Indeed, no global treaty on fresh water existed until 1962, when the International Union for Conservation of Nature (IUCN) and other non-governmental organizations asked me, as director of the International Waterfowl Research Bureau (IWRB; now Wetlands International), to prepare an international program for the conservation of wetlands. Once again, attention was focused on the formerly disregarded wetlands. The proposal was accepted by a number of government delegations, and IWRB was charged with the elaboration of the text, assisted by the Dutch government. After many meetings and consultations, the governments of the then–Soviet Union and Iran agreed with the Netherlands on a text, which was submitted for signature in Ramsar (Iran) in 1971. One of the difficulties in reaching agreement was that some of the delegations insisted that the full name of the wetlands convention should be "Convention on Wetlands of International Importance especially as Waterfowl Habitat," whereas the majority did not want the reference to waterfowl habitat. Certainly some of the delegations thought that it would be too burdensome to make commitments of such general importance. In the end, the reference to waterfowl was included in the title, but in practice it was never respected.

Today, 160 countries are members of the convention, which convenes a Conference of the Partners (COP) every three years.

This book provides a wide perspective on the critical role of fresh water on the planet and illustrates its many forms and benefits. It is a very welcome document; let us hope it increases awareness and mobilizes the world to action.

Dr. Luc Hoffmann
Vice President Emeritus
WWF International

INTRODUCTION
FRESH WATER THE ESSENCE OF LIFE

Russel A. Mittermeier, Thomas M. Brooks, Tracy A. Farrell, Amy J. Upgren, Ian J. Harrison, Topiltzin Contreras-MacBeath, Richard Sneider, Fabian Oberfeld, Andrew A. Rosenberg, Fredrick Boltz, Claude Gascon, Olivier Langrand

Imagine that Earth is a classroom globe about 30 centimeters (cm) across and just about half a millimeter (mm) thick. That half-mm is the space on Earth within which life lives—the biosphere. From space, our biosphere is blue. Almost 71% of the surface area of Earth is covered by water; about 15% of the biosphere. Fresh water passes through the biophysical environment (atmospheric, marine, terrestrial, surface, and subterranean) as a vapor, liquid, and solid. Groundwater recharge happens aboveground but flows underground, water evaporates from soils into the atmosphere and then falls again as precipitation, and transpiration from plants returns water to the atmosphere as well. Therefore, when discussing strictly fresh water, one must remember that it is a component of this much larger hydrological cycle—which is also connected to the carbon and nitrogen cycles, stimulating plant growth as part of terrestrial and freshwater ecosystems. Fresh water is the ultimate connector, from mountaintops to coral reefs. But freshwater systems must be managed and utilized differently from terrestrial and marine systems, partly because the diversity of species in freshwater systems is quite different.

If we compare the volumes of water in the biosphere, we see that nearly all of it (97.5%) is saline—having salt concentrations of more than 0.5 grams per liter. The remaining 2.5% is "fresh water." Water locked up in glaciers and permanent snow comprises 68.7% of the fresh water on Earth. Another 30.1% is found deep underground, and a small percentage (0.86%) is frozen as ground ice and permafrost. This leaves just under 0.3% of fresh water, or 0.0075% of all water (fresh and salt). This final small percentage of fresh water covers about 0.8% of the total surface of Earth (i.e., only a little more than 4 million kilometers [km]^2), or just under 3% of the terrestrial surface area on the planet. This is equivalent to less than one drop of water spread across our 30-cm classroom globe.

What is more, around 98% of that surface fresh water is found in lakes and swamps and other wetlands, with only a tiny fraction flowing in rivers and streams. In fact, of all the fresh water on the planet, a mere 0.26% is in lakes, 0.03% is in swamps and wetlands, and 0.006% is in rivers and streams.

And yet, this minuscule fraction of a fraction teems with life. The fresh water on Earth is manifested through a tremendous diversity of habitats and supports a third of all vertebrate species—maybe 19,000 species in total—that live in it for some or all of their lifecycles (Baillie et al., 2004; and see chapter 1). Fresh water also hosts high proportions of many plant and invertebrate species, including such well-known examples as dragonflies, mayflies, mollusks, crabs, and crayfish. These are the tip of the iceberg; much of aquatic life remains below the water surface. Our knowledge of freshwater biodiversity and our understanding of the importance of the ecological processes occurring in freshwater ecosystems are shockingly scanty; they have been referred to as

Opposite: European white water lily (*Nymphaea alba*) in a lake in Bohuslän, Sweden. —Magnus Lundgren, Wild Wonders of Europe

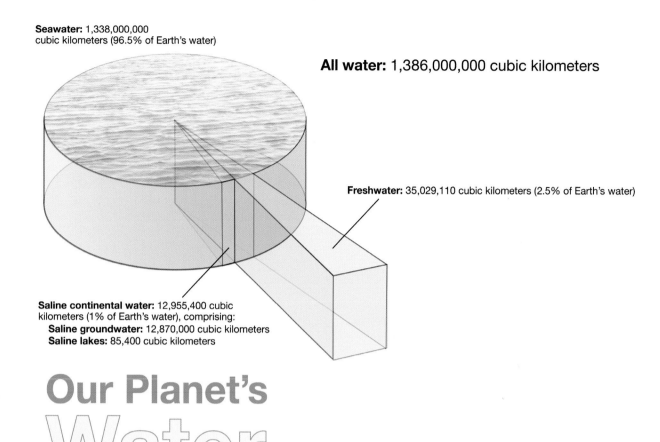

Seawater: 1,338,000,000 cubic kilometers (96.5% of Earth's water)

All water: 1,386,000,000 cubic kilometers

Freshwater: 35,029,110 cubic kilometers (2.5% of Earth's water)

Saline continental water: 12,955,400 cubic kilometers (1% of Earth's water), comprising:
    Saline groundwater: 12,870,000 cubic kilometers
    Saline lakes: 85,400 cubic kilometers

Our Planet's Water

"water blindness" (Falkenmark, 2003). What we *can* say, however, is that, broadly defined, all nonmarine species are dependent on this fraction of a drop of fresh water on the surface of our classroom globe for their survival—maybe two-thirds of all life on Earth.

Every person on the planet depends on fresh water. Approximately 65% of our bodies are made of it. Humanity uses about 28 kilometers (km)³ of water every day. But we are not managing our fresh waters wisely, or the species that live within them. We harvest freshwater species, especially for food, to the point of extinction. We move species around, often introducing large predators, noxious weeds, and pathogens into new places where they cause havoc. We use the world's waters as our waste-disposal system, choking them with sediment and chemical excess. We fight

gravity with engineering, building dams and canals and draining wetlands for power, transport, and water for consumption. Most dramatically, we appropriate vast quantities of water for agriculture and for uses in our homes and industries—an estimated 10,400 km³ per year, or approximately 10% of the surface fresh water on Earth. This intensive water use impacts access and availability of clean water, which has grave consequences for people and for nature. At least 1.1 billion people lack access to secure sources of clean water, another 2.4 billion lack adequate sanitation, and half of our world's wetlands have been degraded and lost over the past century (WHO, 2004; MEA, 2005).

The British ecologist Norman Myers developed the concept of "biodiversity hotspots" in 1988, pinpointing places with exceptional concentrations of life that face exceptional levels of threat, and arguing that with-

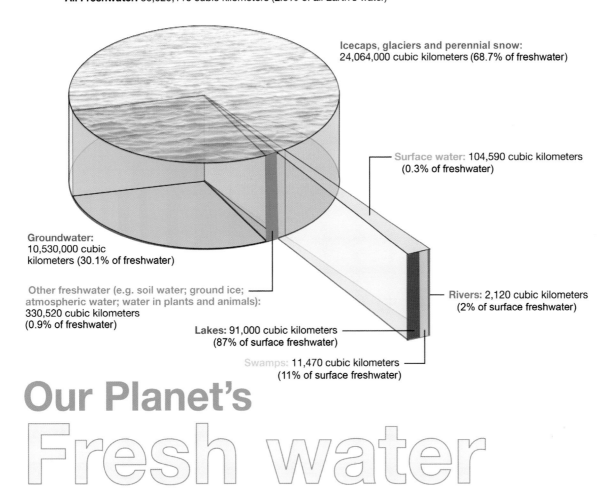

All Freshwater: 35,029,110 cubic kilometers (2.5% of all Earth's water)

Icecaps, glaciers and perennial snow:
24,064,000 cubic kilometers (68.7% of freshwater)

Surface water: 104,590 cubic kilometers
(0.3% of freshwater)

Groundwater:
10,530,000 cubic
kilometers (30.1% of freshwater)

Rivers: 2,120 cubic kilometers
(2% of surface freshwater)

Other freshwater (e.g. soil water; ground ice;
atmospheric water; water in plants and animals):
330,520 cubic kilometers
(0.9% of freshwater)

Lakes: 91,000 cubic kilometers
(87% of surface freshwater)

Swamps: 11,470 cubic kilometers
(11% of surface freshwater)

Our Planet's
Fresh water

out urgent conservation action, biodiversity will be lost (Myers, 1988; Myers et al., 2000). His concept has steered billions of dollars of conservation funding toward such regions over the last two decades (Brooks et al., 2006). We have reported on these at length in earlier volumes published by CEMEX (Mittermeier et al., 1999, 2004). This book presents the case that freshwater ecosystems are the ultimate biodiversity hotspot. Even if we grouped the entire freshwater ecosystems of the world into one hotspot, its surface area (just over 4 million km²) would be only about 17% of the combined surface area of the thirty-four currently recognized biodiversity hotspots (Mittermeier et al., 2004). The Indo-Burma biodiversity hotspot, *just one* (albeit the largest) of the biodiversity hotspots, is equivalent to more than half (58%) of the surface area of Earth's freshwater ecosystems. Nevertheless, those freshwater ecosystems contain a greater con-

centration of life than anywhere else, and are seriously imperiled. Moreover, they provide the most essential ecosystem service for all life. Action is desperately needed to protect aquatic biodiversity and freshwater ecosystems—our own life-support system.

The aim of this book is to highlight the urgency of freshwater biodiversity and ecosystem conservation, and to recommend actions capable of reversing current trends of degradation and loss. If we are to be successful, we must undergo a massive societal redefinition of our relationship to this tiny water droplet available to us, one based on ensuring that the needs of nature are met first, then sustainably and equitably managing the remainder for all humanity. Without such a societal awakening, much of the teeming life of fresh water will be lost—to the detriment of our environments, our livelihoods, and ultimately, our lives.

Following Spread: Glacier-fed stream in Kings Bay, Prince William Sound, Chugach National Forest, Alaska, USA. —Carr Clifton

FRESHWATER BIODIVERSITY

The first chapter introduces the realm of life that lives in fresh water. Some 126,000 species rely on freshwater ecosystems for a part of their life cycle beyond the simple need for water itself (Balian et al., 2008a,b). There are undoubtedly many additional species that have not yet been discovered or scientifically described because there have been so few comprehensive studies of freshwater biodiversity. Most of our knowledge concerns easily observable, abundant, and in some cases iconic species.

Among vertebrates, waterbirds such as ducks, geese, swans, storks, herons, egrets, and kingfishers fall into this category. There are few freshwater mammal species (about 145 species in total), but a wealth of knowledge exists for the more charismatic of these, including otters, beavers, hippos, and platypus. A

Endangered (International Union for Conservation of Nature [IUCN], 2010).

Fishes are the most characteristic vertebrates of freshwater environments. Almost 13,000—about 45% of all known fish species—are wholly restricted to fresh water (Lévêque et al., 2008). Others are dependent upon both fresh water and the oceans. Anadromous salmon, herrings, and other groups breed in fresh water but return to the sea, and catadromous eels breed in the sea but return to the river. Species that live only in fresh water tend to be found almost anywhere where fresh water is present, even at high altitudes and in deserts. For example, the Devil's Hole pupfish, *Cyprinodon diabolis,* lives in Death Valley, Nevada, in the United States. As another example, small nemachiline loaches in Tibet exist at more than 5,000 meters (m) above sea level (Kottelat and Chu, 1988). In fact, freshwater fishes are found

This book presents the case that freshwater ecosystems are the ultimate biodiversity hotspot. They contain a greater concentration of life than anywhere else and are seriously imperiled.

handful of freshwater dolphins found in a few rivers of Asia and South America have also attracted a great deal of human interest. (In one of several Amazonian myths, for example, the enigmatic pink river dolphin in South America, *Inia geoffrensis,* is believed to change into a handsome man at night.) Another freshwater dolphin, the *baiji,* or Yangtze river dolphin, *Lipotes vexillifer,* may have become extinct in the last decade. Two ancient reptile lineages are predominantly aquatic: the twenty-three known species of crocodiles and 268 species of freshwater turtles. By contrast, amphibians *specialize* in fresh water, with an estimated 4,245 species of frogs, toads, and salamanders living underwater for portions of their life cycles. These also include some remarkable species, such as the more than one-meter-long Chinese giant salamander, *Andrias davidianus,* which is Critically

everywhere but Antarctica: in the middle of very hot deserts, on remote oceanic islands, and on top of the highest snow-covered peaks.

Freshwater fishes are remarkable for their diversity, not just in numbers but in their evolutionary and ecological strategies, which occur over thousands and even millions of years. There are six known species of lungfishes, descendents of a group that first appeared up to 410 million years ago. By contrast, the 500 or more fishes found in eastern Africa's Lake Victoria have evolved more recently, within the last 100,000 to 400,000 years; some have even evolved within the last 14,600 years (Witte et al., 2008). These waters host hundreds of species of cichlid fishes, including species that eat other fish species, fish scales, snails, or invertebrates, and species that brood their young in their own mouths. Freshwater fishes also include a mixture of sizes, including many remarkably tiny species (Miller, 1979, 1996). The smallest known vertebrate is an Indonesian cyprinid, *Paedocypris progenetica,* with mature females only 7.9 mm in length (Kottlelat et al., 2006). Conversely, "megafishes" such as the freshwater whipray from Southeast Asia, *Himantura chaophraya,* can reach 4 m long, be more than 2 m wide, and weigh 600 kilograms (kg) (Lundberg et al., 2000).

Although we pay much more attention to vertebrate species, about 60% of the documented freshwater species are insects, about half of which are dipterans (flies, mosquitoes, and midges). Crustaceans are also relatively rich freshwater species, and may form an important part of subterranean systems—especially copepods, isopods, and amphipods. It is likely that the diversity of species in subterranean systems is much greater than currently documented. These and other unique ecosystems, and the highly specialized and range-restricted species they support, are discussed by Stiassny et al. in this book.

Diversity differs depending on geography. Many freshwater invertebrate groups, especially insects, crustaceans, and mollusks, are richest in species in the Palearctic Region of Europe, Russia, and parts of central Asia and North Africa. Vertebrate species are richer in the tropical regions of Asia, Africa, and especially in South America. The neotropics of Central and South America contain one-third of all freshwater vertebrate species, mainly due to the huge diversity of fishes found in the extensive and diverse river and wetland systems in this region. Of the places on Earth with high numbers of endemic animal species—species found in these regions and nowhere else—small streams, pools, and wetlands are well represented. There are also many large, often ancient lakes that are rich in endemic species. Madagascar, which has been geographically isolated from other landmasses for the last ninety million years (Wells, 2003), is especially rich in endemic species.

There is less information available for Earth's aquatic plants than for its animals. More than 2,000 species of freshwater plants have been documented, mostly those that are widespread. This is certainly an underestimate of the actual number. Aquatic plants are very important components of freshwater ecosystems, shaping water movement and providing food and other services for many organisms. Similarly, there is very little information on species diversity and distribution of microorganisms such as viruses, bacteria, protozoans, algae, and fungi, despite the fact that they are critical components of freshwater communities.

FRESHWATER ECOSYSTEMS

The species present in freshwater ecosystems depend upon the diversity, distribution, and ecological connections between the various types of freshwater ecosystems—including lakes, rivers, wetlands, and below-ground water flows— as well as on connections with terrestrial and marine ecosystems. These freshwater regions support diverse habitats and complex systems, shaped by topography, geology, and climate. A global database and map of "freshwater ecoregions" was created to describe freshwater regions of the world based on ecological characteristics (Abell et al., 2008). Chapter two (Stiassny et al.) reviews the main types of freshwater ecosystems, discussing their physical, chemical, and biological features. The authors also explain how the diversity of ecosystems and their associated habitat types allow fresh water to support a large number of species, and how high endemism is due to differences between ecosystems and their geographic or historical isolation.

The terminology and definition of freshwater ecosystems varies. The Convention on Wetlands of International Importance, or Ramsar Convention, defines "wetlands" to include rivers, lakes, pools, swamps, and bogs, as well as marine waters out to 6 m below the low tide level of the sea. Some freshwater definitions also capture fresh waters that extend out to sea. The Amazon, which has the largest average freshwater

Following Spread: Pink Amazon river dolphin (*Inia geoffrensis*) underwater, Rio Negro, Amazon, Brazil. —Kevin Schafer

discharge of any river in the world, has a freshwater plume that extends more than 300 km into the Atlantic Ocean.

Reference to *inland waters* may also include water that is brackish or even more concentrated in salts, such as the very salty Great Salt Lake in Utah, in the United States. The high salinity of this lake (up to 270 grams per liter of salt, compared to 30 to 50 grams per liter in seawater) prevents most species from living in the water itself, even though its surrounding wetlands support many waterbirds. Mono Lake in eastern California is another salty inland lake (with

length, area of the drainage basin, number of tributaries, or size of water or sediment discharge. The Nile and the Amazon are the longest rivers in the world, and the Amazon drains the largest area, 6,145,186 km^2 (Revenga and Kura, 2003). Another key variable is seasonality and regularity; some rivers only run at particular times, while others are effectively permanent. The dynamic integration of the quantity, quality, and timing of water flows are among the most important factors that determine the function of freshwater ecosystems, and hence the kinds of resources they provide to humanity. There has been much recent work in measuring and modeling the environmen-

Some of the most dramatic extinctions have hit North American freshwater mollusks, with up to 37 species of mussels extinct or possibly extinct.

about 80 grams per liter of salt); it similarly supports large numbers of migrating waterbirds, but also its own species of brine shrimp, *Artemia monica,* found in very large numbers in the lake but nowhere else in the world.

Freshwater ecosystems fall into four classes: flowing watercourses (rivers, streams, creeks); standing or slow-moving water (lakes, ponds, pools); wetlands (including peatlands, swamps, and marshes); and subterranean groundwater systems. All of these systems are highly dynamic, evolving with Earth just as the species that live with them have. Rivers flood to form lakes and pools that may fill with sediment to form wetlands. Water flows drain from the surface into groundwater, and groundwater emerges from the earth as springs or forms underground rivers that return to the surface through geological faults and erosion. There is considerable value in classifying these systems, for conservation and for landscape management. The simplest systems to classify and analyze are watercourses. For these, the basic parameter is size, usually described in terms of river

tal flows, or "eFlows," that are necessary to sustain ecosystem function (Forslund et al., 2009; Poff et al., 2009). The application of this work to water resource management will be an essential part of ensuring that human needs for fresh water can be met while sustaining the integrity of the ecosystems that moderate these flows and are equally dependent upon them.

For lakes and ponds, the primary variables are once again size (particularly depth and area) and seasonality. The largest lake in terms of surface area is Lake Superior (82,414 km^2) in North America, although Russia's Lake Baikal is deeper (1,637 m) and has greater volume (23,600 km^3). Water chemistry is also important, particularly for brackish or saline continental lakes such as the soda lakes in the Kenyan and Tanzanian Rift Valley, and the Makgadikgadi Pan in Botswana. The age of a lake can also tell us a great deal about the evolution of the species present. Older lakes often support greater numbers of endemic species. Lake Baikal is Earth's oldest and deepest lake, with many endemic species ranging from freshwater sponges to a subspecies of seal.

Wetlands are the most varied freshwater ecosystem type and the hardest to define. They include all types of bogs, marshes, swamps, fens, and peatlands, which vary in size, seasonality, and extent and timing of dryland emergence. The Pantanal in Brazil is the world's largest wetland (210,000 km2) (Mittermeier et al., 2005). Riparian zone vegetation, at the edges of rivers and lakes and seasonally inundated forests, are also considered important wetland systems. They link terrestrial and aquatic systems, support many different species, and provide diverse ecological functions. Geothermal wetlands such as those found in Yellowstone National Park in the United States, are a particularly unusual subset of wetlands, supporting highly specialized species uniquely capable of living in these harsh habitats.

Groundwater ecosystems comprise water reserves within the soil and between subterranean rock layers. They also contain underground pools and rivers eroded by underground water-forming soluble karst landscapes such as those found in Mexico's Yucatán Peninsula. Groundwater systems are the least accessible and understood freshwater ecosystems. What we do know is that groundwaters are home to species highly specialized to this environment, found only below ground with very restricted distributions. We also know that groundwater is an important resource that is increasingly expropriated by humans to meet their water needs, threatening unique assemblages of species before they have even been discovered, as well as the ecological functions provided by these systems.

THREATENED FRESHWATER BIODIVERSITY

The characteristics of many of the freshwater ecosystems of the world, described by Stiassny et al. in this book, place them under threat; Thieme et al. review these threats in more detail in chapter 3. The imperiled status of freshwater species sounds a loud warning bell, even though global statistics on change in the extent and flow of freshwater ecosystems are almost nonexistent (Darwall et al., 2009; IUCN, 2010). The Living Planet Index (Hails, 2008) showed that populations of 458 freshwater animal species declined by an average of 35% between 1970 and 2005, compared to an average 33% decline in 887 terrestrial species and a 14% decline in 341 marine species. These are most likely underestimates, considering the lack of comprehensive large-scale inventories of the most species-rich regions and the lack of taxonomic expertise for many invertebrate groups (Chung Kim and Byrne, 2006). The four most threatened groups of species in North America are mussels, crayfish, freshwater fishes, and amphibians—all freshwater species. Globally, a total of 54 of 126 (43%) non–Data Deficient (IUCN, 2010) freshwater mammals; 202 of 1,970 (10%) birds; 102 of 158 (65%) turtles; and 1,109 of 3,265 (34%) amphibians are threatened. The equivalent figures for freshwater crabs are 209 of 652 species, or 32% (Cumberlidge et al., 2009).

In too many cases, freshwater species have already been lost forever. Three grebe species have vanished: the Atitlan grebe (*Podilymbus gigas*) from Lago Atitlan, Guatemala (Hunter, 1988); the Colombian grebe (*Podiceps andinus*) from wetlands around Lago Tota in Colombia; and, most recently, the Alaotra grebe (*Tachybaptus rufolavatus*) from east Madagascar, which was declared extinct in 2010 (IUCN, 2010). The Lago Tota, Colombia wetlands were also once home to a now-extinct species of catfish (Fjeldså, 1993; IUCN, 2010). There have been nineteen confirmed freshwater amphibian extinctions in the wild (IUCN, 2010). In terms of geographies, Mexico stands out, with twenty-one freshwater fish extinctions (sixteen completely extinct, and five extinct in the wild, but with surviving captive populations); this represents 20% of the global total reported to date. Some of the most dramatic extinctions have hit North American freshwater mollusks, with up to 37 species of mussels extinct or possibly extinct, and similar levels of threat expected for freshwater snails (see chapter 3).

Freshwater species face numerous threats. Excluding cichlids in Lake Victoria (where it has been especially difficult to determine the numbers of extinct species), Harrison and Stiassny (1999) found that habitat modification (including the effects of water extraction) was a contributing factor to more than 70% of fish extinctions, and that the introduction of species was a contributing factor to the extinction of more than 50% of endemic species of fishes. The Alaotra grebe in Madagascar suffered from the introduction of carnivorous fish to the lakes in which it lived. Habitat modification has also severely impacted many species of freshwater mollusks, crabs, and odonates (an order of aquatic insects represented by dragonflies and damselflies). The growing effects of global climate change will further compromise water availability, resulting in even greater fluctuations in droughts and flooding (Bates et al., 2008), affecting environmental flow regimes in river basins throughout the world (Forslund et al., 2009), and compounding existing impacts on freshwater species and humans. These impacts affect freshwater species and ecosystems, and the related delivery of goods and services needed by people.

PROTECTED AREAS

Chapter 4 (Allan et al.) discusses the status, design, and effectiveness of freshwater protected area systems in safeguarding species, ecosystems, and watersheds from threats. This chapter is complemented by an appendix that provides a history of the Ramsar Convention as well as the role of the WWF in protecting wetlands (Landenbergue and Peck). Freshwater ecosystems are the least-protected and most threatened of ecosystems. Most of the protection is provided by Ramsar sites, but even the 1,218 inland wetland sites designated under Ramsar cover only about 12% of the total 16.94 million km^2 protected in terrestrial areas (Jenkins and Joppa, 2009).

The most immediate response to the freshwater biodiversity crisis is the oldest of all conservation tactics: safeguarding important sites using protected areas and other mechanisms to ameliorate site-level threats. The "Important Bird Area" (IBA) approach of the BirdLife International partnership (BirdLife International, 2008) has been extended by IUCN to identify important sites for freshwater biodiversity (Darwall et al., 2005), helping define "Key Biodiversity Areas" (Eken et al., 2004). Of particular note are sites identified by the Alliance for Zero Extinction, which contain the entire population of at least one highly threatened species (Ricketts et al., 2005). WWF, The Nature Conservancy, and others defined 426 freshwater ecoregions of the world to represent major regions possessing distinct freshwater fish communities, and to help determine the status of freshwater ecosystem protection (Abell et al., 2008).

The second step in preserving freshwater biodiversity is to ensure that existing freshwater protected areas are managed effectively. Data on the world's protected areas are stored in the World Database on Protected Areas (WDPA, 2009), but it is unclear how many of these represent important freshwater ecosystems, and harder still to document the effectiveness of their management. Assessing these points, and adjusting management of protected areas accordingly, is therefore essential (Abell et al., 2007).

The Ramsar Convention provides a formal intergovernmental mechanism by which nations can designate and protect networks of important freshwater biodiversity sites. The convention calls for the identification of freshwater key biodiversity areas as "shadow lists" (BirdLife International, 2002). At national levels, the urgency of conducting gap analysis of protected area coverage has spurred renewed attention to the identification of important sites (Langhammer et al., 2007). The Program of Work on Protected Areas of the Convention on Biological Diversity calls for species conservation and gap analyses, and will integrate freshwater protected areas and ecosystem services as part of its Inland Waters program. Global targets for biodiversity will also include freshwater species.

Rice needs ample water in order to grow.
Hoa Village in the western part of Vietnam near Lao PDR. —Karen Kasmauski

Vietnam

Dhaka, Bangladesh | More than half the world's population now live in cities. Many, like Dhaka in Bangladesh, are overcrowded, with sanitary and health infrastructures badly strained as people flock to urban centers for economic opportunities. These people are illegally taking fresh water from a pipe. —Karen Kasmauski

Despite living in the shadow of one of Nigeria's newest oil export facilities, the people of this village have no piped water, sanitation facilities, electricity, or sufficient drainage (which causes the flooding shown here). —George Steinmetz

Nigeria

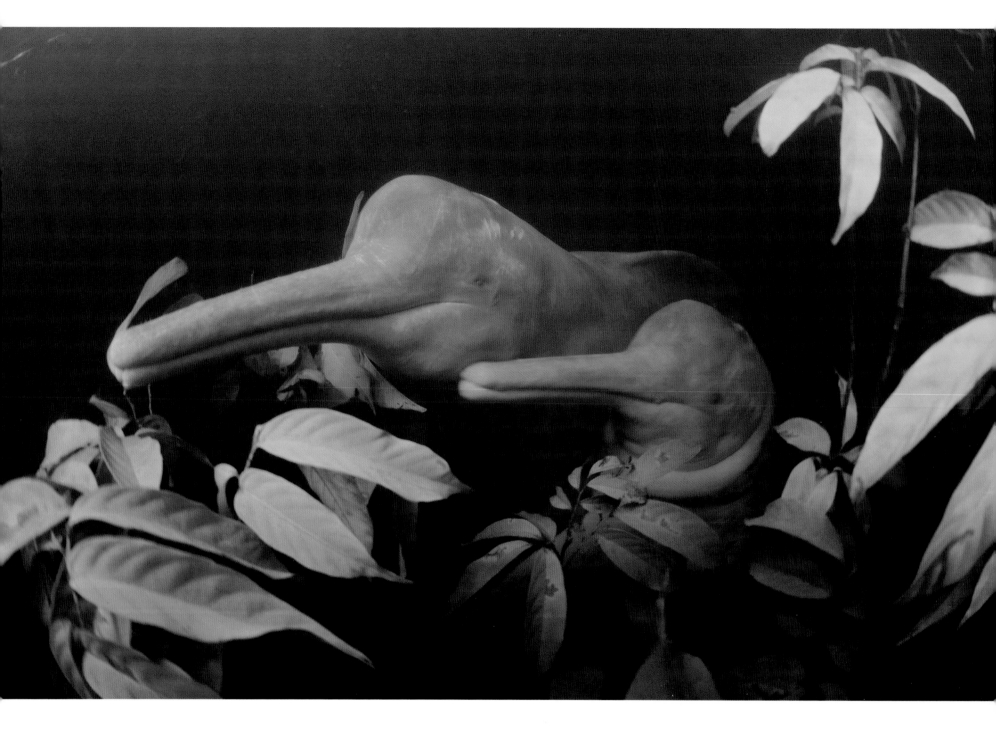

Amazon, Brazil | Amazon river dolphins or *botos* (*Inia geoffrensis*) underwater, Rio Negro, Amazon, Brazil. —Kevin Schafer

CATCHMENT MANAGEMENT'

While much freshwater biodiversity can be appropriately conserved at the site level, catchment-level conservation management is also essential to ensure connectivity between upstream and downstream areas, and between above- and below-ground waters; maybe more so than for any other biome (Boyd et al., 2008). Where threats are low, policy designations such as that of Wild and Scenic Rivers, a national system created by the U.S. Congress in 2007 and of which there are 156 examples in the nation, can provide powerful preemptive conservation.

Ultimately, restoration, among other intensive land and water resource-management activities, will become essential for catchment-level management. Restoration has been implemented most effectively for wetlands and lakes, although some rivers, such as the Thames in the United Kingdom, have also attracted restoration attention. Even more ambitious aspects of restoration include removing invasive species and decommissioning dams. The Everglades' thirty-year $10 billion restoration plan exemplifies the degree to which such large-scale freshwater ecosystem restoration is feasible.

Management of entire drainage basins across large regions and crossing national boundaries is challenging, especially given the serious potential for international conflict over water resources. New approaches to zoning, and focusing on core areas for water-resource extraction versus protection show promise for balancing competing water needs. River basin management policies and institutions have also been formed, including transnational bodies such as the Lake Victoria Development Program (Kenya, Tanzania, Uganda). The Mekong River Commission brings together Cambodia, Lao PDR, Thailand, and Viet Nam—although the non-participation of China and Burma (Myanmar) from the body limits its effectiveness. The European Union Water Framework Directive and the United Nations Watercourses Convention offer water allocation and management frameworks to manage water and permit sufficient water for nature or environmental flows. When ratified, the UN Watercourses Convention would impact management of more than 260 international river basins.

EX-SITU FRESHWATER CONSERVATION

Given the pervasiveness of threats to freshwater biodiversity, *in situ* establishment of protected areas and catchment management needs to be supplemented with *ex situ* conservation tactics: captive breeding, assurance colonies, and reintroduction. A number of freshwater species are classified as Extinct in the Wild and survive only in aquariums; examples are the Mexican fishes *Cyprinodon alvarezi, Cyprinodon longidorsalis,* and *Cyprinodon veronicae,* which now only survive in aquariums, including those at the Chester Zoo and London Zoo in the United Kingdom. The World Association of Zoos and Aquariums published a strategy for conservation and sustainability of freshwater species and ecosystems, supported by several conservation organizations such as Wetlands International and Conservation International (Penning et al., 2009). The strategy provides recommendations for integrating zoo and aquarium roles in *in situ* and *ex situ* conservation, and in public outreach, engagement, and education.

ECOSYSTEM SERVICES VALUE AND PAYMENT

Freshwater ecosystem services, defined by the Millenium Ecosystem Assessment as "supporting," "regulating," "provisioning," and "cultural" services (MEA, 2005), benefit people. Chapter 5 (Farrell et al.) is a discussion of how humanity depends upon—and therefore needs to better value and pay for the protection of—our freshwater ecosystems.

Following Spread: Iguazu Falls, Brazil. —Frans Lanting

ECOSYSTEM SERVICES

Supporting services, such as the hydrologic cycle and nutrient cycling, are the foundational processes that permit the delivery of all the other services. As such, they are perhaps the most important. For example, the hydrologic cycle interacts with the carbon and nitrogen cycles to allow plants to grow and transpire water back into the atmosphere—processes that permit life to exist on our planet. Because these services are the most challenging to quantify and measure, it has been difficult to mitigate threats to their protection in land and water resource management.

Regulating services are the benefits provided to humanity by the moderation of ecosystem processes. Ecosystems mitigate extreme events in the hydrologic cycle, notably droughts, flooding, and mudslides. Upland catchment habitats, especially forests, play a central role in reducing the magnitude of peak flow events, while in the lowlands, river floodplains serve as natural safety nets to contain their impacts. Humanity undermines these insurance mechanisms at its own peril. Deforestation and related flooding events in tropical mountains have been shown to dramatically increase human mortality (Bradshaw et al., 2007). Similarly, the last century has seen great increases in building and agriculture on attractive, fertile floodplain lands, without recognition that these natural systems buffer us from irregular but extreme flooding.

Freshwater species play an important role in maintaining water quality and healthy ecosystems. The role of freshwater mollusks and other species in preserving water quality is well documented. More recently, amphibians have also been shown to be a factor in sustaining healthy freshwater ecosystems. The recent dramatic decline in amphibian populations has been linked to ecosystem-wide changes in streams, including changes in populations of other riparian species (see chapter 1).

An even more encompassing regulating service provided by freshwater ecosystems is the maintenance of water quality. At least four distinct components can be identified within this fundamentally important ecosystem service. In upland catchments, forests and other ecosystems control the erosion of topsoil; erosion is driven to a large extent by running water, resulting in concentration of high sediment loads in fresh water. Along watercourses, water is purified by marshes and other wetlands, which allow deposition of suspended sediment and removal of dissolved chemicals. By extension, rivers themselves also provide waste disposal, transporting excess organic material for redeposition downstream or in the ocean. Finally, this constant hydrological flux also regulates diseases transmitted through waterborne vectors. Clean freshwater sources support species such as dragonflies and some species of fishes that predate upon pest insects such as mosquitoes and, therefore, may be important for bio-control of malaria and other diseases.

Provisioning services include water for drinking, washing, generating energy, growing food, and transportation. Around the world, domestic water use varies from 575 l per day, per person in the United States to 4 l per day, per person in Mozambique (UNDP, 2006). The largest human use of fresh water is agriculture, which consumes approximately 70% of all fresh water withdrawn for human uses globally (Shiklomanov, 2000; Margat and Andréassian, 2008; FAO, 2009). All crops depend on water, and its availability often limits global distribution and success of agricultural development. Highest productivity occurs in moist regions; where water availability is lower or less predictable, irrigated agriculture using stored, diverted, or groundwater is often the only option. Given the huge volumes of foodstuffs traded around the world, agriculture also has the effect of transferring massive quantities of food-locked fresh water from producers to consumers across the planet.

Agriculture requires large water inputs. For example, about 1,000 l of water are needed to produce one kg of wheat, and more than 12,000 l are needed to produce the same amount of beef (World Water Council, 2004). This virtual water trade has been estimated at as much as 700 to 1,100 km3 per year (*ibid*, 2004). Energy production uses large quantities of water, especially as a coolant in power stations (roughly a hundred trillion gallons, or about half of Lake Erie's volume, are used annually in the United States alone) and directly through hydroelectric power. Other particularly thirsty industries include manufacturing, chemicals, and food processing.

People also depend upon fresh water for wild-capture freshwater fisheries. We harvest 8.64 million metric tons of freshwater fishes annually, which accounts for 20% of animal-derived protein in low-income food-deficit countries and 13% in the industrialized countries (Allan et al., 2005; FAO, 2007, 2008). Turtles,

Cultural services are the nonmaterial goods we derive from the environment. Recreation through swimming, boating, and fishing is made possible by the resources and ecosystems supporting these activities, and can be quite lucrative. In the United States, 35 to 60 million adults engage in recreational fishing, spending $38 billion to $41 billion annually; multiplier effects indicate that the sport represents a global overall value of US$116 billion a year (Helfman, 2007). Recreational fishing accounts for at least 4% of the world's fish catch.

However, these economic valuations are gross underestimates of the true cultural value provided by recreational water use; the full but unaccounted-for benefits include human happiness, increased productivity, and improved social relations (see chapter 5.)

In the USA alone, nearly 40% of all rivers and streams are too polluted for fishing and swimming due to sewage, agricultural run-off, and precipitation of industrial airborne pollutants out of the atmosphere.

frogs, snails, and crayfish also provide important food contributions (Revenga and Kura, 2003; Bogan, 2008; Strong et al., 2008). Several groups of economically important plants are harvested from wetlands, including phragmites reeds, lotus root, wild rice, and water chestnut (Li et al., 2000). Rice (*Oryza spp.*) is the most important food crop for humans; more than 2.7 billion people rely on it as a major food source (Chambers et al., 2008).

Aquarium-keeping is a $15 billion–to $30 billion-per-year international industry, with some 350 million aquarium specimens traded annually. Fishes dominate the trade, accounting for 80% to 90% of the total. Although 60% of income from the sale of fishes goes to tropical developing countries, non-fish components are produced more widely, and much of the profit from those go to developed nations (Helfman, 2007).

Another cultural activity associated with freshwater species is the growing number of aquariums being created in all regions of the world. According to the World Association of Zoos and Aquariums (WAZA), some 450 million people visit aquariums globally each year (Penning et al., 2009).

MINIMIZING THREATS THROUGH PAYMENT FOR ECOSYSTEM SERVICES

Freshwater ecosystems are obviously important for human lives and livelihoods—indeed, without fresh water, humans could not have evolved and could not survive. These systems can sustain some level of human use...but we appropriate 50% of accessible freshwater flows each year from rainfall, surface-and-groundwater stocks, and soil moisture (Postel et al., 1996). Even with this appropriation, the world's pop-

ulation facing water deficits is projected to rise to 1.8 billion by 2025 (UNDP, 2006). It is widely predicted that climate change will exacerbate water scarcity in many places, and this scarcity is emerging as a leading cause of conflict. Potential water wars seem imminent in Central Asia, much of Africa, and, above all, in the Middle East. Our greed for water, as well as our inability to sufficiently manage, value, and pay the costs for ensuring that ecosystems deliver our fresh water-related services, render our usage unsustainable.

Water diversion projects, such as dam construction, drive agricultural development and provide electricity generation, but they represent serious threats to aquatic ecosystems. They divert river waters from their channels, flood the areas behind the dams, and increase methane emissions through vegetation. More than 50% of the world's major rivers are now dammed (Nilsson et al., 2005), and a current global average of 160 to 320 new large dams are built every year (World Commission on Dams, 2000). Levees destroy floodplain habitat and invite human settlement and agriculture in areas prone to flooding. Add to that the direct destruction of aquatic ecosystems, primarily through the drainage of wetlands, about whose range of biodiversity there is often little knowledge, and whose system services are therefore undervalued (Darwall et al., 2009).

This enormous appropriation of the planet's fresh water is neither equitable over territory nor sustainable over time. Many of the world's major rivers—including the Nile, the Ganges, Central Asia's Amu Dar'ya and Syr Dar'ya, China's Yellow River, and the Colorado in the United States—no longer reach the sea, and a number of major lakes are disappearing (Postel, 1995). Already, 1.4 billion people live in river basins that have "closed" (Falkenmark and Molden, 2008), and some of the world's great ecological disasters are over-exploited rivers. In places such as the Aral Sea (which depended on flows from the Amu Dar'ya and Syr Dar'ya), northern Africa's Lake Chad, and the Colorado River delta, they have collapsed. Much of the Aral Sea's native floras and faunas have

been killed off, the regional fishing industry has collapsed, and the health of the human population is compromised by polluted water and by salt and dust from the desiccated land. Eight species or subspecies of whitefishes may have been driven to extinction in the Great Lakes of North America and the rivers and lakes of Europe, due in part to overfishing in the last century (Harrison & Stiassny, 1999; Kottlelat & Freyhof, 2007). The introduction of game species, such as trout and charr, and of aquatic plants, such as water hyacinth (*Eichhornia crassipes*), have caused serious declines and extinction of native species in several parts of the world and loss of fishing income in others (Harrison & Stiassny, 1999; Revenga & Kura, 2003; Revenga et al., 2005).

Fresh water is renewable, but only to the extent that it is replenished faster than we expropriate it, and depending on the extent to which we degrade its quality; once degraded, it is useless to us (Gleick et al., 2009). An estimated 25,000 million tons of topsoil are lost each year, choking rivers with massive sediment loads and degrading their quality (FAO, 1995). Some of these sediment inputs—for example, the bleeding of Madagascar's red soils into the Indian Ocean because of indiscriminate upland devegetation—are so dramatic as to be visible from space. In the United States alone, nearly 40% of all rivers and streams are too polluted for fishing and swimming (American Rivers, 2010) due to sewage, agricultural runoff, and precipitation of industrial airborne pollutants out of the atmosphere. Current research is also slowly revealing nonpoint sources of water pollution, including endocrine disruptors from hormones, as well as pesticides, plastics, and other industrial effluents.

If we are to reverse current trends of freshwater loss and degradation, we must value these ecosystems and their service flows and incorporate those values into our economic decisions. One of the best-known examples of paying for ecosystem protection to generate clean water services is the Catskill/Delaware Watershed serving New York City (Forslund et al., 2009; Vintinner, 2009). Many

Opposite: A micro-hydro project on the Tapanahony River in eastern Suriname. Small hydroelectric projects such as this one can generate significant amounts of energy for remote local communities, while minimally disrupting river flow. —R. A. Mittermeier

countries have been experimenting with methods of "payments for freshwater services," whereby downstream (urban, industrial, and agricultural) users pay highland communities directly, to maximize compensation for their conservation and minimize transaction costs.

MANAGING WATER FOR THE FUTURE

Safeguarding key sites and better managing watersheds and river basins for multiple water needs is enabled through policy, governance, and markets that promote use of integrated watershed management and attribute value to functioning freshwater ecosystems. Water for human consumption needs to be priced in a way that more accurately reflects its value. Public utilities generally price water so low as to create perverse incentives for wasteful consumption. Subsidies for agricultural development also encourage water waste and pollution. Pricing and market failures, including these subsidies, need to be corrected if we are to change the way in which we use and abuse our water and surrounding lands. Regional and global markets for freshwater ecosystem services are also needed; this would be a far-reaching but necessary advance. In the final chapter, Smith discusses water management needs in the face of global economic and climate change, proposing governance and policy frameworks as well as the market changes required to secure a future rich in freshwater biodiversity and ecosystem services.

Projected increases in human population from 6.8 to more than 9 billion people by 2050, and growing wealth in many countries, will continue to fuel growth in water demand. More and more people require water for drinking and food, and developing economies are switching to more water-intensive diets based on meat and dairy products (WWAP, 2009). Climate change is in many cases an additive pressure, not only changing hydrology, but also increasing water consumption and driving energy and carbon policies that are consuming even more water (i.e., biofuels, hydropower, and carbon capture and storage) (Bates et al., 2008; WWAP, 2009). Impacts across geographies will differ, but many arid areas will become drier, and wetter areas will become wetter. Seasonality, changes to the hydrologic regime, and uncertainty related to hundred-year flood calculations, will make it even harder to manage water security challenges—exposing more and more people to droughts and floods, among other climate-related hardships.

Water access, allocation, and use are critical societal issues. They often drive political tensions, which may result in conflict within or between states. Privatization of water supplies and depletion or pollution of water in a shared river basin can greatly limit access, and has already resulted in violent conflict in many already weak nation states. Tensions over water also have the potential to exacerbate other, non-water-related violent conflicts (OECD, 2005). Poor water governance is an important source of serious intrastate conflict and is projected to be a major source of such conflict in the future (CNA, 2007). Fresh water must be available, and of sufficient quality, in the right times and in the right places; and these conditions are determined by ecological processes, water flows, and up- and downstream dynamics.

Integrated River Basin Management (IRBM) is a well-tested approach to help minimize conflict and ensure the holistic and sustainable management of water bodies based on natural boundaries. This method has been adopted by Ramsar and others to ensure that there is a sufficient focus on the environment and ecosystems (UNEP, 2007). Integrated Water Resource Management is more widely recognized, but conservationists favor IRBM, given its stronger emphasis on environmental needs.

Managing environmental flows in a river basin context can provide a framework for making decisions about protecting ecosystem services of forested watersheds, freshwater ecosystems, and coastal waters.

This approach has been used to address complex and shared problems, such as water scarcity, habitat change, insufficient protected-area management, corridor and migratory pathway protection, aquatic species recruitment, and pollution reduction.

Effective governance of water can occur within eFlows and IRBM frameworks, as long as necessary institutions are built and policies are in place to coordinate multiple water needs. Safeguards should include transparent roles and responsibilities that are appropriate at local, provincial, national, and regional levels. People must be empowered to have a voice in the decisions that affect them, including assurances that the water needs of ecosystems and the services they provide are represented and incorporated into planning and decision making.

To survive and thrive under ever-increasing insecurity over water in the face of global changes, we depend on resilient freshwater ecosystems—that is, systems capable of withstanding and recovering from shocks and stresses, of protecting the full complement of species, and of delivering services to meet human needs. Our forests, soils, wetlands, and floodplains represent part of the natural infrastructure that stores water, regulates flows, and moderates the hydrograph (fluctuations in river discharge), and needs to be recognized as such within development planning.

We must and can redefine the relationship between humanity and nature to ensure that the freshwater requirements of nature are met first, and that remaining available water is then shared equitably among the world's peoples. Without such changes, we can be sure that we will continue to lose aquatic biodiversity and the life-support system on which we depend. *

* Please see Appendix for elaboration on The Ramsar Convention, WWF, and Conservation International's "Freshwater Strategy".

TLALOC

The Aztec and Mesoamerican cultures understood clearly that irreverence angered the god Tlaloc and his wives. They believed that the ire of the god would lead to bad times—*inic cemayan tlayouaz tlalticpac:* "Darkness will dawn upon us."

Tlaloc was revered by the Aztecs as one of their greatest deities. He was the god who gave life and sustenance; without Tlaloc, god of rain and water, there could be no life. The literal translation of Tlaloc comes from Tlali, meaning earth; *Tlaloc* is often translated as "path beneath the earth." For the Aztecs and Mesoamerican cultures, the very essence of Earth—rain and water, fertility and life—was manifested in Tlaloc.

The Aztecs believed that the world had four corners. The corners were called four Tlalocs, because they held the sky and the earth, and framed the rising and setting of time. Timing, crops, sustainability, and the calendar in general were all within Tlaloc's domain. Three particular gods honored by the Aztecs—Quetzalcoatl, Huitzilopochtli, and Tlaloc—are manifested at the pyramids of Teotihuacán in central Mexico; one of the two main shrines is dedicated to Tlaloc, demonstrating his influence in the culture.

If a worshipper found favor in Tlaloc, he or she was granted a life of sensual pleasure and fulfillment in "Tlalocan"—Tlaloc's paradise. Tlalocan was thought of as the unending spring, a paradise of green. One translation of Tlaloc's name was "a green giver, the genesis of life"; another was "he who makes things sprout."

The Mesoamerican cultures revolved around this god of rain and water. They practiced praising, respecting, and revering him, understanding that their actions would result in fruitful lives, green paradises, crops, order. The Aztecs considered the ultimate gift to him—sacrificing their children—an honor. The sacrifices were made to gain his favor, to seek to ensure that he would reciprocate graciously, with rain. His goddesses would fill the streams, rivers, and lakes. However, disrespecting or ignoring Tlaloc would enrage him, bringing devastation and famine. He was a much-feared and revered god.

Reverence for such a god pre-dates the Aztecs in most Mesoamerican cultures. The Mayans named theirs Chaac; the Totonacas called him Tajin; and the very early culture of the Olmecs worshipped Epocatl. Tlaloc's goddesses represented extensions of his character, his ability to give life. Xochiquetzal was the goddess of spring; Matlolcueti, the goddess of corn; Chalchiuhtlicue, the goddess of lakes, streams, and running water; and Tecciztecatl was the goddess of fertile harvest. The god and his goddesses represented the essential identity of most Mesoamerican cultures—and the attributes they needed for survival.

The Aztec culture has a rich allegorical heritage; descriptions of the essentials of life are articulated and made clear. Tlaloc represented the vital qualities that were crucial to life: heavens and Earth, rain, rivers, and water. The message of the Aztecs is relevant today, as we strive to honor Earth in our care of it. Irreverence toward Tlaloc, to the Aztec and Mesoamerican cultures, led to dire consequences—*in ualpachiuiz topan mani:* "the heavens over us [to] sunder." Lack of proper regard implied that the god would *quipoloquiui tlalli, in quiquaquiui maceualli:* "come to destroy Earth and devour the people."

We do well to learn what the Aztecs lived.

Richard Sneider
Principal
One World, LLC.

Following Spread: Since its construction in the 1930s, the Bonneville Dam on the Columbia River has provided power for industrial development and water for irrigation, but the effectiveness of fish ladders installed for migratory salmon has been disappointing.
—Gary Braasch

Opposite: Apoala cascade in cloud forest on land that was historically part of the Aztec empire, Puebla, central Mexico. —Claudio Contreras-Koob

Bangladesh

A woman in Mohakhali Korail slum in Dhaka, Bangladesh, fetches drinking water from the Buriganga River. One of the world's most densely populated cities, Dhaka sends industrial chemical waste and sewage into the river without treatment. —Karen Kasmauski

Previous Spread, Las Vegas

With water and hydroelectric energy from the Colorado River, even the Mojave Desert can yield lush greenery, as seen here at a private golf course in Las Vegas. Excessive water demand from the Colorado in Nevada, Arizona, and Southern California causes the river to dry before reaching its terminus in the Gulf of California. —George Steinmetz

Fishing-net scaffold on the Dhanaghoda River in Bangladesh. Fish is the staple protein source for much of humanity. —Karen Kasmauski

Dhanaghoda River, Bangladesh

Brook cascading into Lake Superior, the largest freshwater lake in the world by surface area, and the third-largest by volume. Pictured Rocks National Lakeshore, Michigan, USA. —Carr Clifton

Following Spread: Michigan, USA

ONE
A WEALTH
OF LIFE

A WEALTH OF LIFE
SPECIES DIVERSITY IN FRESHWATER SYSTEMS

Estelle Balian, Ian J. Harrison, Helen Barber-James, Stuart H. M. Butchart, Patricia Chambers,
Jay Cordeiro, Neil Cumberlidge, Ferdy de Moor, Claude Gascon, Vincent Kalkman,
Peter Paul van Dijk, Darren Yeo

F resh water provides a thread of life and resources across the planet. It has been described as the spark of life that has allowed evolution and speciation to flourish over millennia through geographically isolated and protected freshwater ecosystems (McAllister et al., 1997). An understanding of the diversity and distribution of species in freshwater ecosystems can tell us much about how Earth has evolved, and how freshwater ecosystems support humans and all other life found not only within those waters, but also in adjacent terrestrial ecosystems. These freshwater and terrestrial ecosystems extend from the sources of rivers in the peaks of mountain ranges to the estuaries and wetlands along the continental coasts. Indeed, distributions of freshwater species have been used to interpret the historical patterns of plate tectonics and other geological processes on Earth. For example, the distribution patterns of a range of aquatic insects can be used to show the sequence of events that resulted in the breakup of Gondwana between 127 and 165 million years ago, and consequent isolation of today's southern continents (South America, Africa, Antarctica, Australia), along with more recent dispersal within the last 65.5 million years (Dingle et al., 1983; Briggs, 2003; Yoder and Nowak, 2006).

However, there is a more urgent concern to develop baseline information about the current patterns of diversity and distribution offreshwater species. This information forms the basis on which to assess how freshwater ecosystems are being directly changed over time by human activities; for example, by habitat modification, impacts of pesticides on species physiology and community structure, introduction of alien species, or overfishing, as well as the impacts of climate change (Revenga et al., 2005; Dudgeon et al., 2006; Heino et al., 2009; Hayes et al., 2010). Many freshwater species are sensitive to water quality or flow, and therefore good bioindicators of the environmental condition of aquatic systems and neighboring terrestrial ecosystems. Freshwater fishes, mollusks, crabs, and several groups of insects (e.g., dipterans, ephemeropterans, plecopterans, trichopterans, and odonates; see table 1.1 for English names) are well suited for use in evaluating long-term and short-term environmental change in aquatic and riparian ecosystems (Daniels, 2001; Revenga and Kura, 2003; Leclerf et al., 2006; Sterling et al., 2006; Dijkstra, 2007; Kalkman et al., 2008; Strong et al., 2008; Cumberlidge et al., 2009). Freshwater mollusks contribute to nutrient exchange and help maintain good water quality by controlling algal blooms and cleaning substrates for other benthic invertebrates (Dillon, 2000). Aquatic vegetation is important in promoting water clarity (Kosten et al., 2009), providing refuge for fishes and invertebrates (Petr, 2000), and

Previous Spread: Katydid drinking water in a river, Altas Cumbres, Tamaulipas, northeast Mexico. At least 126,000 species depend on fresh water for at least part of their life cycle. —Claudio Contreras-Koob

Opposite page: Entirely aquatic and tolerant of a wide range of salinity, the Florida manatee (*Trichechus manatus latirostris*) makes its home in rivers, estuaries, and shallow coastal waters. The closely related Amazonia manatee (*T. inunguis*) is adapted exclusively to freshwater habitats in the Amazon basin. —Art Wolfe

altering water and sediment chemistry (Carpenter and Lodge, 1986). Aquatic vegetation may also be used as an indicator of water quality (Penning et al., 2008). Thus, each species in a freshwater ecosystem contributes to the overall biodiversity and complexity of that ecosystem. It is that complexity that results in what has been termed an "ecosystem service" to that community, and to the humans that depend on it (Reaka-Kudla et al., 1997).

WHAT IS A FRESHWATER SPECIES?

Before one can describe the diversity of species in freshwater systems, it is necessary to have a clear definition of what constitutes a "freshwater species." This is any species that lives at least part of its life cycle in fresh water (Balian et al. [2008a] refer to these as "real aquatic species"), or any species that shows a close and specific dependency on freshwater habitats (Balian et al. [2008b] refer to these as "water dependent" or "paraquatic" species). It is important to note that the ancestors of most "freshwater species" lived in marine environments; possible exceptions include aquatic spiders, mites, many insects, pulmonate gastropods, and perhaps rotifers, cladocerans, and phyllopodus branchiopods. Also, other than Echinodermata (starfish, sea urchins, sea cucumbers, and their relatives), all major phyla have at least some freshwater representatives, but only a select few (e.g., insects, rotifers) have a higher diversity in fresh water than in marine systems. Some aquatic species spend their entire lives in fresh water (e.g., fishes, some crustaceans, some mollusks, most algae), but other species may have only a specific phase of their life cycle completely restricted to fresh water (e.g., parasites that present an aquatic free-living form; many insects, including odonates, mayflies, stoneflies, caddisflies; and amphibians). However, species that are dependent on a water matrix within a terrestrial habitat (termed limno-terrestrial species) are generally not regarded as aquatic species, because they have a more specific dependency on the interface between these media. Microorganisms that live in the moisture between soil particles are an example of such limno-terrestrial species.

There are several definitions of aquatic species that have been specifically applied to plants. For example, Cook (1970) considered vascular aquatic plants to be those "whose photosynthetically active parts are permanently or, at least, for several months each year submerged in water or float on the surface of water." Subsequently, Denny (1985) and Pieterse (1990) defined aquatic plants as those whose vegetative parts actively grow either permanently or periodically (for at least several weeks each year) submerged below, floating on, or growing up through the water surface.

There are many water-dependent species (following Balian et al.'s [2008a] definition; see above) that are not restricted to fresh water at any stage of their life cycle, but are heavily dependent upon it for specific aspects of their ecology. For example, many reptiles and aquatic birds rely on freshwater ecosystems as a source of food (e.g., ospreys and snakes that feed on fishes; diving ducks that feed on aquatic plants). Other species rely on freshwater systems for their habitat. Certain hymenopteran insect species are dependent on mud and water for constructing nests. The hippopotamus, *Hippopotamus amphibious,* uses freshwater systems during the day to stay cool, and as a safe place to give birth to young. Many aquatic species of plants require seasonally flooded habitats to survive. (It is important to note that these various definitions of water-dependent species of plants and animals do not include the need for fresh water for ingestion to support cellular metabolism [i.e., the simple requirement of the water medium itself, rather than the ecosystem that the medium supports] because that would include all life on Earth.)

There are also freshwater species living in temporary water bodies and in transitional systems that link fresh water with terrestrial and marine environments. Some species of large branchiopods, such as fairy shrimp, clam shrimp, and tadpole shrimp (*Artemia monica, Lynceus brachyurus, Streptocephalus sealii*), occur in pools that never dry completely, or in wetland or vernal pools that dry completely and may not become wet again for years or even decades (e.g., *Branchinella, Thamnocephalus, Triops spp.*) (Brendonck et al., 2008). The water in these temporary pools, or in transitional systems linking rivers and wetlands to the sea, may change in salinity and become brackish or even hypersaline (see below and chapter 2). Freshwater species may also be found in these brackish waters, or in fully marine waters. From an evolutionary standpoint, it is in these brackish environments where adaptation toward or away from fresh water perhaps begins. Species that are tolerant of wide ranges in salinity are termed "euryhaline." Examples include

WHAT IS A FRESHWATER ECOSYSTEM?

The preceeding discussion indicates that the definition of a freshwater species directly relates to how we define a freshwater ecosystem. Fresh water, which has less than 0.5 g per liter of dissolved salts, exists in many ecosystems both above and below ground. These freshwater ecosystems are highly diverse: temporary or permanent, large or small, stationary or flowing, intermittent or continuous, hot or cold, surface or subterranean (see chapter 2). As noted above, there are also transitional systems that link fresh water with terrestrial and marine environments. In the latter case, where fresh water mixes with seawater, for example in estuaries and coastal marshes, the water will be higher in salts and hence "brackish" (i.e., between 0.5 g

The decline of stream-dwelling frogs in Central America is projected to have large-scale and lasting effects on the quality of water flowing downstream and on the function of the stream ecosystems.

many fishes that migrate between marine, brackish, and fresh waters. Many aquatic birds are also found in both marine and inland waters. Euryhaline species can also be classified as being freshwater species only if the majority of the individuals of the species rely on freshwater habitats for at least some stage of their life cycle or aspect of their ecology. Indeed, besides diadromous fishes that regularly migrate between marine and fresh water, species of fishes have been classified as primary or secondary freshwater fishes based on whether they are strictly intolerant of salt water (primary), or are usually confined to fresh water but may be tolerant of salt water for short periods (secondary) (Myers, 1951; Lévêque, 1997). However, species that spend all, or nearly all, of their lives in brackish or marine environments are excluded from the present discussion.

per liter and 35 g per liter of dissolved salts). Although these brackish environments may include freshwater species that are tolerant of brackish conditions for at least part of their life cycle (see above), they are quite distinct from freshwater ecosystems and are not considered further in this chapter.

The majority of Earth's fresh water exists as ice, snow, and permafrost. This frozen water does not provide a habitable aquatic ecosystem for many organisms— although bacteria and other microorganisms may be present in viable states frozen into ice (Zhang et al., 2002), and fairy shrimp (*Branchinecta gaini*), can survive complete freezing of its habitat in Antarctica (Peck, 2005). Therefore, frozen fresh water can also be excluded from our definition of a freshwater ecosystem. Nevertheless, it is important to recognize that these frozen freshwater systems are upstream

Following Spread: Lake Kussharo on the Japanese island of Hokkaido is an important stopover for migrating whooper swans (*Cygnus cygnus*). When the lake is frozen over in winter, the swans exploit areas of open water created by volcanic hot springs. —Tim Laman

sources of meltwater that maintain flowing freshwater ecosystems downstream. Therefore, frozen fresh waters are essential physical components for persistence of freshwater ecosystems (See chapter 2 for further discussion of connectivity of freshwater systems.)

THREATS TO SPECIES

It is widely accepted that the human impacts on fresh waters are severe, causing profound declines in the resident freshwater biota (Harrison and Stiassny, 1999; Stiassny, 1999; Revenga et al., 2005; Dudgeon et al., 2006) (see chapter 3 for further discussion of threats to species). These changes in the diversity of species alter the way freshwater ecosystems function, and may eventually lead to totally different systems (through the loss of species that are major components of the food webs, energy flow, and chemical cycling, or that shape the physical structure of the freshwater ecosystem). Declines in freshwater crab populations in rivers in Kenya due to competition and replacement by introduced invasive crayfishes have resulted in declines in the populations of one of the crabs' predators, clawless otters (Cumberlidge et al., 2009). This is probably because of competition with predators of the crayfishes. It is projected that the decline of stream-dwelling frogs in Central America will have large-scale and lasting effects on the quality of water flowing downstream and on the function of the stream ecosystems. Moreover, the decline in frogs may affect the community structure of neighboring riparian ecosystems and the transfer of energy between the stream and riparian systems (Whiles et al., 2006; Colón-Gaud et al., 2008). Changes in the abundance and diversity of aquatic vegetation can also have profound effects on aquatic ecosystems. This is because aquatic plants serve as water filtration organisms (limiting pollution and sedimentation) and provide habitat for a variety of aquatic fauna. For example, declines in abundance of submersed plants in shallow lakes are associated with turbid water and,

in turn, impairments to food-web dynamics and water quality (Scheffer et al. 1993; Kosten et al., 2009).

SPECIES RICHNESS IN FRESHWATER ECOSYSTEMS

Despite the importance of freshwater species to ecology and human well-being, there have been a lack of comprehensive, synthesized data on the total number of freshwater species in the world, their patterns of geographic distribution, and their regional and global evolutionary diversity (i.e., the number of genera, families, orders, etc., that are represented) (Revenga and Kura, 2003). Without these data, it is impossible to quantify the taxonomic scale and breadth of the anthropogenic impacts to freshwater ecosystems. Indeed, this dearth of easily accessible information on freshwater biodiversity has long been a major justification for the lack of appropriate conservation and management for freshwater systems (Stiassny, 2002; Lévêque et al., 2005). Meaningful attempts to provide a global overview of the biodiversity of freshwater systems have only been developed in the last decade (for example, see Revenga and Kura, 2003; Lévêque et al., 2005). The most recent study is the global overview provided by the Freshwater Animal Diversity Assessment (FADA) project (Balian et al., 2008a, b; and see table 1.1).

Although fresh water (e.g., in lakes, rivers, and wetlands) makes up less than 0.008% of the volume of all water on Earth, and covers only 0.8% of the surface area of the planet, freshwater ecosystems harbor exceptional diversity (Dudgeon et al., 2006). That diversity generates nearly 3% of the total net primary production on Earth (Alexander and Fairbridge, 1999). FADA estimates the number of known freshwater animal species to be about 126,000. This is about 7% of the total number of described species on Earth, which is estimated at 1.8 million (Hilton-Taylor et al., 2009). However, other studies have estimated that the percentage of freshwater

Taxonomic Group	Number of freshwater species	Number of freshwater species as percent of total described species for the taxonomic group	Number of freshwater species in taxonomic group as percent of all described freshwater species	Reference
Vascular macrophytes (plants)	2614	1	1.9	Chambers et al. (2008)
Porifera (sponges)	219	1.5	0.2	Manconi and Pronzato (2008)
Cnidaria	40	0.6	0.0	Jankowski et al. (2008)
Turbellaria (free-living flatworms)	1303	20	0.9	Schockaert et al. (2008)
Rotifera (rotifers)	1948	96	1.4	Segers (2008)
Nemertea (nemerteans)	22	1.8	0.0	Sundberg and Gibson (2008)
Nematoda (nematodes)	1808	6.7	1.3	Abebe et al. (2008)
Nematomorpha (hairworms)	326	16	0.2	Poinar (2008)
Bryozoa (bryozoans)	88	1.1	0.1	Massard and Geimer (2008)
Tardigrada (tardigrades)	62	6.8	0.0	Garey et al. (2008)
Annelida: Polychaeta (polychaetes)	168	1.9	0.1	Glasby and Timm (2008)
Annelida: Oligochaeta, Clitellata (oligochaetous clitellates)	1119	22	0.8	Martin et al. (2008)
Annelida: Hirudinea (leeches)	482	71	0.3	Sket and Trontelj (2008)
All Annelids	1769	12	1.3	Balian et al. (2008b)
Mollusca: Bivalvia	1026	6.8	0.7	Bogan (2008)
Mollusca: Gastropoda	3972	9.9	2.8	Strong et al. (2008)
All Mollusks	4998	4.3	3.6	Balian et al. (2008b)
Crustacea: Large branchiopods (Branchiopoda)	500	100	0.4	Brendonck et al 2008)
Crustacea: Cladocera	620	100	0.4	Forro et al. (2008)
Crustacea: Ostracoda	1936	6.5	1.4	Martens et al (2008)
Crustacea: Copepoda	2814	22	2.0	Boxhall and Defaye (2008)
Crustacea: Branchiura (fishlice)	113	100	0.1	Poly (2008)
Crustacea: Mysidae	72	6.8	0.1	Porter et al. (2008)
Crustacea: Spelaeogriphacea & Thermobaenacea	22	N/A	N/A	Jaume (2008)
Crustacea: Cumacea & Tanaidacea	25	1.1	0.0	Balian et al. (2008b)
Crustacea: Isopoda	994	9.9	0.7	Wilson (2008)
Crustacea: Amphipoda	1870	21	1.3	Vainola et al. (2008)
Crustacea: Syncarida	240	100	0.2	Camacho and Valdecasas (2008)
Crustacea: Decapoda, Anomura, Aeglidae (hermit crabs)	63	100	0.0	Bond-Buckup et al. (2008)
Crustacea: Decapoda, Brachyura (true crabs)	1280	20	0.9	Cumberlidge et al. (2009); De Grave et al., (2009)
Crusatcea: Decapoda, Caridea (shrimps)	655	20	0.5	De Grave et al. (2008, 2009)
Crustacea: Astacidae, Cambaridae, Parastacidae (crayfish)	638	100	0.5	Crandall and Buhay (2008)
All crustaceans	**11842**	**24**	**8.4**	Balian et al. (2008b)

Table 1.1: Numbers of Freshwater Species for Major Taxonomic Groups. Continued on next page

Taxonomic Group	Number of freshwater species	Number of freshwater species as percent of total described species for the taxonomic group	Number of freshwater species in taxonomic group as percent of all described freshwater species	Reference
Acari: Hydrachnidia (water mites)	6000	100	4.3	Di Sabatino et al. (2008)
Acari: Halacaridae (halacarid mites)	56	5.3	0.0	Bartsch (2008)
Acari: Orabatida (orabatids)	90	0.9	0.1	Schatz and Behan-Pelletier (2008)
All Acari (mites)	**6146**	21	4.4	Balian et al. (2008b)
Insecta: Ephemeroptera (mayflies)	3138	100	2.2	Barber-James et al. (2008)
Insecta: Odonata (dragonflies and damselflies)	5680	100	4.0	Kalkman et al. (2008)
Insecta: Plecoptera (stoneflies)	3497	100	2.5	Fochetti and Tierno de Figueroa (2008)
Insecta: Heteroptera (true bugs)	4656	12	3.3	Polhemus and Polhemus (2008)
Insecta: Trichoptera (caddisflies)	13574	100	9.6	Morse (2010)
Insecta: Megaloptera (dobsonflies, fishflies, alderflies)	328	100	0.2	Cover and Resh (2008)
Insecta: Neuroptera (lacewings, antlions, snakeflies)	118	1.8	0.1	Cover and Resh (2008)
Insecta: Coleoptera (beetles)	12600	3.2	9.0	Jach and Balke (2008)
Insecta: Mecoptera (scorpioflies and hangingflies)	8	1.6	0.0	Ferrington (2008a)
Insecta: Diptera; Chironomidae (midges)	4147	28	2.9	Armitage et al., (1995); Ferrington (2008b)
Insecta: Diptera; Tipulidae (craneflies)	15178	99	11	de Jong et al. (2008)
Insecta: Diptera; Simuliidae (black flies)	2000	100	1.4	Currie and Adler (2008)
Insecta: Diptera; Culicidae (mosquitoes)	3492	100	2.5	Rueda (2008)
Insecta: Diptera; Tabanidae	5000	N/A	3.6	Balian et al. (2008b)
Other Diptera	13454	N/A	9.6	Wagner et al. (2008)
All Diptera	**43271**	22	31	Balian et al. (2008b)
Insecta: Lepidoptera (butterflies)	740	0.6	0.5	Mey and Speidel (2008)
Insecta: Hymenoptera	150	0.1	0.1	Bennett (2008)
Insecta: Orthoptera (grasshoppers, locusts, crickets)	188	0.8	0.1	Amedegnato & Devriese (2008)
All Insecta	**87948**	8.7	63	Balian et al. (2008b)
Pisces (fishes)	12740	44	9.1	Lévêque et al. (2008)
Amphibia (amphibians)	4245	66	3.0	IUCN (2010)
Reptilia: Lacertilia (lizards)	73	1.5	0.1	Bauer and Jackman (2008)
Reptilia: Crocodilia (crocodiles)	23	100	0.0	Martin (2008)
Reptilia: Chelonii (turtles)	268	80	0.2	Turtle Taxonomy Working Group (2009)
Reptilia: Serpentes (snakes)	153	5.1	0.1	Pauwels et al. (2008)
Mammalia (mammals)	145	2.6	0.1	IUCN (2010)
Aves (birds)	1979	20	1.4	BirdLife International (2010)
TOTAL	**140759**			

Table 1.1, continued

Opposite page: Duckweed (*Lemna sp.*), Iroquois National Wildlife Refuge, Niagara Region, New York, USA. —Carr Clifton

species is even larger, perhaps up to 12% of all species (Abramovitz, 1996; and see information compiled in table 1.1). The disproportionate relationship between high species numbers found in the relatively small habitable volume of fresh water on Earth has been termed "the paradox of freshwater biodiversity" (Martens, 2010).

Based on the results of the Freshwater Animal Diversity Assessment of 2008, more than 60% of the documented freshwater species that live in or are closely associated with fresh water are insects (table 1.1), because a large proportion of insects have aquatic larval phases. Almost half of the aquatic insects are dipterans, which play an important role in aquatic environments, particularly as a food source for many other species (Revenga and Kura, 2003). Some of the other important invertebrate groups include crustaceans (8% of documented freshwater species; decapods and copepods being the most species-rich groups), and mites (ca. 4%). Mollusks also represent about 4% of the aquatic species; in healthily functioning river systems, freshwater snails alone number in the millions (in terms of numbers of individuals) and serve as an important food source for other animals. Rotifers, annelid worms, nematode worms, and turbellarian flatworms each represent 1% to 2% of documented freshwater species. About 39% of all vertebrate species are dependent on fresh water, although these are mostly freshwater fishes (which represent 9% of the total number of documented freshwater plant and animal freshwater species). The 2,614 known species of freshwater vascular macrophyte plants represent about 1% of the total number of vascular plant species documented, and 2% of all known freshwater animal and vascular plant species.

Viruses, bacteria, simple eucaryotes (including a vast array of microorganisms that are often called protozoans, protists, and algae; see Tudge, 2000), and fungi are also critical components of freshwater communities, driving important biogeochemical cycles

(Dudgeon et al., 2006). Although there was insufficient information to include these groups in the Freshwater Animal Diversity Assessment of 2008, some general estimates of overall species numbers exist. There are an estimated 2,390 species of free-living protozoans in freshwater ecosystems (Finlay and Esteban, 1998), along with 3,047 aquatic species of fungi, more than 500 species of meiosporic ascomycetes, 405 species of miscellaneous mitosporic fungi, and ninety species of aeroaquatic mitosporic fungi (Shearer et al., 2007). However, the total number of freshwater species could be much larger for protozoans and fungi, reaching as many as 10,000 to 20,000 species of protozoans and 1,000 to 10,000 species of fungi (Palmer et al., 1997); the same authors also estimated up to 20,000 freshwater species of algae. AlgaeBase (Guiry and Guiry, 2010) includes about 25,000 species of algae, of which about 11,000 are thought to be freshwater or terrestrial. However, because of the uncertainty of the classification of diatoms, the total number may be much greater. Six thousand species of diatoms are noted in AlgaeBase, but the actual species number may be greater than 100,000 species (M. Guiry, pers. comm.).

The species numbers and percentages given above are, nevertheless, probably underestimates of the total number of freshwater species, because many remain undiscovered or scientifically undescribed. For example, the number of recognized species of amphibians increased by 48% between 1985 and 2006 (Frost et al., 2006). A small proportion of these are cases where species were removed from synonymy with another species. Synonymy occurs when two or more species that were originally described as different are subsequently thought to be the same species (i.e., the differences between the species were considered to be insignificant). Thus, removal from synonymy occurs when the synonymized species are, even later, recognized once again as distinct and different species. Despite these cases of removal from synonymy, most of the newly recognized species of amphibians are genuine new discoveries of species

(Köhler et al., 2008). Many more species are awaiting proper scientific description, and there is no doubt that many species remain to be discovered. Similarly, between 1976 and 1994 an average of 309 species of fishes were newly described or resurrected from synonymy each year (Stiassny, 1999). Eschmeyer and Fricke (2010) cited 500 new species of fishes in 2008, than 500 species over the past twenty years. One mayfly family alone, the Baetidae, realized an 18% increase in species numbers and a 20.5% increase in the number of genera known globally (data derived from Gattolliat and Nieto, 2009). For Odonata (dragonflies and damselflies), an average of thirty-eight species have been described annually since

The number of recognized species of amphibians increased by 48% between 1985 and 2006

and 287 in 2009. Although these numbers are for both marine *and* freshwater fishes, a reasonable proportion of them can be expected to be freshwater fishes.

Global estimates of the species richness of freshwater invertebrates vary widely, and total species numbers are typically underrepresented, for many of the same reasons as noted above for vertebrates. Those reasons are compounded by the facts that the taxonomy of many of the invertebrate groups is less well known than for vertebrates, and that large parts of the world remain unexplored or undersurveyed for freshwater invertebrates. For example, a new species of freshwater leech was recently described based on collections made in 2006, just 50 km north of New York City (Hughes and Siddal, 2007). Nearly 25% of the approximately 500 globally known species of large branchiopods are represented by specimens from fewer than three localities (Belk and Brtek, 1995, 1997). In many cases those species are known only from a single collection point, the "type locality"; this is the collection locality for the "type specimens" on which the description of the species is based.

The total number of recorded Trichoptera (caddisflies) has risen from 11,532 in 2005 to 13,574 (Morse, 2010). This represents a 17.7% increase in species in a five-year period. Similarly, for the Ephemeroptera (mayflies), Brittain and Sartori (2009) indicated the addition of ten new families, ninety genera, and more

1970. In 2008 the number of described species of Odonata was 5,680, but it was estimated that well over a thousand species remain to be discovered and described (Kalkman et al., 2008). The taxonomic underrepresentation is greatest for the least-known invertebrate groups, fungi and microalgae. For example, in 1994 a new species of microorganism, *Limnognathia maerski*, was collected from a cold spring on Disko Island, West Greenland (Kristensen and Funch, 2000). This new species also represents an entirely new genus (*Limnognathia*), family (Limnognathiidae), class (Micrognathozoa), and order (Limnognathida). Some scientists, in fact, view the Micrognathozoa as a new phylum. Genomic analyses have shown that freshwater microbial diversity is likely to be much greater than presumed from nonmolecular analyses (Dudgeon et al., 2006).

CRYPTIC SPECIES

There are frequent cases where a single, widespread species has been found to include several "cryptic species" that appear so similar morphologically that they were not previously recognized as distinct. The freshwater turtle fauna of Australia is rich in cryptics and has exceeded that of Brazil in total species number—at least for now, since Brazil also has a number of cryptic turtle species waiting to be described (R. A. Mittermeier, pers. comm.). A careful

Left: Great pond snail (*Lymnaea stagnalis*) in a hardwood forest pond at Gornje Podunavlje Ramsar site, Serbia. This species serves as host to the larvae of a number of cryptic species of flatworm. —Ruben Smit, Wild Wonders of Europe

mix of anatomical, biogeographic, and molecular analyses is often required to distinguish these cryptic species. Bain et al. (2003) used these techniques to identify six additional cryptic species of cascade frog from Southeast Asia that had previously been conflated as a single species.

Numerous examples of cryptic species of the freshwater snail family Hydrobiidae have recently been uncovered in the Great Basin of Australia (Ponder, 1997; Ponder and Walker, 2003) and the American West (Hershler, 1998, 1999). As recently as 1980, the primary North American reference for freshwater snails listed approximately thirty hydrobiid snail species in western North America (Burch and Tottenham, 1980), but subsequent surveys coupled with more modern taxonomic methods now recognize more than 300 species and subspecies (Hershler, 1998, 1999).

The distribution of these closely related, cryptic species is important for defining patterns of biodiversity and for planning conservation actions (Cook et al., 2008). Cryptic sibling species (i.e., those that are most closely related to each other) are particularly important to identify when one is dealing with mosquitoes and blackflies, for instance, which are vectors of parasites such as *Plasmodium* (which causes malaria) and *Onchocerca* (a roundworm that causes river blindness). Not accurately knowing the species can lead to an overly broad-scale control of the pest-vector species which, in some cases, can in turn lead to controlling the harmless sibling and favoring the carrier of the disease (e.g., *Anopheles funestus*, studied in Malawi; Spillings et al., 2009). Detection of cryptic species is also critical when assessing the range extension of a species. Estimation of impacts and management actions will differ when the range extension is associated with a native species compared to a nonnative strain (for example, Saltonstall (2002) discussed cryptic invasion of the common reed, *Phragmites autralis*).

MAPPING FRESHWATER SPECIES

When mapping and analyzing patterns of species distributions, it is important to use methods that account for the ecological and environmental characteristics that define the species' ranges. This is necessary for any spatial analyses of overall numbers of species, numbers of endemic species, or species thought to be economically important, or threatened. The methods must also be appropriate for planning habitat conservation and for ecologically effective resource management. The patterns of species distributions across freshwater ecosystems on Earth are defined by historical processes of geology, extinction, and speciation, as well as current processes of species dispersal and, of course, the impacts of humans. These factors, when considered together, allow us to describe species distributions relative to the ecology and geography of Earth—that is, the "biogeography" of the species—rather than just relative to political boundaries, for example.

Freshwater species distributions are often described according to the river and lake basins, or subbasins, from which they have been collected. In practice, the ranges of the species may not always extend throughout an entire subbasin. For example, a waterfall or some other geological barrier may restrict the distribution of the species, but this is impossible to know without fine-scale biophysical and distribution data, which are often lacking. Also, the distributions of some species, such as dragonflies, mayflies, and stoneflies, often correspond less well with basins than with the dividing mountain ranges between the basins. Nevertheless, conservation planning for freshwater ecosystems, and management of these resources, are usually implemented for complete basins or subbasins, rather than partial subbasins (Abell et al., 2008). For these reasons, the method of describing species distributions by subbasins has been adopted by IUCN for the freshwater fishes, mollusks, crabs, dragonflies, and damselfies, and for aquatic plants included in the IUCN Red List of Threatened Species™ (Darwall et

Botswana

A baby Nile crocodile (*Crocodylus niloticus*) hides in an algal veil in the Okavango River Delta in Botswana. —David Doubilet

Dragonfly (*Libellula sp.*) in the Pantanal, Mato Grosso, Brazil. —Thomas Marent

Mato Grosso, Brazil

Ecuador | Marsupial frog tadpole (*Gastrotheca riobambae*) with back legs developed. Once common in the gardens and parks around Quito, Ecuador, their populations have declined. —Pete Oxford

A network of elephant (*Loxodonta africana*) trails crisscrosses the green grasses of Lake Amboseli, at the center of Kenya's Amboseli National Park. The elephants migrate from the dry surrounding plains almost daily in the dry season to drink and graze. —George Steinmetz

Lake Amboseli, Kenya

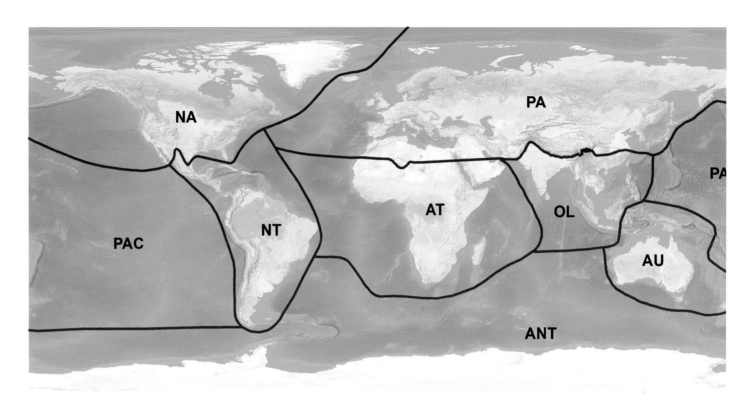

FIGURE 1.1 Zoogeographic regions used in the Freshwater Animal Diversity Assessment. PA: Palearctic Region; NA: Nearctic Region; AT: Afrotropical Region; NT: Neotropical Region; OL: Oriental Region; AU: Australasian Region; ANT: Antarctic Region; PAC: Pacific Region and Oceanic Islands. Based on Balian et al. (2008a). Created with Natural Earth datasets. Free vector and raster map data at naturalearthdata.com.

al., 2005, 2009; Smith and Darwall, 2006; Kottelat and Freyhof, 2007; IUCN, 2010). Similarly, NatureServe (2010) has used subbasins for mapping New World freshwater species.

WWF has proposed a slightly different spatial unit for mapping and analyzing the distribution of freshwater biodiversity, based on "freshwater ecoregions" (Abell et al., 2008). These ecoregions encompass one or more freshwater hydrological systems with a distinct assemblage of natural communities and species. Although the boundaries of freshwater ecoregions often match those of river basins, they are not constrained to them, because the ecoregions also account for various other factors, such as species composition and associated ecological and evolutionary processes. Currently, however, most of WWF's freshwater ecoregions are based only on fish distributions.

For these reasons, the distributions of many species can only be mapped at a much coarser level than basins. The 2008 Freshwater Animal Diversity Assessment mapped species numbers only to the level of eight large, zoogeographic regions (figure 1.1). These are:

The Palaearctic Region (PA)—Europe, Russia, North Africa (not the Sahara), the northern and central Arabian peninsula, and Asia to the southern edge of the Himalayas.

The Nearctic Region (NA)—North America, Greenland, and the high-altitude regions of Mexico.

The Afrotropical Region (AT)—Sub-Saharan Africa (south of the Sahara), the southern Arabian peninsula, and Madagascar.

Taxonomic Group	Region								Total for taxonomic group
	Afrotropical	*Antarctic*	*Australasian*	*Nearctic*	*Neotropical*	*Oriental*	*Pacific*	*Palearctic*	
Macrophytes	614	12	439	644	984	664	108	497	3962
Annelids	186	10	210	350	338	242	10	870	2216
Mollusks	483	0	557	936	759	756	171	1848	5510
Crustaceans	1536	33	1225	1755	1925	1985	133	4499	13091
Arachnids	801	2	708	1069	1330	569	5	1703	6187
Collembolans	6	1	6	49	28	34	3	338	465
Insects	14428	14	7510	9410	8594	13912	577	15190	69635
Vertebrates	3995	1	694	1831	6041	3674	8	2193	18437
Other phyla	1188	113	950	1672	1337	1205	181	3675	10321
Total for Region	23237	186	12299	17716	21336	23041	1196	30813	129824

Table 1.2. Number of Species by Zoogeographic Region, for Major Taxonomical Groups (based on Balian et al., 2008b).

The Neotropical Region (NT)—Southern and coastal parts of Mexico, Central America, the Caribbean Islands, and South America.

The Oriental Region (OL)—India and Southeast Asia south of the Himalayas to Indonesia, as far as Wallace's Line (passing between Borneo and Sulawesi, and through the Lombok Strait between Bali and Lombok [Wallace, 1876]); and including the Philippines, Taiwan, and Japan's Ryukyu Islands.

The Australasian Region (AU)—Australia and New Zealand, New Guinea, and Indonesian islands south and east of Wallace's Line.

The Antarctic Region (ANT)—the Antarctic continent, and the Antarctic and sub-Antarctic islands.

The Pacific Region and Oceanic Islands (PAC)—the islands in the North and South Pacific Ocean.

(See Balian et al. [2008a] for further information).

These data for large zoogeographic regions are of limited value for conservation planning, but are very useful for global analyses of patterns of species' abundance and endemism. De Moor and Ivanov (2008, fig. 4) had suggested a different approach when mapping Trichoptera (caddisflies). They identified an alternative set of regions to that used in the Freshwater Animal Diversity Assessment that more closely describe biogeographic characteristics and relationships of species within the group.

An important point to note is that most studies of freshwater species diversity are focused on species found in surface waters. Although groundwaters, those below Earth's surface, do not have the same extent of species richness as surface waters, their diversity should not be overlooked (Sket, 1999). Those subterranean ecosystems represent important conservation priorities. Further discussion on groundwater ecosystems and the species present is given in chapter 2.

BIOGEOGRAPHY AND SPECIES RICHNESS

Results of the Freshwater Animal Diversity Assessment (Balian et al., 2008b) indicate that the Palearctic Region is the richest in freshwater animal species, followed by the Afrotropical, Oriental, and Neotropical regions

Following Spread: Dalmatian pelican (*Pelecanus crispus*) at Lake Kerkini, Macedonia, Greece. —Jari Peltomaki, Wild Wonders of Europe

of the tropics, and then the mostly temperate Nearctic Region (table 1.2). The general trend, of a lower abundance of animal species in the tropical regions than at higher latitudes of the Palearctic, is in contrast to the usual pattern of latitudinal diversity of species (Gaston and Williams, 1996). Although some invertebrate groups are evidently rich in species in the Palearctic (see below), the overall trend of species abundance is probably biased by less extensive field sampling and taxonomic knowledge for freshwater species in the tropics than for the more northerly Nearctic and Palearctic regions (Lundberg et al., 2000; Graf and Cummings, 2007; Balian et al., 2008b). Indeed, some well-sampled invertebrate groups, such as dragonflies and damselflies, as well as freshwater crabs, are richer in species numbers in the Neotropical, Australasian, and Oriental regions of the tropics than at higher latitudes.

Aquatic vascular plants are noted for having many species with a widespread distribution. Nevertheless, freshwater plants generally show greatest species richness in the tropical regions, especially the Neotropics. The Oriental, Nearctic, and Afrotropic regions are the next-most species-rich for aquatic plants, and lower numbers have been recorded from the Palearctic Region and from Australasia. Species richness is low in the Pacific Oceanic Islands (for reasons discussed below) and lowest, not surprisingly, in the Antarctic Region.

PALEARCTIC

Insects account for approximately half the total number of freshwater Palearctic species documented in the Freshwater Animal Diversity Assessment. For example, stoneflies (plecopterans), caddisflies (trichopterans), and various dipterans such as midges (chironomids) and craneflies (tipulids) show high levels of species richness in the Palearctic. However, high concentrations or hotspots of endemism in Trichoptera are to be found in high-rainfall montane ecosystems in both temperate and tropical regions

worldwide (de Moor and Ivanov, 2008). Crustaceans, which have considerably more species in the Palearctic compared to other parts of the world, account for another 15% of the total number of freshwater Palearctic species. About 34% of the total documented freshwater species of mollusks are reported from the Palearctic (table 1.2), although particular evolutionary lineages of mollusks shower high diversity elsewhere (see "Biogeography and Species Endemism," below). Although vertebrates tend to show greatest species diversity in the tropics, the Palearctic realm supports a disproportionately large number of fresh water– dependent species of birds, reflecting the high diversity of migrant shorebirds that breed in wetland habitats at high latitudes.

AFROTROPICAL

The Afrotropical Region has 22% of the recorded freshwater vertebrate species diversity, making it the second richest region for vertebrate species after the Neotropics (see below). It also follows the Neotropics in being the second-most species- rich area for freshwater fishes. The Congo basin and Lakes Malawi, Tanganyika, and Victoria in the Rift Valley of East Africa are identified as areas of high species richness in freshwater fishes, mollusks, and freshwater crabs (Abell et al., 2008; Cumberlidge et al., 2009). These taxonomic groups, together with frogs, are also rich in species in the Lower Guinea region, roughly encompassing western Central African river basins from Cameroon to the Republic of Congo; (Stiassny et al., 2007; Abell et al., 2008).

The Afrotropical Region has relatively few families of dragonflies and damselflies, but relatively many recent evolutionary radiations within those families. Nevertheless, the region still has a relatively low total number of species of dragonflies and damselflies compared to the fauna of the Oriental and Neotropical regions. This relative species poverty has been attributed to the unstable climatological history of the Afrotropical Region, in which a sustained dry period in the past resulted in a strong contraction of tropical forest cover, which may have resulted in declines in species diversity (Dijkstra and Clausnitzer, 2006).

ORIENTAL

The Oriental Region is rich in several groups of insects, most noticeably dragonflies and damselflies, which have greatest species numbers in Indo-Malaya (Kalkman et al., 2008; Clausnitzer et al., 2009). This region also has the highest species richness for freshwater crabs, with more than 800 species known (Yeo et al., 2008; Cumberlidge et al., 2009). China and Southeast Asia in particular are centers of species richness for freshwater crabs and shrimps (Kottelat and Whitten, 1996; Dudgeon, 2000); there are at least 224 species of freshwater crabs and fifty species of shrimps in the southern half of China (more than any other country in Asia). There are about 219 species of freshwater mussels in the Oriental Region (Graf and Cummings, 2007). Twenty percent of recorded freshwater vertebrate species are found in the Oriental Region, with several river basins being especially rich in vertebrate species. The Mekong River supports an exceptional level of biodiversity. Estimates of the number of fishes in the Mekong River range from 500 to 2,000 species, with about 32% endemism (Kottelat and Whitten, 1996; Rainboth, 1996); only the Amazon and perhaps the Congo rivers have a greater diversity of freshwater fishes. The Lower Mekong has the greatest known species diversity of gastropod mollusks (ca. 140 species, 79% endemic) of any large river in the world (Strong et al., 2008), and the Mekong basin has 300 to 350 species of odonates (dragonflies and damselflies) and more than eighty-nine species of freshwater crabs (Cumberlidge et al., 2009). The annual inland fisheries production of the Mekong may be as much as 25% of the entire freshwater fish catch for the world (Baran et al., 2008). Lake Tonle Sap, on the Mekong, is Southeast Asia's largest and most productive lake (Motomura et al., 2002). Fishes provide an essential source of calcium and protein, and human consumption of

fishes in the lower Mekong basin is one of the highest in the world. Tragically, the Mekong River is perhaps one of the most threatened freshwater ecosystems in Southeast Asia (see Kottelat and Whitten, 1996; Dudgeon, 2000; Roberts, 1995, 2001).

The Yangtze, Ganges, Brahmaputra, Chao Phyraya (in Thailand), and Kapuas (in Kalimantan) rivers also have high levels of species richness (Kottelat and Whitten, 1996; Abell et al., 2008). Indeed, globally high richness of freshwater fishes is reported from both the Yangtze and Pearl rivers in China (Abell et al., 2008). The Yangtze has an estimated 360 species and subspecies of freshwater fishes, of which 177 species (i.e., about half) are endemic (Fu et al., 2003). The lowland plains and modest elevations of the mainland Oriental Region (the Ganges plains to South China and to Peninsular Malaysia) are the world's most species-rich area for freshwater turtles (Buhlmann et al., 2009). However, as noted above for the Mekong River, many of these other rivers and associated wetlands of the Oriental Region are also highly impacted through river fragmentation and flow regulation caused by dams, and the attendant habitat loss (see chapter 3).

NEOTROPICAL

The Neotropics are especially diverse in freshwater vertebrates (which are the most comprehensively and consistently analyzed group at a global level); 33% of the total number of species of freshwater vertebrates are found in this region (table 1.2). Amphibians are generally richest in species in the Neotropics: Central America, the Andes, the Amazon basin, and the Atlantic Forest of Brazil (Stuart et al., 2008). There are also about 4,500 species of freshwater fishes in the Neotropics (more than any other region), with Characiformes (characins and their relatives) and Siluriformes (catfishes) being large components of this fauna (Lundberg et al., 2000; Reis et al., 2003; Ortega et al., 2007). The Neotropics are also rich in dragonfly and damselfly species (Kalkman et al., 2008; Clausnitzer et al., 2009), and vascular plants (Chambers

India | A tigress crosses a creek in Bandhavgarh National Park, India. Tigers (*Panthera tigris*) are powerful swimmers; some populations, especially those of Southeast Asia, spend much of their time in rivers or wetlands, feeding on fish and turtles. —Theo Allofs

Eastern long-neck turtle (*Chelodina longicollis*) at Piccaninnie Ponds Conservation Park, South Australia. —David Doubilet

South Australia

et al., 2008). The high diversity of freshwater species is supported by the networks of large rivers, tributaries, and extensive wetlands. For example, the Pantanal, which is the largest wetlands on the planet, covers between 140,000 and perhaps 210,000 km2 of lowland floodplain and incorporates many different habitats (Harris et al., 2005; Mittermeier et al., 2005a). The Amazon basin contains Earth's most diverse riverine fish fauna, with about 2,500 species described and another 1,000 species that may be present but not yet discovered (Junk et al., 2007). Some other large, Neotropical rivers flowing to the Atlantic are also rich in fish species, including the Orinoco (with about 1,000 species) and the Paraguay-Parana-Rio de la Plata system (about 400 species) (Lundberg et al., 2000; Quirós et al., 2007; Rodríguez et al., 2007). Brazilian inland waters are also rich in species of freshwater algae (with 25% of the world's species), Porifera (Demospongiae, 33%), Annelida (12%), Rotifera (25%), Cladocera (Branchiopoda, 20%), freshwater Decapoda (10%), and parasites of aquatic organisms (Agostinho et al., 2005; and see table 1.1 for English names of taxonomic groups).

NEARCTIC

The Nearctic Region is less species-rich than the Neotropical, Afrotropical, and Oriental regions, but has some groups with notably high species numbers. For example, 77% of the world's diversity of crayfishes is from North America (particularly the southeastern United States, contained within the Nearctic Region). Mollusks, especially, show high species richness and endemism (see below for discussion on endemism). North America contains about 302 of the world's 840 to 1,000 known species of freshwater mussels (Unionioda) (Lydeard et al., 2004; Strayer et al., 2004; Graf and Cummings, 2007); this represents as much as 36% of the world's freshwater mussel species richness, compared to 1.3% of the richness in Europe (Graf and Cummings, 2007). The world's greatest diversity of pleurocerid snails occurs in rivers and streams of the southeastern United States (Neves

et al., 1997; Brown et al., 2008). Also, high levels of species richness of hydrobiid snails are reported from the American West (see "Cryptic Species," above).

AUSTRALASIAN

The freshwater species richness of Australasia is generally low, considering the size of this region (table 1.2), with less than 4% of the total numbers of freshwater vertebrate species. The land surface area of Australasia is comparable to that of Brazil, with a similar percent coverage of fresh water (about 0.8% of the land area; CIA, 2010), but it has only about 26% of the number of species of fishes compared to Brazil (Froese and Pauly, 2010). This difference is partly because of the extraordinary species richness of the Amazon basin, with its combination of large channel rivers and minor tributaries, and partly because the freshwater fauna of Australasia is incompletely documented (Lundberg et al., 2000). There are, however, some notable exceptions to this documented pattern. For example the diversity of odonates (dragonflies and damselflies) is relatively high in Australasia, and so is freshwater turtle diversity.

PACIFIC ISLANDS

The Pacific Islands have relatively low freshwater species richness for all groups (fewer than 1,200 species in total, according to the Freshwater Animal Diversity Assessment (Balian et al., 2008b; see table 1.2.). This might be an underestimate; for example, the Assessment records only eight species of vertebrates, which is much lower than other published estimates (see Mittermeier et al., 2005b). Nevertheless, the low overall species numbers on the Pacific Islands is not surprising, because of the small surface area of these islands, the restricted size of any freshwater systems, and the isolation of many of the islands from large land masses. However, most of the islands have been colonized by species of dragonflies flying from the Oriental Region, and these species are typically widespread. Several of the islands or island groups are home to endemic dragonfly species. There are several cases in which a large portion of the dragonfly diversity of an island comprises a large radiation of species within a single genus (Polhemus, 1997). If one estimates freshwater species richness relative to freshwater ecoregion area, then New Caledonia, Vanuata, and Fiji in the Pacific become especially noteworthy as regions of high species density within their small areas (Abell et al., 2008).

BIOGEOGRAPHY AND SPECIES ENDEMISM

A species whose distribution is restricted to a particular region is said to be "endemic" to that region. For example, a small species of carp-like fish, *Squalius keadicus,* is known to be endemic to just one river, the Evrotas River, in southeastern Greece (IUCN, 2010). One should note that a species can be "native" to a region without being endemic to it, because it may also be found elsewhere. For example, a species of dragonfly, *Oxygastra curtisii,* is native to southwestern Europe (i.e., it is naturally distributed there), but it is not endemic there because small populations also naturally occur in Morocco (Kalkman et al., 2010). Thus, the proportion of truly endemic species found in a region is an indication of the biological uniqueness (and hence irreplaceability) of the fauna or flora in that region.

Global patterns of species endemism vary for different taxonomic groups. For example, distributions of aquatic insects are quite variable; some species tend to show greater tendency for flight dispersal and may be more widespread (e.g., some dragonflies and damselflies [Odonata]; Dijkstra, 2007), whereas mayflies (Ephemeroptera) have a weak dispersal ability that, along with the antiquity of the order, has resulted in their generally high endemism. Similarly, amphibians and freshwater reptiles show high levels of endemism because of their reduced ability to disperse. Several regions of the southeastern United States are important areas of endemism for

salamanders and freshwater turtles (Buhlmann et al., 2009). Many islands host only endemic species of amphibians: Jamaica, São Tomé and Principé, New Zealand, Fiji, Palau, and the archipelago of Seychelles where all caecilians and frogs are endemic.

Madagascar is an example of a much larger island with high endemism. It has long been recognized as one of the world's most important biodiversity hotspots (Myers et al., 2000; Groombridge and Jenkins, 2002), mainly due to the unique species found on the island and to the high level of threat they encounter. Of the natural habitats present on Madagascar before human settlement, about 2,000 years ago, only 10% remain intact. Despite extreme habitat loss, Madagascar has a surprisiningly high rate of new species discovery for many taxa, even for some well-known groups such as amphibians; a recent study suggests that the number of known species of frogs may still be an underestimate, and that between 129 and 221 new species of frogs could be added to the total known species from the island (Vieites et al., 2009). In addition to a high species richness, the level of endemism in Madagascar is tremendous. According to Goodman and Benstead (2003, 2005), endemism for several taxonomic groups is as follows: all species of Ephemeroptera (mayflies) except for one (>100 species); 73% of Odonata (dragonflies and damselflies; 132 of the 181 described species); 100% of Plecoptera (stoneflies; twelve species); 100% of freshwater crabs (fifteen species); 65% of freshwater fishes (ninety-three of 143 species); 99% of frogs (197 of 199 species). Among the other endemic vertebrates are the aquatic tenrec, *Limnogale mergulus,* from a family of insectivorous mammals; the rare turtle, *Erymnochelys madagascariensis;* and a large aquatic lizard, *Scelotes astrolabi.* In addition, at least twenty species of atyid shrimps, five species of palaemonid shrimps, seven species of freshwater crayfish, and fifteen species of potamonautid crabs inhabit the island's rivers and streams. All seven genera of freshwater crabs and the single genus of crayfish found in Madagascar are endemic (Cumberlidge, 2008; Cumberlidge et al., 2009).

Australia | The platypus (*Ornithorhynchus anatinus*) has declined in parts of its historic range because of urban development, agriculture, and other human activities. Yarra River, Victoria, Australia. —David Doubilet

The common kingfisher (*Alcedo atthis*) is an indicator of freshwater ecosystem health across Europe and Asia. The sparrow-sized birds hunt most successfully in habitats with good water clarity. —Laszlo Novak, Wild Wonders of Europe

Europe & Asia

Yucatán Peninsula, Mexico | Ghost crab (*Ocypode quadrata*) sheltering in a cenote, one of numerous karst caves and sinkholes in Sian Ka'an Biosphere Reserve, Yucatán Peninsula, Mexico. —Claudio Contreras-Koob

The freshwater pearl mussel (*Margaritifera margaritifera*), native to Europe and eastern North America, has disappeared from much of its historic range due to habitat loss and over-harvesting for the occasional pearl. Umeälven tributary, Sweden. —Michel Roggo

Sweden

As noted above for Madagascar, often those areas that are rich in species numbers also have a high percentage of endemism. Some lakes may have high levels of endemism because these habitats are more isolated than river networks. For example, fishes, mollusks, and crustaceans show high levels of endemism in lakes. Several ancient lakes are centers of endemism, a phenomenon that reflects their greater age and relative isolation compared to rivers. In the Palearctic Region, Lake Biwa, in Japan, is about four million years old and has endemic plankton and thirty-eight species of gastropod mollusks, of which 50% are endemic (see also Kottelat and Whitten, 1996). Lake Baikal in Russia and Lake Tanganyika in Africa, both older than Lake Biwa and with high levels

interest because of their large numbers of endemic fishes and invertebrates (Kottelat and Whitten, 1996; Dai, 1999). In Sulawesi, the Malili lake system includes endemic radiations of crabs, shrimps, mollusks, and fishes, in particular small sailfin silversides (Herder et al., 2006), several of which are listed as threatened in the IUCN Red List (IUCN, 2010). Nearby, in Lake Poso, endemic species of halfbeak and goby fishes are threatened or may already be extinct (Harrison and Stiassny, 1999; IUCN, 2010). Similarly, Lake Lanao in the Philippines was a center of endemism, with a species flock of eighteen cyprinid fishes, fourteen of which may be extinct (due to the introduction of a species of goby). In the case of Lake Lanao, the cyprinid fishes disappeared from the lake even before

Although fresh waters cover less than 1% of Earth's surface, they provide habitat for more than 10% of the known animals and about one-third of all known vertebrate species.

of endemism, are discussed in more detail in chapter 2. Several of the other African Rift Valley lakes besides Tanganyika are well known for their high levels of species endemism for cichlids and gastropods. There are more than 800 species of cichlids in Lake Malawi, 99% of them endemic (Thieme et al., 2005). Fresh water–dependent birds, amphibians, and some reptiles (turtles and crocodiles are an exception) also tend to show great levels of endemism in the Afrotropical Region (Balian et al., 2008b).

In Lake Titicaca in South America, 63% of the twenty-four gastropod species are endemic. The lake is also an area of endemism for fishes (Abell et al., 2008), where at least one endemic cyprinodontid fish has become extinct due to the introduction of exotic fishes (Harrison and Stiassny, 1999). Freshwater endemism has also been noted for several lakes in the Oriental and Australasian regions. Many lakes of the mountainous Yunnan region of China are of special

their taxonomy could be fully investigated (Harrison and Stiassny, 1999).

Endemism is also found in other freshwater ecosystems. The relative importance of wetlands, rivers, and creeks, in terms of endemism, is much greater, proportionately, than would be suggested by their global water volume. Many of the approximately forty-nine genera and 330 species in the aquatic vascular plant family, Pdostemaceae, are found in rapids and waterfalls and are endemic to small geographic areas—even a single river or waterfall (Rutishauser, 1997). Freshwater fishes show high levels of endemism in the geographically isolated headwaters and small tributaries of the Neotropics (Junk et al., 2007; Quirós et al., 2007). The Atlantic Forest and Guianas ecoregions in South America are noted for high species endemism and richness of fishes. Many of the freshwater crabs and shrimps in the Oriental Region are restricted to single streams, or to a small group of streams associated with a single hillside or a small range of hills (Kottelat and Whitten, 1996; Cumberlidge et al., 2009). China has 96% freshwater crab endemism, and Southeast Asia has 69% to 98% freshwater crab endemism. Also in the Oriental Region, high levels of endemism for mollusks are reported from the Lower Mekong River. Similarly, the Congo River basin in Africa has high mollusk endemism (Strong et al., 2008).

The freshwater springs and groundwater of several parts of Australia show high species richness and endemism of hydrobiid snails (Strong et al., 2008; and see "Cryptic Species"). Of the numerous species of mollusks found in North America (see "Biogeography and Species Richness"), many are restricted to only one or a few river basins of the United States; for example, the basins of the Tennessee, Cumberland, and Apalachicola rivers, as well as drainages to Mobile Bay, and in the Ozark highlands (Abell et al., 2008). The basins of the southeastern United States are also a focus of threat and extinction for these species (Bogan, 2008; and see chapter 3).

Several wetlands of Southeast Asia, including the tropical peatland systems of Indonesia and Malaysia, have a large amount of freshwater endemism (Ng, 1994; Kottelat and Whitten, 1996). The small river networks found in Korea and Japan have high proportions of range-restricted species. About 42% of the 211 species or subspecies of freshwater fishes in Japan are endemic (Yuma et al., 1998). Among groups such as dragonflies and aquatic bugs, most species with a small range inhabit rivers or streams, often in tropical forest in mountainous areas. These range-restricted species are less commonly endemic to lakes. Trichopterans (caddisflies), which show some similarities to odonates in species distributions, have high levels of endemism in the Neotropical and Australasian regions, where 73% and 69% of the genera and subgenera are endemic (de Moor and Ivanov, 2008). The Ephemeroptera (mayflies) have their highest generic endemicity (90%) in the Australasian Region, yet this region has the lowest number of mayfly species per biogeographical realm. In contrast, the Palaearctic has the highest number of recorded mayfly species, but the lowest percentage generic endemism (Barber-James et al., 2008). This trend is true whether considering the order as a whole, or one particular family in detail; for example, Gattolliat and Nieto (2009) show the lowest number of Baetidae species in the Australasian Region when compared with other realms, but the highest endemicity. This implies that the lineages in the Australasian are old and stable, with little recent speciation, whereas the Palearctic species have been shaped by more recent extreme climatic conditions such as glaciation, resulting in higher species numbers.

The discussion above cannot do justice to the enormous range of species diversity and endemism in the freshwater ecosystems of the world. But it highlights some general trends and some important considerations for ensuring that we continue to conserve this biodiversity and safeguard the important ecosystem services it provides to humans. Readers who wish to find more comprehensive discussion of any of the taxonomic groups discussed above should consult the references cited, and especially the publications of the Freshwater Animal Diversity Assessment.

Veracruz, Mexico

The northern jacana (*Jacana spinosa*), seen here at Catemaco Lake, Veracruz, Mexico, is a common wading bird. —Claudio Contreras-Koob

Exploiting a nocturnal niche that is more commonly the domain of diurnal birds, a greater bulldog bat (*Noctilio leporinus*) in Panama swoops low over water and uses echolocation to detect ripples on the surface made by its prey—small fish. —Frans Lanting

Panama

A relative of the Arctic ringed seal, the nerpa (*Pusa sibirica*), endemic to Russia's Lake Baikal, is the only pinniped adapted exclusively to a freshwater habitat. —Boyd Norton

Following Spread:
Lake Baikal, Russia

TWO
AQUATIC
ECOSYSTEMS

AQUATIC ECOSYSTEMS
DIVERSITY AND DYNAMISM

Melanie L. J. Stiassny, Carmen Revenga, Patrick Comer

F reshwater habitats—the lakes, rivers, wetlands, and subterranean networks that freshwater species call home—are highly dynamic systems molded by a complex interplay of topography, geology, and climate. They are constantly created and replenished as precipitation, in the form of rain or snow, enters the terrestrial environment and flows above and below ground, shaping the landscape. This continuous cycling of water between the oceans, the atmosphere, and the land is what sustains life on Earth. Without the flow of water, life as we know it would cease, and few of the complex aquatic habitats that harbor so much of the planet's biodiversity would exist today.

Despite a relatively small footprint on Earth's surface—less than 0.008% of the volume of the planet's fresh water is found in rivers, freshwater lakes, and wetlands (Gleick, 1996)—freshwater ecosystems are extraordinarily rich and diverse. This diversity, in many ways, is created by the tremendous power of water, which constantly shapes and remodels the landscape. Rivers and glaciers erode away mountains, excavate valleys, and carry massive volumes of sediment that shape river floodplains and replenish the coastal zone. Surface water percolates through permeable portions of Earth's crust to create vast caves, sinkholes, and tunnels where water collects and forms underground aquatic networks—aquatic havens where numerous species colonize, diverge, and evolve. The power of water to remodel our planet is extraordinary; an average thunderstorm releases more energy than a 120-kiloton bomb, and the energy expended by the world's rivers as they seasonally flood landscapes and remodel their own channels, transport sediment, and build coastlines, exceeds that produced by our own species' energy-generating projects by two orders of magnitude (Leopold and Davis, 1966).

Freshwater ecosystems are not only disproportionally rich in species; they tend also to harbor high numbers of endemic species, species that are found only in a very small range—or even in just one particular location—and nowhere else. Such patterns of high species richness and endemism, in large part, are the result of the relative isolation of freshwater systems. Although shallow groundwater underlies most of the rivers, lakes, and wetlands, and contributes to their base flow, from a biological point of view, many aquatic systems are more or less isolated from one another, and usually have remained so for thousands, if not millions, of years. We can think of freshwater ecosystems—whether they are rivers or lakes, swamps or sinkholes—as "inverse" islands of water surrounded and separated from one another by land. Here isolation has allowed genetic mutations to accumulate and local adaptations to arise, ultimately resulting in the evolution of new species. Over time, many of those species have been able to disperse from river drainage to river drainage through headwater capture and flooding, or during times of major climatic change and geological upheaval, but many appear

Previous Spread: Atlantic salmon (*Salmo salar*), like these in Sweden, spend the first few years of their lives in freshwater streams and rivers before heading out to sea to mature. Along with overfishing, degradation of salmon rivers around the northern hemisphere has led to a precipitous decline among wild anadromous salmonid populations.
—Michel Roggo

Opposite: Water shamrock (*Marsilea mucronata*) grows in isolated playas and temporary pools from Mexico to Canada; its spores are dispersed in the digestive tracts of waterfowl. Peck Canyon, Coronado National Forest, Arizona, USA.
—Jack Dykinga

to have remained restricted to their natal drainages, lake basins, or wetland refuges. This has resulted in the patterns of endemism we see today.

Some regions, such as the humid tropics, have ample year-round supplies of fresh water and consequently a wide array of relatively stable aquatic habitats. Tropical and subtropical freshwater ecosystems tend to have high numbers of species, from the more than 1,000 fish species found in the main channel of the Congo River to the sixteen (and perhaps as many as nineteen) species of freshwater turtles found in the Mobile-Tensaw basin, in Alabama. In Florida, which neighbors Alabama, the Apalachicola River has fifteen (and perhaps as many as nineteen)

they burrow into mud or sand and become dormant when conditions become too dry or cold.

For scientists and conservationists, classifying and aggregating similar ecosystems into categories is a common goal. Classifications allow knowledge gained in one system to inform the conservation and management of similar systems in other locations, where information may be limited. It also facilitates management of, and communication about, these systems for policy makers and the public. But classifying the numerous kinds of freshwater habitats found today is not easy. No two water bodies are exactly the same, and no single water body is the same throughout the year; each is characterized by a unique combination

Rivers flow both above and below ground, and for many of the world's larger rivers the amount of free-flowing water visible in the channel is actually greatly exceeded by the "under-river flow" of groundwater.

species of freshwater turtles. Despite the similarity in numbers of species, and the geographical proximity of the Apalachicola and Mobile-Tensaw systems in the American South, the species lists for the two systems differ substantially; combined, the Apalachicola and Mobile-Tensaw systems contain one of the world's richest freshwater turtle fauna (Hoekstra et al., 2010; P. P. van Dijk, pers. comm.). In other parts of the world, such as the planet's large arid regions, far fewer surface freshwater ecosystems persist year-round, and these often experience wide fluctuations in water availability. These places tend to be more challenging for aquatic life, and species diversity is often low—although endemism can be high, with specialized plants and animals adapted to life in these harsh, isolated environments. In the southwest of the United States and in northern Mexico, numerous endemic species of desert pupfish (Cyprinodon spp.), for example, live in isolated warm waters, often extremely saline due to evaporation, and in individual desert springs, where

of geographical location, timing and duration of flow, and watershed connectivity. One way of looking at these habitats is to consider whether the waters they contain are flowing (rivers and streams) or still (lakes and ponds), or whether they are found above or below ground (surface water versus groundwater). Yet boundaries are often blurred. Rivers flow both above and below ground, and for many of the world's larger rivers the amount of free-flowing water visible in the channel is actually greatly exceeded by the "under-river flow" of groundwater in subsurface rocks in and around the river channel. These unseen waters often extend far out below the river's banks and floodplain, forming a dynamic and biologically important zone—the hyporheic zone—where surface and ground waters are in constant interaction and exchange (Edwards, 1998). Unlike terrestrial ecosystems, which are readily classified into broadly accepted major habitat types such as temperate grasslands, boreal forests, or Mediterranean scrub, the complex and dynamic nature of freshwater ecosystems makes it difficult to create a standard global classification. It is possible, of course, to recognize seemingly discrete forms such as lakes, rivers, ephemeral wetlands, and subterranean systems, but in many ways these are oversimplifications that denote what are essentially continuous and dynamic patterns of interconnectivity as if they were static, and completely discrete entities (Turak and Koop, 2008).

Most global and regional assessments have focused on a broad classification of the world's freshwater ecosystems into four main types: lotic (flowing) **fluviatile** systems (rivers, streams, brooks, creeks, etc.); lentic (slow-moving) **lacustrine** systems (lakes, ponds, oxbows, pools, etc.); **palustrine** wetlands (swamps, marshes, bogs and fens, etc); and subterranean **groundwater** systems (shallow and deep aquifers, sink holes, cenotes, etc.). Again, there is no clear-cut boundary between these. Rivers expand and contract with the seasons, and the paths they follow may change extensively over the years, as old channels become filled with sediment and new channels are formed. The Kosi River, a tributary of the Ganges, has moved about 120 km west of its historic channel over the last 220 years (Gopal et al., 2000). Some rivers give rise to lakes as they become dammed through accumulated sediment or, in the case of oxbow lakes, when bends in the river course become cut off from the main channel as it erodes a new course. These lakes may further fill with sediments, transitioning to palustrine wetlands and eventually to dry land. In other cases, lacustrine systems may themselves be the sources of rivers, and groundwater continuously seeps or flows in and out of all surface systems supplying much of their fresh water. Despite this seasonal ebb and flow, and the dynamic interconnectedness of each of these categories, such classification does provides a useful framework to begin to catalog the extraordinary diversity of aquatic "living spaces" over the planet's surface.

FLOWING WATERS

Rivers are perhaps the most visible manifestations of fresh water as it moves over the planet's surface. Since the earliest times, human civilizations have risen and fallen alongside the great rivers that provided food, water, a highway to travel along, and protection from outside intrusion. It is the rivers of the world that drain most of the land's surface, and they are found throughout climatic zones from humid to arid and from boreal to tropical. There is no hard-and-fast rule as to what makes a river a river (rather than a stream, a creek, a brook, or any other of the numerous designations we have to name these flowing waters), but all share a familiar tree-like (dendritic) organization consisting of a main river channel and relatively smaller river "branches," or tributaries. One of the most common ways of describing rivers is by categorizing the tributaries that feed into any given river network relative to their order within the landscape, starting with the highest-elevation streams. This is called the "stream-order" concept, and it recognizes a morphological hierarchy common to all rivers. All water flows downhill, and channel segments are ordered numerically with the highest elevation streams assigned a value of 1: "first order" streams. First-order streams are those with no joining tributaries and which arise entirely from springs, glaciers, or precipitation They are usually small, high-elevation streams, characterized by fast-flowing waters. The joining of two (or more) first-order streams forms a "second order" stream, and the downstream joining of second-order streams forms a third. A "third order" stream continues until joined by another third-order stream and there the "fourth order" begins, and so on, until a main trunk (or channel) is formed. As stream order increases, so does the length of the river, the volume of water it contains, and the area of the watershed it drains. The largest of the main trunks—the main river channel—carries the most water and also the river's name, and usually flows to the sea...but not always. Numerous rivers flow into lakes, some disappear underground,

Following Spread: Peat swamp forests in Indonesia, like these in the Kerumutan region of Sumatra, are being drained, logged, and converted to agricultural land at an astonishing rate. In addition to destroying important freshwater habitat, the desiccation of peat forest sets the stage for gigantic fires that release millions of tons of carbon stored in the peat.
—Daniel Beltrá

and others flow to the lowest point in the landscape, fanning out to form rich inland deltas or, in arid regions, evaporating into desolate saltpans. The shortest river in North America is the D River, a first-order effluent of Devil's Lake in Oregon that flows a mere 130 m from the lake before entering the Pacific Ocean. At the other extreme is the Mississippi River, which reaches the tenth order, the highest in all of North America; at 3,730 km in length it is also the longest river in North America. Worldwide, the highest-order "stream" is the massive Amazon, with no fewer than 1,000 joining tributaries draining a watershed of 6,144,727 square kilometers and carrying almost one-fifth of the world's river water to the sea. It is so huge and so complex that hydrologists are still trying to determine whether it is a twelfth- or thirteenth-order stream. The Amazon exhibits a typical dendritic hierarchical network, but—like many large rivers during high water—it floods its banks, inundating vast tracts of floodplain forest, dispersing sediment, and creating numerous seasonal lacustrine and palustrine habitats. The large floodplain lakes of another very large river, the Yangtze in China, are used as critical wintering grounds by waterfowl, including 98% of the world's population of the endangered Siberian white crane (Dudgeon, 1992).

Regardless of whether rivers occur in temperate or tropical basins, first- through third-order streams are usually considered "headwaters" that drain the upper reaches of a watershed, and these high-energy, fast-flowing waters form the erosive, sediment-production zones of most rivers. With decreasing elevation and increasing stream order, the channel width, water depth, and volume increase, and the sediment and debris generated primarily in the headwaters and suspended in the water column are transported in these middle reaches—often over large distances—and ultimately deposited, as the river's gradient inexorably declines in the highest-order channel and at the river mouth. Here the channel may fan out, forming a wide, nutrient-rich delta where estuarine conditions prevail and marine and inland faunas intermix along the tidal reaches.

As rivers course from headwaters to lower reaches, many of the physical and biological features that characterize each segment of the network also change, in a somewhat predictable fashion (Vannote et al., 1980). In headwaters, gradients are usually steep, with many rapids, riffles, and falls. The waters tend to be cool and well-oxygenated. The stream channels are narrow and shallow, and often shaded from direct sunlight by dense overhanging vegetation, so photosynthesis is limited and most energy is derived from leaves and other terrestrially derived material falling into the stream. In the mid-reaches, the gradient decreases and fewer rapids and falls are present; the stream channel widens, and sunlight penetrates the water's surface, allowing for the proliferation of aquatic plants and algae. As stream order increases further, the channel widens, deepens, and often meanders in wide sinusoidal bends. Terrestrial organic inputs become considerably less significant (compared with the water volume now in the channel) and energy is supplied primarily by dissolved organic material derived from upstream reaches. Phytoplankton and zooplankton, and organic inputs from floodplains during flood pulses, provide the food base, and water turbidity increases. As these physicochemical gradients change from source to mouth, biological communities shift and change in response. The communities of organisms—and the myriad specializations and adaptations needed to survive in low-order headwater streams—will be very different from those necessary to thrive in the more turbid, meandering flow farther downstream. Many of the endemic species in riverine systems are found in the more isolated, high-energy headwater systems, where endemics often exhibit an array of anatomical and physiological specializations suited to life in fast-flowing waters. Main river channels, on the other hand, tend to host larger, more widespread, and more ecologically generalized species. Understanding and mapping the way in which species are distributed *within* river basins, and the range of features that underlie those patterns, has only just begun for most of the world's rivers; this is an active field of research. Indeed, the rate at which new freshwater fishes are described is higher than for many other animal groups (see chapter 1).

One of the lesser-understood aspects of life in flowing waters is how important the unique combination of timing, duration, temperature, and flow volume (characteristic of each river system) is in sustaining essential processes and species interactions in rivers and wetlands (Lytle and Poff, 2004). To a large extent these physical factors rule life in lotic fresh waters; they can cue species to migrate, spawn, feed, and avoid predators. They also underpin essential dynamic processes such as bank erosion, channel reshaping and formation, and the relocation and deposition of riverborne material to form sandbars, sandbanks, and other essential habitats. Alteration of these elements—largely by dams and their reservoirs, by excessive water withdrawals, or by canalization of river reaches—is one of the primary threats to freshwater ecosystems and their species (Revenga et al. 2000; Postel and Richter 2003). Fish migration and reproduction are often triggered by changes in flow regime, such as spring peak floods, so changes in the timing and volume of these floods can disrupt migratory behaviors, destroy nesting habitats, wash away eggs, or bury nest sites (sometimes called "redds") with sediment. Similarly, decreased summer flows can reduce the number of upstream juvenile growing pools or block migration where water levels are too low to pass. The loss of migratory-fish runs not only impacts freshwater ecosystems; it can also affect ecosystems far inland. The renowned migrations of the many species of Pacific salmons, for example, bring nutrients from the Pacific Ocean far into upstream areas along the Pacific coast of North America, releasing nitrogen and phosphorus into upland rivers and streams as a huge biomass of salmon spawn and die. The released nutrients not only support aquatic food webs, but also those of terrestrial species such as bears, raccoons, and eagles,

as well as the forest ecosystems these species call home (Gende and Quinn, 2006). Similarly, benthic (bottom) river habitat, where filtering invertebrates live, can be altered by changes in sediment transport, often resulting in major impairment of water quality in rivers and estuaries. Sustaining these complex interrelationships between biological and hydrological factors by designing and operating dams to mimic natural river flows is becoming an emerging field in aquatic conservation, one that is aimed at meeting the needs of both people and nature (see chapter 5).

STILL WATERS

LACUSTRINE SYSTEMS

Most natural lakes are formed after glaciers, volcanoes, and earthquakes create depressions and faults on the land that fill with water. Reservoirs look like lakes and are often referred to as such, but they are created when a dam is built on a river channel, interrupting its flow and flooding the land behind it. When reservoirs transform river ecosystems into lakelike environments, native faunas are not usually able to adapt to the radically altered hydrological regimes; their populations are often extirpated or reduced to minimal numbers. As a result, many reservoirs are stocked with nonnative fish species such as trout, bass, or tilapia to enhance food production or to foster recreational fisheries. While there are still many more natural lakes than reservoirs, there are now reservoirs on most river systems on Earth, and the resulting altered flow regimes have often severely impacted downstream hydrology, ecosystem functioning, and biodiversity.

Unlike the highly dynamic fluviatile systems, lakes and reservoirs are landscape receivers, or "sinks," for runoff and sediments scoured from their watershed. As these sediments are continuously deposited, the water bodies gradually fill in. Over time, most lacustrine systems go through a typical "aging" process,

Sweden European white water lily (*Nymphaea alba*) is an aquatic flowering plant commonly found across Europe. Bohuslän, Sweden.
—Magnus Lundgren, Wild Wonders of Europe

Meltwater from winter snowpack on the east side of the Sierra Nevada flows into California's Owens River, supporting a rich riparian habitat in an otherwise arid valley. Several miles north of the river's natural terminus in Owens Lake, it is diverted via an aqueduct to supply a thirsty Los Angeles. —Justin Black

Owens River, USA

A lake sturgeon (*Acipenser fulvescens*) crosses the bottom of the St. Lawrence River, Canada. This keystone species is an indicator of healthy river and lake ecosystems. In the 1800s, populations plummeted due to over-harvesting and destruction of spawning habitat, but today they appear to be on the rebound in the Great Lakes, the St. Lawrence River, and the Lake Winnebago system. —David Doubilet

Following Spread, Canada

Okavango Delta, Botswana | A school of three-spotted tilapia (*Oreochromis andersonii*) glides through the floodwaters of the Okavango Delta, Botswana. The Okavango is home to more than seventy freshwater fish species. —David Doubilet

Aerial view of forest and swamps in the Yimas Lakes area, East Sepik Province, Papua New Guinea. Subject to seasonal fluctuations in the flow of the Sepik River, these extensive freshwater wetlands support diverse and dynamic habitats. —Tim Laman

Yimas Lakes,
Papua New Guinea

with a predictable sequence of decreasing depth and oxygen content, and a changing biological community structure. Before ultimately drying up, many pass through palustrine stages, becoming swamps, marshes, fens, or bogs until (after hundreds of years, in most cases) terrestrial vegetation invades and dry land eventually replaces them. The inexorable process of the filling in of lakes can take a long time, but lakes in different settings age at markedly different rates. Deep lakes and lakes with nutrient-poor, resistant watersheds can remain youthfully oligotrophic (nutrient-deficient but high in oxygen) for millions of years, while others (such as in the tropics, where heat and humidity act to rapidly accelerate the growth and decay of plants) will eutrophy, or gain in nourishment, more quickly.

Despite their geological transience, lakes, ponds, pools, and reservoirs currently contain about 87% of Earth's surface fresh water (a mere 2% is found in free-flowing rivers) (Gleick, 1996). Once again, there is no hard-and-fast rule as to what makes a lake a lake (rather than a pond or a pool), but surface area and depth are usually the arbiters. Smaller water bodies are termed ponds or pools, and larger ones considered lakes, but no internationally accepted definitions exist. Regardless of terminology, lacustrine ecosystems are dominant features on the planet's surface and are found from boreal regions to the tropics. But they are not distributed evenly across the globe; higher, northern latitudes have around 60% of the world's lakes and more than 40% of all of the planet's surface water. The wide range of lacustrine habitats and the rich variety of life they support is remarkable, and many different classifications have been proposed to categorize them.

How a lake has been formed typically determines its size and shape, as well as many of its biological properties. Most lakes, particularly in the upper latitudes of the northern hemisphere, have been formed by the ebb and flow of the vast glacial sheets of the last ice age. The advance and retreat of these massive glaciers stripped away soil and scoured bedrock. Glacial ice scooped out deep basins and, often in combination with tectonic mechanisms, created many of the lakes found throughout the northern hemisphere and, to a lesser extent, in the Chilean Andes, Tasmania, and New Zealand in the south. The North American Great Lakes—the largest interconnected system of inland waters on Earth—were formed in this way. Vast amounts of rock, gravel, and soil left behind by retreating glaciers (and called glacial drift) dammed rivers and blocked valleys, creating yet more lakes. Massive blocks of ice remained behind retreating glaciers and, insulated by glacial drift, often took many decades to melt, leaving behind characteristic, circular basins that filled with water to form the familiar kettle lakes, ponds, and bogs that dot the northern expanses of the planet. Because the great majority of lake formation dates from the last glacial maximum, most lakes are considerably less than 20,000 years old, and while many are rich in life, they are not (with few exceptions; see chapter 1) rich in endemic or highly specialized species. Not all of the planet's lacustrine systems are young, and a handful of lakes scattered over several continents can be considered, at least by lacustrine standards, truly "ancient." Most of these lakes are millions of years old, and are the products of tectonic faulting and uplift of Earth's crust. Examples of ancient lakes are Lake Biwa in Japan, Lake Ohrid in the Balkans, Lake Malawi in eastern Africa, the Andean Lake Titicaca, and Lake Lanao in the Philippines. While each has its own complex geomorphological history, geographical setting, bathymetry (variations in depth), and limnological characteristics, their collective longevity and isolation have resulted in the evolution of the highest levels of species richness and endemism of any of the planet's insular freshwater systems (Rossiter and Kawanabe, 2000). This is well-exemplified by two of the largest ancient lakes: Lake Baikal in southern Siberia and Lake Tanganyika in eastern Africa.

Lake Baikal is the world's oldest and deepest freshwater lake. Formed by rifting of Earth's crust more than 25 million years ago, it holds approximately one-fifth of the world's fresh water and at its deepest point reaches 1,637 m. Lake Baikal is outstanding not only in terms of its size, but also for a rich community of plants and animals that have evolved and adapted to the lake's environment. In all, 2,635 species of plants and animals are found in Lake Baikal, and more than 75% of these are found nowhere else on Earth (Russian Ministry of Natural Resources, 2007). Despite great depth, Baikal's waters remain oxygenated year-round; as a result, life can flourish in its depths. Among the fifty-two species of fishes

(Coulter, 1991). Of the 325 fish species living there, 290 are known only from the lake; among the seventy thiariid gastropod snails, thirty-five are endemic; and all eighty species of ostracod crustaceans are found only in this lake. Both Lakes Baikal and Tanganyika include radiations of freshwater sponges, which are otherwise uncommon in fresh water. Of the total of approximately 5,000 species of sponges in the world, only 197 are found in fresh water, and fourteen of those species (7%) belong to one family that is endemic to Lake Baikal (Lévêque et al., 2005). Each

In all, 2,635 species of plants and animals are found in Lake Baikal, and more than 75% of these are found nowhere else on Earth.

living in the lake, thirty-five are endemic and include fourteen species of highly specialized deepwater sculpin (Abyssocottidae). There are also more than 255 species of small amphipod crustaceans, called gammarids, and eighty flatworm species (Russian Ministry of Natural Resources, 2007), and 77% of the 147 species of the lake's gastropod mollusks are endemic (Strong et al., 2008). Such high richness and endemism is striking when compared to the ten to twelve fish species, two to three gammarids, eight or so flatworms, and half-dozen gastropod mollusks found in a typical European lake.

Lake Tanganyika, the largest lake in Africa, is nine to twelve million years old (Cohen et al, 1993). This is considerably younger than Baikal, but a similar picture of extraordinary species richness and endemism emerges here too. With a maximum depth of 1,470 m, Lake Tanganyika is second in depth only to Lake Baikal, but due to its tropical setting, Tanganyika is permanently stratified and nearly all of its waters are anoxic, so most of the life in the lake is concentrated in the upper 200 m of oxygenated water. Lake Tanganyika is home to about 1,400 species of animals and plants, more than 50% of which are found nowhere else

of the planet's ancient lakes harbors different plant and animal communities, but nearly all of them are home to concentrations of diverse, unique, and often highly specialized freshwater species (Rossiter and Kawanabe, 2000).

All lake waters contain dissolved minerals, but when their concentration exceeds 35 parts per thousand or 3.5% (or 35 g salt per liter), the water body is considered saline. The number of lacustrine bodies that are saline is surprisingly high, and saline lakes occupy almost as much of Earth's surface as do freshwater lakes. They are found primarily in the arid regions of every continent, and with a few notable exceptions such as the Caspian "sea," which began life more saline than it is today, most saline lakes began as freshwater bodies that have become isolated in closed (endorheic) basins. Water entering such basins from inflowing rivers, or by precipitation, can leave only by evaporation or seepage into underlying groundwater. With time, salts accumulate in the basin and the salinity of the water increases, resulting in a wide range of lakes of differing levels of salinity, concentrations of dissolved solids, and pH levels. Despite such seemingly inhospitable conditions, many

Following Spread: Russia's Lake Baikal is the world's oldest, deepest, and most voluminous freshwater lake, holding 20% of the liquid fresh water on Earth's surface. Of the 2,635 species of animals and plants that live there, three-quarters occur nowhere else. —Galen Rowell

of these salt and soda lakes and seasonal pans are extraordinarily productive. They can support a huge biomass of bacteria, algae, and highly specialized crustacean and insect communities, which in turn form important aggregation grounds for numerous feeding and nesting birds. For example, 75% of the global populations of lesser flamingo, *Phoeniconaias minor,* return each year to the alkaline Lake Natron in Tanzania to nest. In California's highly alkaline Mono Lake, considered one of the world's most productive ecosystems, dense blooms of blue-green algae (Cyanobacteria) support vast populations of endemic brine shrimp (*Artemia monica*) and Mono Lake alkali fly (*Ephydra hians*). The population sizes of these highly specialized species are enormous. The alkali fly, for example, occurs in Mono Lake in the highest densities of any saline aquatic ecosystem known, and as many as 4,000 flies have been counted in a single square foot (0.09 m2) of shoreline (Herbst, 1988). Mono Lake is also home to nesting colonies of 85% of the state's California gulls and 11% of the snowy plovers, and is visited by more than 80 species of resident and migratory water birds. Although highly productive (and some soda lakes are even home to a few physiologically adapted fish species), these harsh aquatic ecosystems tend to host low overall diversity.

PALUSTRINE WETLANDS

Palustrine wetlands are important ecotones existing at the interface of terrestrial and aquatic ecosystems. They are broadly defined as areas where water covers the soil, or is present at or near the surface at all times (perennial wetlands) or for varying periods of time during the year (ephemeral wetlands). Such wetlands support numerous aquatic and terrestrial species, and the prolonged presence of water favors conditions that promote the growth of specially adapted vegetation types as well as characteristically rich soils. They are ubiquitous around the globe, and highly varied in their physical and ecological characteristics and in the biodiversity they harbor and attract (Fraser and Keddy, 2005). Wetlands also vary enormously in

extent, from the massive Pantanal, which spans the borders of Brazil, Bolivia, and Paraguay and covers an area of 140,000 square kilometers in the dry season to as much as 210,000 square kilometers during flood (Harris et al., 2005; Mittermeier et al., 2005), to the smallest ephemeral bogs, fens, and vernal pools found studded throughout the terrestrial landscape. Some of these wetlands are amongst the most highly productive ecosystems on the planet; they play critical roles in maintaining water quality, nutrient cycling, and flood control, and can be extraordinarily rich in life. For example, in a small ephemeral pool of 0.16 ha in northern Florida, 16,155 individuals of forty-two species of amphibians and reptiles were captured over a five-year period (Dodd, 1992). A broad-brush analysis of the value of the world's ecosystem services estimated that wetlands are 75% more economically valuable than rivers and lakes (Costanza et al., 1997; and see chapter 5). While some have stressed caution in the interpretation of such analyses (e.g., Mitsch and Gosselink, 2000), there can be no question as to the essential roles of wetland systems in maintaining natural cycles and as refuges for huge numbers of plants and animals.

Fringing riparian zones, along river margins or around lakes, form an important interface between land and water and are often considered a distinct wetland type. Increasingly, riparian zones are recognized as key landscape features that perform vital ecological functions linking terrestrial and aquatic systems within watersheds (Pusey and Arthington, 2003). Riparian zones' combination of water availability, complex vegetation cover, and corridor-like connections to other landscapes provide critical connectivity and habitat for many species. On the Canadian prairie, for example, riparian zones have been found to contain seven times more bird species than surrounding grassland communities, and Nilsson (1992) reported that 13% of the entire Swedish flora of vascular plants occurs along a single river corridor.

Other wetland systems are equally complex and rich in life, and many wetland classifications exist. Generally speaking, wetlands can be grouped into four major types: marshes, swamps, bogs, and fens. Distinctions between them are not always clear-cut, and a number of the characteristics of each may be overlapping; most large, and many smaller, wetlands are made up of a complex mosaic of different wetland types. Nonetheless, broadly speaking, marshes and swamps are usually distinguished primarily by the dominant type of emergent vegetation (although there is considerable regional variation in the application of these names). Woody plants and trees dominate in swamps, whereas in marshes the dominant vegetation tends to be soft-stemmed herbaceous plants, reeds, and grasses, as well as floating and submerged plants.

Marshes are generally classified as either tidal or nontidal. Tidal marshes (which may be fresh, brackish, or salt) are found along secluded coastlines throughout mid- and high latitudes around the globe, where they play a vital role in flood control and nutrient- and runoff absorption, and provide food and habitat for numerous invertebrates, juvenile fishes, and shorebirds. For example, the Fujimae-Higata tidal mudflat Ramsar site, in the heart of the port city of Nagoya, is one of the most important staging sites on the East Asia-Australia flyway and a feeding and resting area for one of the largest congregations of migratory shorebirds in Japan.

Nontidal marshes frequently occur in poorly drained depressions alongside rivers and lakes, where water levels may vary from a few centimeters to many meters. These marshes can be vast, and much of the area of many of the world's largest wetlands are composed of endless expanses of flooded grasses. One such is the Saharan Sudd, where seasonally river-flooded grasslands cover about 16,000 km2 and provide complex habitat mosaics that support rich aquatic faunas and extraordinary congregations of migratory mammals and waterbirds (Rzóska, 1974).

Freshwater swamp forests, or flooded forests, which may be inundated permanently or seasonally, occur along the lower reaches of many rivers and around lakes in many parts of the world. Some of the most extensive of these are the *igapó* forests of the nutrient-poor black water rivers and the *várzea* forests of the nutrient- and sediment-rich white waters of the Amazon basin. These are regularly inundated for extended periods during the flood season, when the Amazon River and its tributaries rise as much as 10 m higher than their dry-season levels (Junk, 1997). These flooded forests provide enrichment of the floodplain and extensive flooded habitat for lateral migration of fishes and other organisms. Species in the *várzea* and *igapó* forests are quite different from each other; whereas plant species in the *várzea* are similar to those found in the upland terra firma, those in *igapó* systems are oligotrophic and distinct from those in upland areas (Vicentini, 2008). Seed dispersal by fishes during residence in such inundated regions is an important mechanism for forest renewal. The bottomland hardwood forests found in the broad floodplains of rivers of the southeast and central United States are another notable example of extensive swamp ecosystems of high biodiversity and global importance, as are the mangroves that are found in many parts of the world and which often take the place of marshes in the tidal and estuarine zones of the tropics.

Fens and bogs tend to differ primarily in the pH of their waters. Fens (and mires), like bogs, are peat lands, but are fed primarily by groundwater seepage; they tend not to be strongly acidic, and are generally higher in nutrients than are acidic bogs. Fens are mostly a phenomenon of the northern hemisphere, and are generally associated with low temperatures and short growing seasons. Fens, although often extremely nutrient-rich because of their northern locations, do not tend to harbor high levels of species diversity or endemism of aquatic life; but many provide refuge for important communities of birds, snails, dragonflies, butterflies, and plants. Bogs, in contrast, occur where

water inputs are primarily from rainwater, which is generally more acidic than groundwater. In bogs, accumulations of dead sedges, mosses, and other plant material form deep layers of peat, raising the surface above the influence of groundwater and staining the water a characteristic tea color. Bogs (and heaths) are scattered throughout the northern hemisphere. Most are small, but some cover large areas, as in the Canadian interior or the western Siberian lowlands of Russia, where a rich mosaic of bogs covers more than 600,000 square kilometers. The acidic conditions and low productivity of boreal bogs make them inhospitable to much aquatic biodiversity, and even insect diversity is often low and restricted principally to the larvae of chironomid water midges and specialized sphagnum moss–associated ground (Carabidae) and rove (Staphylinidae) beetles.

Such depauperate faunas are not the case, however, in tropical peat-swamp forests, which are not only highly productive and one of the largest terrestrial carbon sinks (Jauhianinen et al., 2005), but also extraordinarily rich in species, many of which are endemic to these unique habitats. Worldwide, peat swamps are estimated to cover close to 350,000 square kilometers (UNDP, 2006) and are common to many tropical regions with high rainfall. They occur in parts of Africa's Congo basin, in the Florida Everglades, in Central America, and in Papua New Guinea—but more than 60% of the world's tropical peat lands are found in Southeast Asia, most notably on Borneo and Sumatra. While it has generally been thought that species diversity in these wetland systems was low compared with other forest types, many recent studies have begun to challenge that idea (Yule, 2010). Despite seemingly inhospitable conditions, peat swamps support high numbers of highly specialized, endemic aquatic plants and trees; in addition to peatland-specialized species, representatives of most of the families of lowland dipterocarp forests are also present. Malaysia's peat-swamp forests alone provide sanctuary for more than sixty bird and mammal species listed on the IUCN Red List as globally threatened (Sebastian,

2002), and the rate of discovery of highly specialized, stenotypic species across phyla in these habitats is also extremely high. For fishes in particular, these are habitats rich in species; 200 to 300 have been recorded from the peat lands of peninsular Malaysia, Borneo, and Sumatra—many of them restricted to small areas—and new discoveries are being made each year. In 2006, the smallest living vertebrate, the fish *Paedocypris progenetica,* was discovered in an isolated peat swamp on Sumatra (Kottelat et al., 2006; and see Introduction). Far from being depauperate, tropical peat swamp forests are being recast as centers of high species diversity and endemism, with many of those species having narrow niches and very restricted ranges.

GROUNDWATER ECOSYSTEMS

Groundwater ecosystems are some of the least-studied and most poorly known habitats on Earth, yet these subterranean waters form a vital underground connection for almost all rivers, lakes, and wetlands on the planet's surface. Groundwater reserves represent an enormous reservoir of water—about one hundred times the total amount contained in all rivers and lakes combined—and as much as 30% of the water volume found in rivers, lakes, and wetlands reaches them from this subterranean source (Pringle, 1987). Groundwater is continually replenished as precipitation falling on land drains downward, through loose outer layers of soil, sand, and gravel at the surface. Below this granular layer are porous sandstones and carbonate rocks, through which water slowly seeps through pores and fissures until it is finally stopped by impermeable bedrock. Above the bedrock, groundwater accumulates and spreads out horizontally, saturating vast expanses of subterranean earth with water. Once all of the openings and cracks in the permeable rock layers are fully saturated, the top of this underground zone forms the water table. The depth of the water table anywhere on Earth depends on many factors, but precipitation, climate, and geology are primary determinants. The water

Opposite: The Yucatán Peninsula in Mexico is pockmarked with cenotes like this one at Samula. These water-filled caverns and sinkholes, created by dissolution of the limestone bedrock, are home to numerous endemic species and are tapped by fig trees (*Ficus spp.*) and other vegetation on the surface. —Jack Dykinga

table may be only a few centimeters below ground near wetlands or along river courses and lake bottoms, or it can be thousands of meters deep in arid regions. Any water-saturated layer of rock (usually limestones, sandstones, and gravels) is called an aquifer, and the water table above it rises and falls with the surface topology. In places where the surface contour drops more steeply than the water table beneath it, saturated earth is exposed and a spring or a seep arises. In other places, where the surface contour dips below the water table, a lake or wetland marsh or swamp will form, and across the lowest dip in a valley the water table supplies much of the flow of many rivers. In just about any part of the globe, a hole dug deep enough will gain access to groundwater sequestered in an aquifer. Even in the driest deserts, such as the Sahara in North Africa, large volumes of groundwater can be sequestered deep below the surface in deep, often ancient, aquifers. Many of these fossil aquifers were formed during the last ice age and are no longer replenished by precipitation—over-pumping these aquifers is therefore unsustainable, and eventually results in the loss of the resource.

The great majority of groundwater is present in the interstices of rocks, and in saturated earth. These interstitial groundwater environments may support numerous microorganisms (as do deep artesian basins) but do not provide livable space for many plants and animals. In some places, however, groundwater exists abundantly in clearly defined pools, or flows in identifiable streams; it is in these places where the great variety of subterranean aquatic habitats and biodiversity is to be found (Danielopol et al., 2000, 2003). Such habitats are commonly formed in karst landscapes, in which the extensive dissolution of rock has led to the development of subterranean channels where groundwater flows or pools. Here, the dominant surface formations are carbonate rocks, usually fractured limestones and underlying dolomites that are differentially dissolved by mildly acidic precipitation (formed as water incorporates CO_2 to produce weak carbonic acid). The resultant karsts

are rugged landscapes characterized by numerous sinking streams, underground caverns, and sinkholes. Surprisingly, almost 20% of the planet's land surface is karst, and particularly large and often dramatic formations are found in Madagascar, southern China, Southeast Asia, the eastern United States, Western Europe, and the Yucatán Peninsula of Mexico, and on some Caribbean islands (White et al., 1995). Over time, small voids and fissures are reworked by dissolution into vast caves, caverns, and tunnels, which fill with water and form complex networks of underground rivers and lakes. Many of the unique features of karst landscapes are the result of internal drainage through these conduits, which intimately couple surface and subsurface hydrology. Karst conduits usually drain through high-discharge springs, and it is not unusual for a subterranean system to have several discharge points. Because karst systems are typically highly fragmented and offer stable environments over long periods of time, their cave and spring faunas often have restricted distributions and are highly specialized. The high regional diversity of species in subterranean systems, and particularly in cave systems, may be attributed to several factors (Danielopol et al., 2000), including the low concentration of competitors and predators, such as insects; the often dynamic geology of the environment, creating new habitats for colonization from surface-dwelling species; the relative thermal stability of habitats; and the often low extinction rates and high rates of speciation by colonizing species. As most input of organic materials into these subterranean systems originates from the outside, food resources are often limited, and selection on cave-dwelling animals has tended to produce similar adaptations in diverse animal groups. Most *troglobites* (obligate cave dwellers; aquatic troglobites are often termed *stygobites*) tend to be smaller, have lower fecundity, exhibit slower development and growth, live longer, and have larger fat reserves than most *troglophiles* (facultative cave dwellers) and *epigean* (above-ground) relatives. They also often completely lack pigmentation and have reduced or absent eyes, and typically have highly developed sensory systems.

While these nutrient-poor subterranean systems are not notably rich in species, they are often strikingly rich in highly specialized endemic species. For example, in the single subterranean Movile Cave and associated springs in Romania, forty-eight species of invertebrates have been recorded. Thirty-four of these are thought to be endemic to this system, and they include the first known cave-adapted aquatic hemipteran, a water scorpion (*Nepa anophthalma*), and the first known stygobitic leech (*Haemopsis caeca*) (Lascu et al., 1993; Lascu, 2004).

Another common feature of karst landscapes and other areas underlain by carbonate rocks, salt beds, or porous volcanic rocks are sinkholes. Sinkholes may vary in size from less than a meter to hundreds of meters across, and similarly may be extremely deep or little more than shallow depressions. They form in a number of ways, but most commonly when limestone is dissolved away from below until the roof of an underground cavern collapses. The density of sinkholes in some regions of the world can reach the hundreds in a couple of square kilometers, giving the landscape a characteristic "pockmarked" appearance when viewed from above. Some of the most spectacular sinkholes on Earth are the *cenotes* of Mexico and a few nearby islands in the Caribbean (Schmitter-Soto et al., 2002). Cenotes vary in topology, but typically have a circular opening into a deep, cylindrical shaft that descends in sheer walls to an open groundwater pool, often tens to hundreds of meters below. The Zacatón Cenote in Tamaulipas state on the northeastern coast of Mexico is the world's deepest water-filled sinkhole. Numerous deeper cenotes extend well beyond the reach of exploratory divers, but Zacatón was charted in 2007 by a NASA-designed robotic vehicle that was able to locate bottom at a record depth of 318 m. Many of the cenotes in the Tamaulipas region of Mexico appear not to be connected horizontally by subterranean conduits, but rather to be isolated units where the water is often extremely clear because it derives almost entirely from rainwater infiltrating slowly through the ground. In contrast, the cenotes

along the Caribbean coast of the Yucatán Peninsula feed into a large and complex coastal conduit aquifer system, which is typically sharply stratified with denser salt water overlain by a thick lens of fresh water derived from precipitation. Where cenotes provide deep enough access into the aquifer, the interface between the fresh and saline water can be reached. Cenotes are scattered over much of the Yucatán, but a notable concentration of them rings the edge of the ancient Chicxulub impact crater, buried beneath the northwestern edge of the peninsula. Biodiversity exploration in cenotes is in its infancy, and while these extraordinary habitats appear to harbor reasonably large numbers of aquatic species and provide habitat for numerous bird and bat species (Schmitter-Soto et al., 2002), levels of endemism are not high.

Most of our knowledge of the biodiversity they harbor is restricted to peripheral aquifers and to a few deep cave systems where exploration has been possible despite extremely hazardous conditions and the need for rigorous technical cave-diving and climbing skills. As a result, our knowledge of most of these systems is extremely incomplete, and discovery rates are high. Between 1980 and 2005 the rate of discovery of subterranean fishes, for instance, quadrupled in comparison with discoveries made over the preceding sixty-year period (Proudlove 2006), a trend that suggests that the current number of eighty-six species (Trajano, 2001) may increase by as much as 25% by 2020.

To date, more than 6,600 aquatic vertebrate, invertebrate, and protozoan species have been recorded in groundwater systems, and a global total of 50,000 to 100,000 obligate subterranean species has been proposed (Gibert and Deharveng, 2002). Whereas insects are usually uncommon in groundwaters, crustacean species are an important component of the subterranean macroinvertebrate fauna; copepods, isopods, and amphipods are among the most widespread and taxonomically diverse (Sket, 1999). Holsinger (1993) listed 740 species of the amphipod suborder Gammaridea, representing 138 genera and thirty-six families. Of the twelve orders of crustaceans recorded in subterranean aquatic systems, six are exclusively or essentially stygobite groups (Stoch, 1995, cited in Gibert and Deharving, 2002). Range-restricted species usually account for more than 50% of the subterranean fauna (at least in areas not affected by recent climatic events such as glaciations), and may represent up to 90% of the fauna (Sket, 1999; Gibert and Deharveng, 2002). An increased priority for conserving these subterranean habitats is clearly justified by the fact that subterranean species show unique adaptations, and may represent unique evolutionary lineages, as does the ancient salamander *Proteus anguinus,* which is restricted to caves in southern Europe (Sket, 1997; AmphibiaWeb, 2010).

A remarkably complex and diverse array of aquatic ecosystems supports and connects all life on Earth. But unlike the more familiar terrestrial ecosystems, which are readily classified into well-defined global habitat types, freshwater systems are in an almost constant state of flux. The dynamic nature of these systems as they flow through landscapes, expand and contract with the seasons, and carve new channels, basins, and networks renders their classification into globally "equivalent" units far more challenging. Each system is characterized by a unique combination of geography, climate, and the hydrological timing and duration of flow. While we recognize lakes, rivers, wetlands, and subterranean systems as separate and discrete entities, these distinctions are, in many ways, simply ephemeral manifestations of the dynamic interconnectivity of water as it cycles through the planet. As we have seen, the planet's numerous freshwater ecosystems and associated habitat types support large numbers of species (as discussed in chapter 1) and, on a hectare-for-hectare basis, are far richer than the more extensive terrestrial and marine ecosystems of the planet. Similarly, it is the heterogeneity of these ecosystems and, in many cases, their biologically insular nature that explains the high levels of species endemism found within them.

Opposite: Spelunkers drop down Mystery Hole, a 100-meter-deep limestone pit eroded by a waterfall that pours from its top. Chatanooga, Tennessee —George Steinmetz

Following Spread: Alluvial gold mines, such as this one in the rain forest of Guyana, destroy the riverbed, promote erosion, degrade the forest, and often have unforeseen downstream consequences. —Pete Oxford

THREE
FRESHWATER ECOSYSTEMS UNDER THREAT

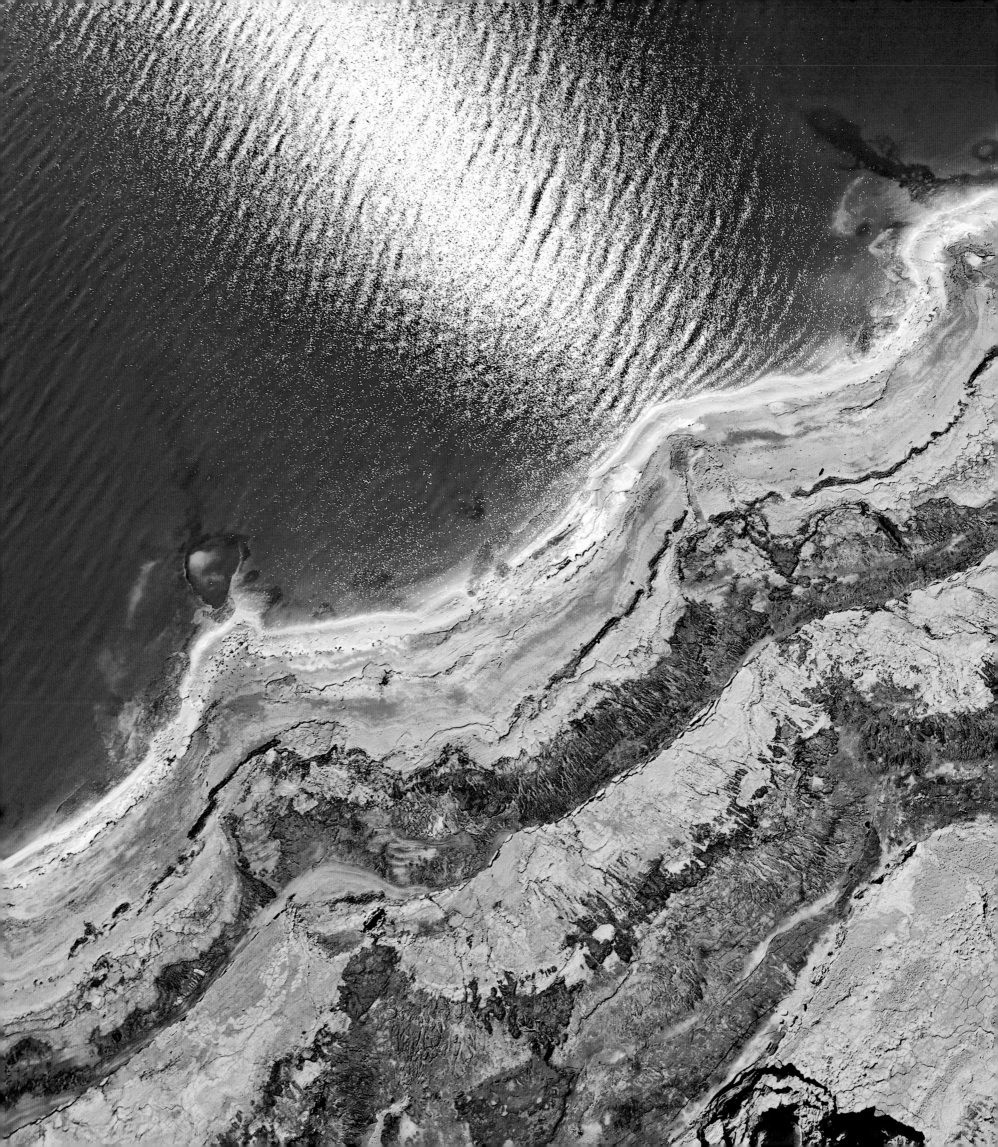

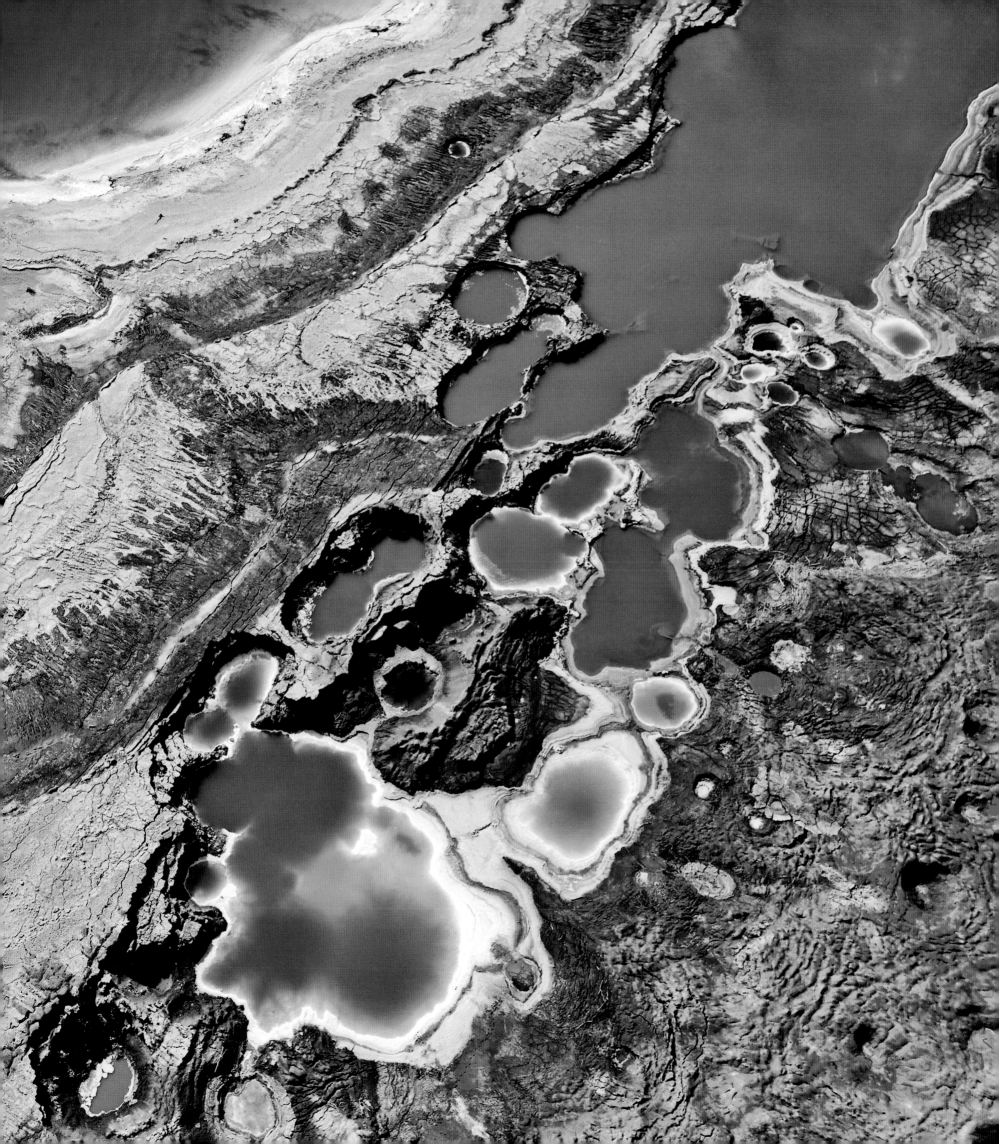

FRESHWATER ECOSYSTEMS UNDER THREAT
THE ULTIMATE HOTSPOT

M. L. Thieme, Eren Turak, Peter McIntyre, William Darwall, Klement Tockner, Jay Cordeiro, Stuart H. M. Butchart

F resh waters have the dubious distinction of occupying the lowest points in a landscape, making the health of rivers, lakes, and wetlands intimately dependent on that of the land. For millennia, human communities have settled along the shores of rivers and lakes, benefiting from the availability of water, productive soils, and bountiful food sources. Freshwater systems, species, and the ecosystem services they provide, though, are increasingly stressed and strained. The health of any given freshwater system is defined by the quality and quantity of its water, its natural connections to other parts of the landscape and water bodies, the condition of its habitat, and its diversity of plant and animal species (Karr and Dudley, 1981). The pressures created by human settlements, water use, and contamination are impinging on all aspects of the health of rivers and lakes. As a result, aquatic species and ecosystems face an uncertain future.

CONSERVATION STATUS OF FRESHWATER SPECIES

Freshwater ecosystems contain disproportionately more species per unit area than do marine and terrestrial ecosystems. Although fresh waters cover less than 1% of Earth's surface, they provide habitat for more than 10% of the known animals and about one-third of all known vertebrate species (Balian et al., 2008; and see chapter 1). Our current knowledge of freshwater species diversity varies greatly between groups of animals, but overall significantly underestimates actual diversity. For example, even among the relatively well-known fishes, current estimates are about 13,000 described freshwater fish species, with many new species being described each year (Abell et al., 2008; Lévêque et al, 2008; Stiassny, 1999).

The paucity of information for many plant and animal groups and the high rate at which new species are being described make an accurate assessment of all species impossible, such that there has been no comprehensive global assessment of the status of freshwater species. Great progress, however, has been achieved in accumulating knowledge of the status of several individual groups in recent years (Vié et al., 2009). Freshwater mammals, crocodiles, turtles, amphibians, and crabs have been assessed globally (Stuart et al., 2004, 2008; Schipper et al., 2008; Cumberlidge et al., 2009; BirdLife International, 2010; IUCN, 2010) and freshwater crayfish are in the final stages of assessment. The results of the completed assessments show that a high proportion of

Previous spread: Diversions of fresh water from the Jordan River into Israel have caused the Dead Sea to drop steadily since 1960. As the water table lowers along with the lake, sinkholes form along the emerging shoreline as subterranean salt deposits are dissolved.
—George Steinmetz

Left: Boy jumping over a trash-choked creek in Moradbad, India. The village's water and soil are contaminated, hampering efforts to immunize against polio. —Karen Kasmauski

Taxonomic Group	Geographic Coverage	Number of freshwater species	Number of freshwater species classified as 'Data Deficient' (IUCN) or 'Unrankable'/'Not yet ranked' (NatureServe)	Number of freshwater species classified as 'threatened' (IUCN or NatureServe), or 'vulnerable/threatened/endangered' (American Fisheries Society Endangered Species Committee); see references for definitions	Number of freshwater species classified as 'Extinct' or 'Extinct in the wild' (IUCN), or Presumed or Possibly Extinct (NatureServe), or Exinct/Possibly Extinct/Extirpated in Nature (American Fisheries Society Endangered Species Committee); see references for definitions.	Percentage of freshwater species (excluding those that are Data Deficient, Unrankable, or Not Yet Ranked) that are classified as 'threatened' (IUCN or NatureServe), or "vulnerable/threatened/endangered' (American Fisheries Society Endangered Species Committee); see references for definitions	Percentage of freshwater species (excluding those that are Data Deficient, Unrankable, or Not Yet Ranked) classified as 'Extinct' or 'Extinct in the wild' (IUCN), or Presumed or Possibly Extinct (NatureServe), or Exinct/Possibly Extinct/Extirpated in Nature (American Fisheries Society Endangered Species Committee); see references for definitions.	Reference
Freshwater vascular plants	Southern Africa	156	23	25	0	19	0	Darwall et al. (2009)
Crustacea: Decapoda, Brachyura (true crabs)	Global	1280	628	209	0	32	0	Cumberlidge et al (2009)**
Crustacea: Decapoda, Potamonautidae (freshwater crabs)	Southern Africa	16	3	1	0	7.7	0	Darwall et al. (2009)
Crustacea: Decapoda (freshwater crabs)	Eastern Africa	37	0	20	0	54	0	Darwall et al. (2005)
Freshwater Gastropoda (snails)	U.S. and Canada	719	8	435	84	61	12	NatureServe (2010)
Freshwater Bivalvia (mussels)	U.S. and Canada	301	1	175	30	58	10	NatureServe (2010)
Freshwater mollusks	Southern Africa	56	33	6	0	26	0	Darwall et al. (2009)
Freshwater mollusks	Eastern Africa	215	90	35	0	28	0	Darwall et al. (2005)
Anostraca (fairy shrimps), Conchostraca (clam shrimps), Notostraca (tadpole shrimps)	U.S. and Canada	91*	0	40	4	44	4.4	NatureServe (2010)
Astacoidea and Parastacoidea (crayfishes)	U.S. and Canada	356	0	185	3	52	0.8	NatureServe (2010)
Ephemeroptera (mayflies)	U.S. and Canada	577*	1	198	13	35	2.3	NatureServe (2010)
Odonata (dragonflies and damselfies)	U.S. and Canada	478*	4	79	3	17	0.6	NatureServe (2010)
Odonata (dragonflies and damselfies)	Europe (geographic)	137*	5	21	0	16	0	Kalkman et al. (2010)
Odonata (dragonflies and damselfies)	Southern Africa	64	18	15	0	32	0	Darwall et al. (2009)
Odonata (dragonflies and damselfies)	Eastern Africa	295	21	21	0	7.6	0	Darwall et al. (2005)
Plecoptera (stoneflies)	U.S. and Canada	666*	0	289	12	43	1.8	NatureServe (2010)
Trichoptera (caddisflies)	U.S. and Canada	1421*	17	636	12	45	0.9	NatureServe (2010)
Freshwater fishes	Europe (geographic)	546	55	200	15	41	3.1	Kottelat & Freyhof (2007)
Freshwater fishes	Mediterranean basin	253	41	142	8	67	3.8	Smith and Darwall (2006)
Freshwater fishes	U.S., Canada, and Mexico	1187		432	36	36	3	Jelks et al. (2008)***
Freshwater fishes	Southern Africa	239	57	40	0	22	0	Darwall et al. (2009)
Freshwater fishes	Eastern Africa	901	73	250	2	30	0.2	Darwall et al. (2005)
Amphibians	Global	4245	980	1109	19	34	0.6	IUCN (2010)
Mammals	Global	145	19	54	4	43	3.1	IUCN (2010)
Birds	Global	1979	9	202	19	10	1	Birdlife International (2010)

Table 3.1. Global and regional assessments of threat for freshwater species (IUCN Red List data based on statistics in the IUCN Red List of Threatened Species as of May, 2010).
* this assumes that all species listed in the NatureServe database are freshwater.
** Cumberlidge et al. (2009) use IUCN Red List criteria to classify species as threatened

species are threatened or extinct. For example, 46% of freshwater mammals, 35% of amphibians, 38% of freshwater turtles, 11% of freshwater birds, and 32% of freshwater crabs that are not data deficient are considered threatened or extinct (Buhlmann et al., 2009; Turtle Taxonomy Working Group, 2009; and see table 3.1). The total number of threatened freshwater turtles is likely to exceed 50% when all turtle assessments are completed.

The Red List Index, which tracks trends in the extinction risk of species based on IUCN Red List assessments, confirms that the status of freshwater species of birds, mammals, and amphibians have been declining worldwide for at least the last fifteen to twenty years (fig. 3.1; Butchart et al., 2005; Hilton-Taylor et al., 2009).

In fact, half the known species of amphibians are declining in numbers, and the rate at which amphibian species are currently being lost from the planet by extinction are one hundred to 1,000 times greater than historical rates, as with other species groups (Stuart et al., 2004, 2008; IUCN, 2010).

A global assessment of freshwater fishes has not yet been completed, but regional analyses show that freshwater fishes are also highly threatened. In North America, 36% of species are threatened and about 3% presumed extinct or extirpated from nature (Jelks et al., 2008). In Europe, 38% (200 species) are listed as globally threatened and an additional 2% (thirteen species) are extinct (Kottelat and Freyhof, 2007). Since 1700, at least fifteen vertebrate species have gone extinct in Europe—one of these is marine, two are terrestrial, and all the rest are freshwater fish species (Tockner et al., 2009). A regional assessment of the Mediterranean, including North Africa, found that the majority, 56%, of Mediterranean endemic freshwater fish species are threatened (Smith and Darwall, 2006). In assessments of East and southern Africa, 27% and 11%, respectively, of freshwater fishes were found to be regionally threatened (Darwall et al., 2005, 2009). Along with the Mediterranean, Madagascar has the highest proportion of globally threatened species, with more than 50% of fishes threatened or extinct (IUCN/SSC, 2004). A recent analysis for the IUCN Red List also determined that an extremely high proportion of

sturgeon species (85%) are at risk of extinction.

Among invertebrates, the trend is similar. In a sample of 1,500 species of dragonflies and damselflies that was selected to be taxonomically and geographically representative of the whole group, 13.9% of the species are threatened (Clausnitzer et al., 2009). Mollusks have the greatest number of documented extinctions of any major animal group (41% of 721 recorded animal extinctions since the year 1500 [IUCN, 2010]). Thirty percent of the documented mollusk extinctions are of freshwater species. In North America, freshwater mussels are generally considered the most endangered group of animals: Between 67% and 70% of North American freshwater mussels are threatened with extinction or are already extinct (Williams et al., 1993; Master et al., 2000; Lydeard et al., 2004; Strayer et al., 2004). In the United States alone, Master et al. (2000) estimated that thirty-seven species of freshwater mussels are extinct or possibly extinct. Preliminary evidence suggests that North American freshwater snails, particularly the families Hydrobiidae and Pleuroceridae, are similarly threatened and may approach the imperilment numbers seen in freshwater mussels (Lydeard et al., 2004; Brown et al., 2008; Lysne et al., 2008; Perez and Minton, 2008), with more than sixty species (possibly as many as eighty) presumed extinct in the United

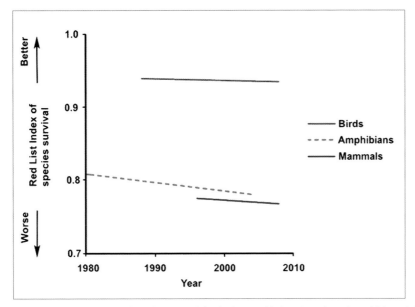

Figure 3.1. Red List Index of species survival for freshwater birds, mammals and amphibians. A Red List Index value of 1.0 indicates that all species are categorized as Least Concern and not expected to become extinct in the near future. A Red List Index of zero indicates that all species have become extinct. (See Butchart et al, 2005; Hilton-Taylor et al., 2009).

Following spread: Hoover Dam on the Colorado River formed Lake Mead, which stores water and produces 2,080 megawatts of electricity for Southern California, Nevada, and Arizona. The dam's construction had significant unforeseen impacts on the river's native floras and faunas, particularly in the wetlands and estuaries of the Colorado Delta across the border in Mexico. —Jenny E. Ross

States (Christian and Harris, 2008; NatureServe, 2010). In the biologically diverse Coosa River basin in the southeastern United States, twenty-six species and three entire genera of freshwater snails (*Amphigyra, Gyrotoma,* and *Neoplanorbis*, plus *Clappia*, which was recently rediscovered) are presumed extinct (Bogan et al., 1995).

Two key traits of freshwater species that make them so imperiled are limited geographic range and limited dispersal pathways. Many species have evolved within an individual lake or river basin, and remain confined to a small area. Essentially, freshwater habitats are akin to islands surrounded by vast areas of unsuitable dry land or salt water. Species living in these habitats are susceptible to the same vulnerabilities as those on oceanic islands with relatively long evolutionary histories essentially in isolation and with limited opportunities for dispersal (Strayer et al., 2006). As a consequence, when conditions in a water body are degraded, many of its animal and plant species may be threatened with extinction. The high proportion of threatened freshwater species noted in Madagascar (see above) is partly because many of the species have restricted ranges (Benstead et al., 2003). In particular, taxonomic groups with limited dispersal abilities and narrow habitat tolerances, such as certain species of freshwater mussels, freshwater crabs, crayfish, and freshwater vascular plants, are unable to colonize new areas quickly when conditions become inhospitable due to ongoing threats. In addition, many freshwater organisms such as diadromous (migratory between fresh and salt waters) fishes, aquatic insects, and amphibians have complex life cycles restricted to different habitats during larval and adult stages, which makes them highly vulnerable to multiple pressures.

MAJOR THREATS TO FRESHWATER ECOSYSTEMS

Human activities have profoundly altered the physical, chemical, and biological characteristics of freshwater ecosystems around the world. Throughout recorded history, humans have relied on fresh water for drinking, waste disposal and treatment, fishing and aquaculture, irrigation and farming, power generation, and recreation (see chapter 5). The vast majority of the world's population centers lie either in coastal areas or along rivers and lakes. Jackson et al. (2001) estimated that one-half of accessible freshwater runoff across the globe is now utilized in some way by humans. No corner of the planet remains unaffected, and most freshwater ecosystems suffer from multiple threats (Ormerod et al., 2010). In response to threats, many freshwater ecosystems exhibit distinct regime shifts leading to dramatic alterations in biodiversity and ecosystem functioning (Dent et al., 2002; Carpenter, 2003). Fresh waters may shift from a clear to a turbid state, from permanent to temporary waters, from flowing to still waters, from well-oxygenated to anoxic states, or from connected to disconnected landscape elements. Threats include dams, diversions, and associated water infrastructure; changes in land use and direct conversion of aquatic habitats; invasive species; overexploitation; chemical pollution; and climate change (Allan and Flecker, 1993; Malmqvist and Rundle, 2002; Dudgeon et al., 2005; Strayer, 2006). These threats rarely act in isolation; rather, they have synergistic effects that complicate management priorities and responses.

DAMS, DIVERSIONS, AND OTHER WATER INFRASTRUCTURE

The hydrologic regime, or "hydropattern," is considered the "master variable" in determining the overall function and health of freshwater systems (Poff et al., 1997; Jackson, 2006). Dams, water diversions, and stream-channel straightening (channelization) disrupt the hydrologic regime and alter natural processes within aquatic ecosystems. These structures fragment the physical connectivity of aquatic systems—blocking species movements between habitats and during migration, and disconnecting rivers from their floodplains and associated wetlands. More than half of 292 large rivers around the world

Left: The common grayling (*Thymallus thymallus*) has become less common in Swiss rivers. Pollution and damming that decrease oxygen content have reduced size and contiguity of useful habitats, while increased sedimentation covers the rocky river bottom on which the fish lay their eggs. Lake Thun, Switzerland. —Michel Roggo

Owens Lake went dry when the Los Angeles Department of Water and Power diverted the flow of the Owens River 320 km to the south to serve the needs of its growing population in the early 20th century. Today, bubblers dampen the lakebed to mitigate hazardous particulate pollution, frequently lifted aloft by strong winds in the valley. —Jenny E. Ross

are already fragmented by large dams on their main stems, with only arctic tundra regions drained primarily by unimpounded rivers (Nilsson et al., 2005). Continental assessments in the northern hemisphere show widespread impoundment damming of rivers and streams of all sizes. In the United States alone, more than 80,000 large dams and 2.5 million smaller impoundments occur (Graf, 1999; Smith et al., 2002). Dams and other infrastructure, interbasin transfers, and water extraction also modify the flow regime by changing the seasonal or daily flow volume, velocity, and temperature patterns, and by altering sediment movement through the system. The resulting dams and reservoirs also serve as barriers to dispersal, essentially isolating populations. By the end of the twentieth century, more than 45,000 large dams had been constructed in more than 140 countries (Malmqvist and Rundle, 2002). About 20% to 25% of continental runoff and about 25% to 30% of the total global sediment flux in rivers are now held behind reservoirs (Vörösmarty et al., 2003, 2004). These changes often have devastating consequences for species (Pringle et al., 2000). For example, intensive water management, a series of large dams, and introduced species have completely changed the hydrology of the Colorado River in the United States; it no longer runs to the sea during dry periods (Postel, 2003). These changes have caused a large portion of the fauna to decline: Sixteen of the twenty-eight native fish species in the Lower Colorado River have seen a reduction in range by greater than 35%, seventeen species are currently listed on the U.S. Endangered Species List, and one species is extinct (Olden and Poff, 2005). Another example comes from the tributaries of the Tennessee River and Mobile Bay basins, which have been largely reduced to a series of big reservoirs due to impoundments along the main stem. The result has been the loss of much of the most diverse freshwater mussel assemblage in North America, with the global extinction of about sixty species of freshwater mollusks (Neves et al., 1997).

A major driver of dam building is energy production. In 2007, about 2% of the world's energy and 16% of its electricity was produced from hydropower. Much of the developed world has maximized its hydropower production potential, and current focus is on maintaining or decommissioning existing infrastructure. However, the developing world is continuing to build large dams as it expands its hydropower production. China (15.4%), Brazil (11.9%), Canada (11.7%), and the United States (8%) made up nearly half of the world's hydropower as of 2007, and are currently the largest producers of hydroelectricity (Totten, 2008, pers. comm.). China alone plans to more than double its hydropower capacity by 2020 (Totten, 2008, pers. comm.). Several dams currently planned on the lower Mekong main stem could alter the hydrology in the delta and adversely affect the livelihoods and food security of millions that rely on the natural resources of the Mekong Delta (Dugan et al., 2006). In the Yangtze River, large dams affect the survival of the Yangtze sturgeon and Chinese paddlefish, two large and charismatic species that are Critically Endangered (IUCN, 2010).

Beyond energy production, the development of water infrastructure is largely driven by irrigated agriculture, flood protection, and water supply to communities and businesses. Agriculture is the primary source of water extraction. About 70% of withdrawals globally are for irrigated agriculture (Shiklomanov, 2000; FAO, 2009), and about half of the world's large dams were built exclusively or primarily for irrigation (World Commission on Dams, 2000). Demand for water for industrial and domestic uses constitutes the balance of global water withdrawals. As of 2003, about 11% was for domestic purposes and 16% for industrial uses (FAO, 2009).

In some catchments, water extraction has led to partial or complete drying out of freshwater ecosystems. Globally, more than one-third of all waters (streams, lakes, and ponds) dry up seasonally; and the proportion of temporary waters is rapidly increasing due to direct human impacts and climate change–induced precipitation regimes (Larned et al., 2010). For example, water withdrawals and increased

sediment deposition have caused Lakes Haromaya and Adele in Ethiopia to dry completely (Alemayehu et al., 2007). The Aral Sea is the best-known example. Water abstraction for cotton irrigation has reduced water levels to such an extent that the sea is now split into several water bodies and covers only a quarter of the area it did fifty years ago. High salinity and concentrations of toxic pesticides and herbicides in the remaining water have increased disease among nearby human communities, destroyed the commercial lake fishery, and hindered farming on much of the adjacent land (Glantz, 2007). Although restoration efforts are underway in the northern portion of the Aral Sea, the recent history in this region stands as a striking example of the consequences for both human and aquatic health that can occur from over-extraction.

LAND USE CHANGE AND MODIFICATION OF AQUATIC HABITATS

Humanity's footprint on the terrestrial landscape and conversion of wetland habitats are also primary causes of the loss and degradation of freshwater ecosystems. Urban areas, agriculture, deforested lands, mines, and other land uses now cover about 22% of the globe (Hoekstra et al., 2005). It is speculated that about 50% of wetlands have been lost worldwide, but there is insufficient information available to substantiate the actual extent of habitat loss (Brinson and Malvárez, 2002; Finlayson and D'Cruz, 2005). Among floodplain habitats, more than 90% of the original floodplains in Europe are functionally extinct, or have been transformed into agricultural and urban areas, and in Japan about 70% of the human population has settled on floodplains (Tockner et al., 2008). Large-scale losses of habitat are expected to continue, particularly in the developing world, as freshwater systems are further modified to provide power, water for irrigation, and drinking water and sanitation services.

Changes to land cover affect freshwater systems via numerous and complex mechanisms—principally via sedimentation, nutrient enrichment, hydrologic alteration, pollution, and loss of riparian forests (Allan,

2004). In densely populated urban and suburban areas, buildings, parking lots, and networks of roads have replaced the natural land cover. Rainwater flows quickly across these impervious surfaces, draining with more force into nearby water bodies than would have occurred previously, causing flash floods, scouring riverbanks, and carrying pollution from the surrounding area into rivers and lakes. Many freshwater plants and animals are unable to live in these conditions, and the biota of urban streams and wetlands is often composed of only the most tolerant species, if any (Walsh et al., 2005).

Clearing of natural land cover for agriculture and other land uses can have similar impacts on the hydrology of systems, although the interactions are complex and impacts are site-specific. In rivers, increased erosion following deforestation and other land-use change can lead to inputs of sediment, which decrease light penetration, blanket the bottom habitat, and disrupt ecosystem function. In small Amazonian streams, clearing of tropical forest and conversion to pasture has been shown to change the biogeochemical and hydraulic characteristics of the system (Neill et al., 2006). At the extreme, whole mountaintops are removed for mining operations and the resulting dredge material is dumped in nearby valleys, burying entire streams (Palmer et al., 2010).

More subtle degradation of aquatic environments is also commonplace. For instance, removal of wood debris from streams and lakeshores facilitates navigation and human recreation, but at the cost of habitat complexity (Maser and Sedell, 1994; Christensen et al., 1996). This can adversely affect populations of fishes and other aquatic animals (Wondzell and Bisson, 2003). Conversely, adding structures such as docks, sea walls, and boat ramps disrupts the natural movement of water and sediments, leading to siltation in some areas and sediment depletion in others.

INVASIVE SPECIES

Invasive species are those that have been introduced or spread outside of their native range and are causing harm within the systems to which they were introduced. Freshwater systems and their native species are often particularly vulnerable to invasive species, because rivers and lake basins, in particular, are insular with high endemism levels (see chapter 1). Only a very low proportion of species that are introduced ultimately thrive in the new system, but those that do can have devastating impacts (Williamson and Fitter, 1996). Combined costs for the United States, the United Kingdom, Australia, South Africa, India, and Brazil have been estimated at US$314 billion per year (Pimentel et al., 2001, 2005). Primary vectors for the introduction of aquatic species include deliberate introductions; aquaculture, horticulture, and pet-trade escapees; interbasin water transfers; ballast water from ships; canals; and releases from aquariums, gardens, and bait buckets (Strayer, 2010). Deliberate introductions occur for a variety of reasons, including commercial or recreational harvest of the introduced species and biological control of other introduced species. The rate at which nonnative freshwater fishes have been introduced worldwide has doubled in the space of thirty years—39% of introductions occur because of aquaculture, and 17% are for improvement of wild stocks (Gozlan et al., 2010).

Invasive species affect native species in a variety of ways: They prey on them, alter their genetics by breeding with them, parasitize them, introduce diseases, compete with them, or otherwise disturb their habitat. As species invade a region and others are extirpated, assemblages of species that were once distinct from one another are becoming more and more similar (Rahel, 2000; Olden et al., 2008). In extreme cases, invasives have contributed to species extinctions. In East Africa's Lake Victoria, a complex set of threats—including the introduction of Nile perch (*Lates niloticus*), coupled with overfishing of the native fishery, climate change, and habitat degradation—have caused a decline in abundance and the loss of a large proportion of the 500 native cichlid fish species that once inhabited its waters (Chapman et al., 2008, Hecky et al., 2010).

Even where native species have not gone extinct, the effects of exotics can be severe. For example, the zebra mussel, *Dreissena polymorpha,* native to the Ponto-Caspian region, has been introduced widely into lakes and rivers in western Europe and North America. The explosion of zebra mussels has caused the decline of some species and significantly altered habitat conditions for others. Through consumption of phytoplankton and filtration of the water column, zebra mussels change the water clarity, which allows more sunlight to enter and thus changes other aspects of the ecology. They also form thick mats that cover submerged substrates, including rock surfaces, aquatic vegetation, native mollusks, canal and dock walls, watercraft, and water intake pipes and other water infrastructure. Declines in native species and associated changes in freshwater food webs have been recorded; the economic impacts are not fully known, but are estimated to exceed US$100 million (Strayer, 2009).

OVERHARVESTING

Although it is extremely difficult to determine the status of inland fisheries because of under-reported catch data, there are strong indications that inland fisheries in most parts of the world are heavily exploited (Kura et al., 2004; Dugan et al., 2007). In many systems we may be "fishing down the food chain"; as larger species become overexploited and rarely caught, smaller species make up the bulk of the fishery. The catch of the Oueme River fishery in West Africa, for example, was composed of large species reaching about 60 cm in length in the 1950s; by the 1990s, the length of species caught had been reduced to 10 cm to 30 cm (Allan et al., 2005). Evidence exists of similar declines in the largest species in other fisheries in the tropics, as in parts of the Amazon and Mekong basins (Allan et al., 2005; Castello et al., 2009).

Large species of commercial value in the northern hemisphere, such as sturgeon and salmon, are also heavily exploited. A recent review concluded that sturgeon and paddlefish are imperiled across the globe and that long-term survival of these species in the wild is in jeopardy (Pikitch et al., 2005). Inland fisheries and aquaculture are extremely important for human well-being and economic growth, representing about 25% of the world's total fish production (Dugan et al., 2007). Other inland water creatures we eat include turtles, mollusks, and crustaceans. The Chinese giant salamander, found in the Yangtze, is the largest of all amphibians (more than one meter in length) and is Critically Endangered—mainly through exploitation for human consumption (IUCN, 2010). In addition to those aquatic species that we consume, aquatic plants are used in products such as baskets and roof thatching, and some aquatic species are exported for the pet trade.

Beyond fisheries, freshwater turtles are one of the few animal groups for which some data exist on exploitation. The demand for turtle species for use in traditional Chinese medicine and for consumption in East and Southeast Asia has devastated regional turtle populations. In the 1990s and early 2000s, for example, annual exports of wild-caught and farmed turtles from Bangladesh, Viet Nam, Lao PDR, Cambodia, Burma (Myanmar), Thailand, Malaysia, Indonesia, and Taiwan amounted to millions of turtles annually, wiping out one wild turtle population after another in the process. Part of the demand is met by turtle farms, but gourmet demand for wild-collected turtles continues to impact the last remaining populations in Asia, and has led to expansion of harvest into North America (P. P. van Dijk, pers. comm.). Some species are just a few individuals away from extinction: The Yangtze population of the giant softshell turtle, *Rafetus swinhoei,* was extirpated some time in the twentieth century, and the species now hangs on with just three males and one female from the Red River basin in China and Viet Nam still known to survive. Several species of Asian box turtles of the genus *Cuora* are little better off, with some down to fewer than one hundred individuals left worldwide in the wild and captive assurance colonies combined.

Direct harvest has also contributed to the decline of a few freshwater invertebrates. Humans initially utilized freshwater mussels for food and shells; declines were not documented until the pearl button industry depleted many Mississippi and Ohio river basin species in the last 200 years (Claassen, 1994). Harvest of Australian crayfish from the wild for food and the pet trade has contributed to the drastic decline of some species (Horwitz, 1994; Geddes and Jones, 1997).

In addition to the direct impacts on the target species, overharvesting of animals or plants can change the dynamics in the ecosystem. For instance, many rivers in South America have large populations of migratory fishes that consume sediment from the bottom. These species support intensive seasonal fisheries, and their removal leads to the buildup of sediment that changes the productivity and nutrient cycling of the entire system (Taylor et al., 2006).

POLLUTION

Freshwater ecosystems suffer from the input of both nutrients and toxic chemicals due to human activities. Nutrient loading occurs as a consequence of transforming land cover from natural vegetation to farm fields, roads, and cities. Most modern agriculture involves the application of large amounts of fertilizers that contain nitrogen and phosphorus in order to enhance crop growth. A portion of these nutrients washes off the landscape into rivers and lakes, where they encourage overgrowth of both plankton and aquatic plants. In Chesapeake Bay in the United States, high nutrient inputs from upstream have caused large algal blooms, creating dangerously low oxygen concentrations through large portions of the estuary (Malone et al., 1996). In southeastern Australia, nutrients from agriculture contributed to the largest algal bloom recorded in the world's history, affecting

Brazil | The magnificent Pantanal of Brazil is the world's largest wetland. The greatest threat to its survival comes from runoff from the surrounding agricultural lands. —Luciano Candisani

Small-scale gold mining has a colossal impact in Borneo, where thousands of miners use water cannons to wash tons of alluvial deposits into troughs in an attempt to isolate a few grams of gold. Neurotoxic mercury is used to extract the gold from the resulting slurry of heavy particles, poisoning the miners and polluting the water. —Daniel Beltrá

Borneo

more than 1,000 km of the Darling-Barwon River (Donnelly et al., 1997). Emissions from automobiles, power plants, and industry also contribute to nutrient loading. These emissions disperse into the atmosphere, transporting nutrients long distances and elevating inputs of nitrogen even in remote freshwater ecosystems that appear pristine. Phosphorus from wastewater near population centers is also a chronic problem that requires societal investments in proper treatment technologies and in the control of inputs.

Toxins such as pesticides, heavy metals, pharmaceuticals, and organics can reduce water quality and limit the ability of rivers and lakes to support the full complement of species. Acid rain from emissions of sulfur and nitrogen oxides was an acute problem in lakes and rivers of eastern North America and Europe until emissions controls were mandated (Malmqvist and Rundle, 2002). Highly acidic runoff continues to be problematic below abandoned mine sites, making these streams uninhabitable for most species. Toxic

Mills and Chichester, 2005). For instance, inter-sex fish, possessing both male and female characteristics, have been found in nine large river basins sampled in the United States (Hinck et al., 2009).

CLIMATE CHANGE

It is difficult to make accurate predictions about the effects of climate change on freshwater organisms globally, however it is assumed that these effects will likely be widespread and variable. As the climate warms due to increases in greenhouse gas emissions from anthropogenic sources, we can expect to see changes in water temperature, hydrologic regime or hydroperiodicity, sea-level, limnological stratification, water chemistry, and riparian corridor composition. Extreme events are expected to be more frequent and intense—floods are projected to increase in regions with higher rainfall, while droughts will also be more likely, particularly in those areas where precipitation is already low (Kundzewicz et al., 2008). Around the

A growing list of man-made chemicals used in industrial and personal care products have been found in aquatic ecosystems. The prevalence and impact of the newer chemicals are largely unknown, but some are known to disrupt the endocrine system of animals and people.

spills also occur periodically along many waterways. In November of 2005, highly toxic organic compounds were washed into the Songhua River in China and eventually reached the Amur-Heilong River. In a follow-up study nine months after the spill, harmful levels of these toxins were found in the tissue of fishes that occurred up to 1,400 km downstream (Levshina et al., 2009). A growing list of man-made chemicals used in industrial and personal care products have been found in aquatic ecosystems. The prevalence and impact of the newer chemicals are largely unknown, but some are known to disrupt the endocrine system of freshwater animals and people (Jobling et al., 1998;

world, changes to flow regimes resulting from shifts in precipitation and evaporation patterns have already been documented (Rosenzweig et al., 2007). Climate change-induced air temperature shifts are altering a number of phenomena: water temperature and associated biogeochemical processes, the amount and duration of snow and ice cover, and changes in lake volume and thermal structure (Lake et al., 2000; Mohseni et al., 2003; Schindler and Smol, 2006; Wang and Sun, 2009). As a result of temperature changes, aquatic ecosystems in higher latitudes will have a longer growing season and decreased period of ice cover. Water quality is also expected to decline

in some basins due to higher pollutant loads from heavy precipitation events, overload of wastewater treatment plants during extreme rainfall, and greater volume of withdrawal from low-quality sources (Kundzewicz et al., 2008).

Many systems and the species that inhabit them are already under substantial stress from ongoing changes in land and water use—climate change has exacerbated and will only continue to exacerbate the situation. For example, recent modeling suggests that decreased discharges from climate change and increased water withdrawals will put up to 75% of fish species at risk of extinction by 2070 in rivers with reduced discharges (Xenopoulos et al., 2005). Increasing water temperatures in the southwest Australia biodiversity hotspot may exceed the thermal tolerances of the aquatic fauna (Davies, 2010). A few studies have documented changes in freshwater species' ranges in northern regions—in general, northward range shifts of warm-water species are expected and some cold-water species may go extinct in the southern parts of boreal regions (Heino et al., 2009; Hering et al., 2009). Marked changes in the biological communities of many Arctic lakes and ponds have already been documented (Schindler and Smol, 2006). Many aquatic organisms will likely have to disperse to water bodies with suitable habitat and environmental conditions to survive climatic changes. This, however, implies that suitable habitat exists, that dispersal corridors are available, and that aquatic organisms possess the means and capability to disperse to such areas in time (Bohanak and Jenkins, 2003; Mohseni et al., 2003). The inherent isolated nature of river and lake basins as well as human-constructed barriers will limit the dispersal options for most aquatic species. Using the southwest Australia biodiversity hotspot as an example, Davies (2010) stated that global biodiversity hotspots are often geographically constrained. The species present are, therefore, susceptible to the impacts of climate change because they have a limited ability to move to less hostile conditions.

SYNERGIES AMONG THREATS

Most freshwater ecosystems are subjected to multiple threats at once (Ormerod et al., 2010). For instance, habitat alteration and chemical pollution are virtually universal, and create a powerful physical-chemical double whammy. To further complicate the situation, the effects of multiple threats often greatly exceed that expected from each one acting independently. The tragic loss of much of the spectacular fish diversity of East Africa's Lake Victoria exemplifies such synergistic effects. The combination of an introduced predatory fish, an introduced floating plant, and enhanced nutrient loading from deforestation and farming has led to reduced water clarity, enhanced predation risk, and oxygen depletion. Within only a few decades, it appears that up to 200 species found nowhere else have been lost (Witte et al., 2007). In Australia, the reduction of river flows from river regulation and over-abstraction and nutrient runoff from agriculture jointly led to an increase in the frequency and severity of algal blooms in rivers (Young et al., 1996). The freshwater dolphins (the *baiji* or Yangtze river dolphin [*Lipotes vexillifer*], the *susu* or Ganges river dolphin [*Platanista gangetica gangetica*], and the *bhulan* or Indus river dolphin [*Platanista gangetica minor*]) all have low population levels and are impacted by multiple threats, including dams, water development projects, pollution, and direct fishing. Each species is restricted to a single river basin and is highly threatened by the synergies created by multiple threats. The *baiji* has not been seen since 2002 (IUCN, 2010) and may already be extinct.

Interactive effects complicate both prediction and alleviation of impacts. For example, when managers introduced small beetles to control the introduced floating plants that covered much of the surface of Lake Victoria in the 1990s, they successfully countered one problem, yet the overall outlook for the lake and its species remains bleak (Hecky et al., 2010). Not only do different types of threats often have cumulative effects that exceed their individual impacts, restoration efforts targeting one factor may have little overall effect because other threats remain.

RESPONDING TO THE THREATS

A sustained, global response is required to halt the ongoing losses of freshwater species and degradation of freshwater ecosystem health. As described elsewhere (chapter 5), we risk losing the many services provided by aquatic ecosystems as well as the richness of biodiversity that they support. In response, society must devise strategies that leverage scientific understanding to reduce threats in ways that both protect aquatic biodiversity and enhance human well-being.

The actions needed to counter these threats are often quite obvious. For instance, requiring adequate flows below dams, or the complete removal of dams, or not constructing them in the first place are simple solutions to the suite of problems arising from damming rivers. However, resource limitations and human needs constrain the range of feasible options, making it imperative to prioritize actions. Science-based, systematic methods for conservation and restoration planning applied to freshwater ecosystems at national and regional scales have advanced greatly in recent years (Nel et al., 2009). Further work is needed, particularly to guide prioritization at the continental and global scales. Essential requirements for such prioritizations include an understanding of spatial patterns in freshwater species and biological communities and comparable and integrated data on biodiversity, threats, and drivers on global and continental scales. The recent definition of the Freshwater Ecoregions of the World (Abell et al., 2008), ongoing freshwater species status assessments (Darwall et al., 2005, 2009; Smith and Darwall, 2006), and a new initiative to develop a global biodiversity observation system (Scholes et al., 2008) are important steps toward addressing these requirements. At this late stage, given that declines are widespread, threats are ongoing, and extinction of freshwater organisms is imminent, conservation at the species level—as has been applied to terrestrial vertebrates, in particular—may not always be feasible. It may be necessary to prioritize actions by targeting drainages or subbasins with high biodiversity that face impending threats or that contain intact and representative species assemblages.

Unfortunately, public awareness of threats to freshwater ecosystems remains woefully low. Future developments of water resources must consider the potential impacts to freshwater plants and animals and the services that they provide. In some instances, linking freshwater species protection to conservation of freshwater resources could go a long way toward achievement of a mutually beneficial goal. Public officials need to have ready access to information about the distributions, values, and ecological sensitivities of freshwater species so that future development actions within freshwater ecosystems can best limit or mitigate future impacts.

In responding to threats, narrowly focusing on what has changed in the last few hundred years and simply trying to reverse these changes is unlikely to be productive. This is particularly pertinent in planning responses to climate change, because it has the potential to completely change the context within which natural systems currently operate. Responding effectively to climate change in the context of freshwater conservation requires a shift in our own perception of natural systems and the actions that we must take to conserve them. For example, as species' ranges shift to adapt to a changing climate, we may need to see these species not as "invasive species," but as native species adjusting to a changing planet. New approaches to "climate-aware" water management are required in many basins across the globe, as are governance structures with sufficient capacity and authority to deliver that management (Matthews et al., 2009). Flexibility and adaptability will be needed as water managers deal with ever-greater climatic and ecohydrological uncertainty (Milly et al., 2008; Matthews and Wickel, 2009).

Following spread: These fields of alfalfa in Saudi Arabia are irrigated using fossil groundwater that fell during the last ice age. After two decades of pumping, the aquifer is projected to run dry, and the desert will reclaim the fields. —George Steinmetz

Alberta, Canada | The oil reserves of the tar sands in Alberta, Canada are second only to those of Saudi Arabia. The methods necessary to extract the highly viscous petroleum bitumen and separate it from its sand matrix are among the most destructive and polluting used in the oil industry. —Garth Lenz

Sumatra, the world's sixth-largest island, has seen most of its rain forest logged, burned, and converted to agriculture. Around the tropics, the removal of rain forest in favor of crops shifts the hydrological cycle toward a hotter, drier climate; causes soil erosion; and destroys biodiversity. —Daniel Beltrá

Sumatra

Ethiopia | A girl collects water supplied from the Bale Mountains National Park catchment in south-central Ethiopia. A lack of water treatment exposes people in Ethiopia to many water-borne parasites such as trypanosomes. —Robin Moore

A technician monitors samples taken outside the Sellafield nuclear complex on the Cumbrian coast of England. Presently being decommissioned, the site holds the most hazardous industrial building in Western Europe. Numerous discharge incidents here have contaminated local waterways and have been detected as far away as Norway. —Karen Kasmauski

Cumbria Coast, England

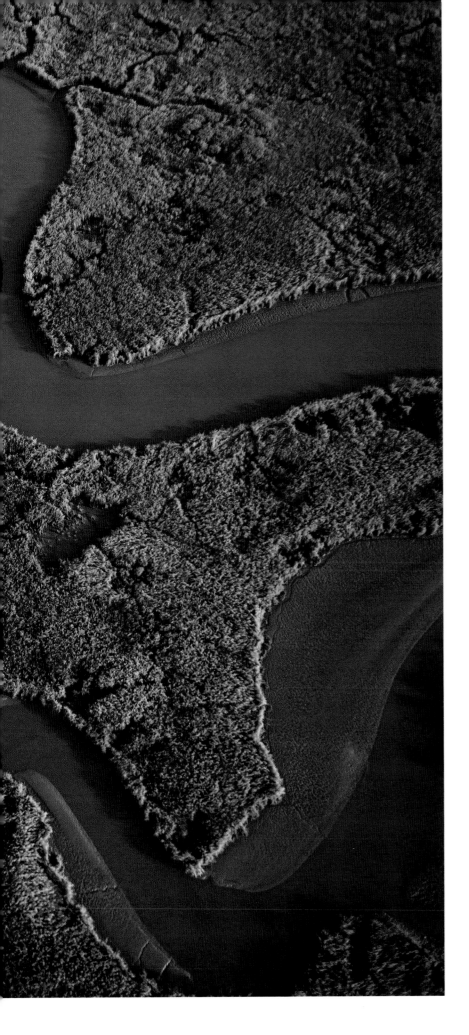

Reliant on fresh water from terrestrial watersheds, coastal estuaries like this one at Jamestown Island, Virginia, USA, are degraded both by upstream pollution and sea-level rise, which also threatens low-lying freshwater systems farther inland.
—George Steinmetz

Jamestown, Virginia, USA

FOUR

PROTECTED AREAS FOR FRESHWATER ECOSYSTEMS

PROTECTED AREAS FOR FRESHWATER ECOSYSTEMS
ESSENTIAL BUT UNDERREPRESENTED

David Allan, Peter Esselman, Robin Abell, Peter McIntyre, Nicolas Tubbs, Harry Biggs, Leandro Castello, Aaron Jenkins, Richard Kingsford

Freshwater ecosystems are the most threatened (chapter 3) and least-well protected (Abell et al., 2007) ecosystem type in the world, a fact that jeopardizes myriad species and essential ecosystem services relied upon by society. Recent compilations of global freshwater biodiversity information (Balian et al., 2008) and analyses of rates of freshwater biodiversity loss (Ricciardi and Rasmussen, 1999) remind us that knowledge of freshwater life may not keep pace with extinctions. Measures that take into account the unique and diverse challenges of freshwater conservation are not yet well developed (Abell et al., 2007). The consequences of failing to protect freshwater resources are significant for both humanity and biodiversity.

Protected areas are a key tool for sustaining aquatic species and water resources. They are designated to limit human use and modification at particular sites, retaining representative ecosystems with their full complement of species and deriving associated goods and services for people. Though protected areas have largely focused on maximizing coverage of ecosystem types, notable landscapes, or species of particular interest, they also provide aesthetic, recreational, and resource benefits to society. Poor management of water resources now jeopardizes human quality of life and economies in most parts of the world. The services provided by wetlands have been tentatively valued at US$14 trillion annually (Finlayson and D'Cruz, 2005). These services are particularly valuable for the poor, who may not have access to alternative sources once services are lost. Thus, it is essential that we account for aquatic ecosystems within protected areas and other environmental management strategies.

The Inner Niger Delta (IND) is a success story of human welfare and species benefits provided through better protection and management of freshwater ecosystems. This vast area is the second-largest floodplain in Africa after the Okavango, with rivers making their way down from the Guinea Highlands of West Africa. The floods vary greatly from one year to the next; a mere 9,500 km2 was inundated in 1984 compared to 44,000 km2 in 1957. These flood patterns greatly impact the people and biodiversity of the IND. The IND's wetlands include swamps, ponds, lakes, flood plains, rice fields, pastures of the bourgou grass (*Echinochloa stagnina*), and flooded forests. The delta has a large supply of water in an otherwise very dry area, benefiting one million people through an abundant supply of fish, and pastoral land containing two million cattle and three million sheep and goats. The IND is also home to populations of hippos, manatees, and twenty-nine species of fishes (Beintema et al., 2007), and 117 species of waterbirds (Wetlands International, 2006).

Opening spread: Catching the bulk of California's water from winter storms off the Pacific Ocean, 15% of the 640-km-long Sierra Nevada range is protected from development, logging, and mining. This includes three national parks, two national monuments, and twenty wilderness areas covering 9,720 square km of watersheds and sublime landscapes, such as this view over Moonlight Lake in the John Muir Wilderness.
—Justin Black

Left: Sunrise over Victoria Falls on the Zambezi River. A short section of the river above and below the falls is protected by Victoria National Park on the Zimbabwe side, and Mosi-oa-Tunya National Park on the Zambia side. The parks contain small rain forests, unusual in this region, that are sustained by the ceaseless mist rising from the falls.
—Galen Rowell

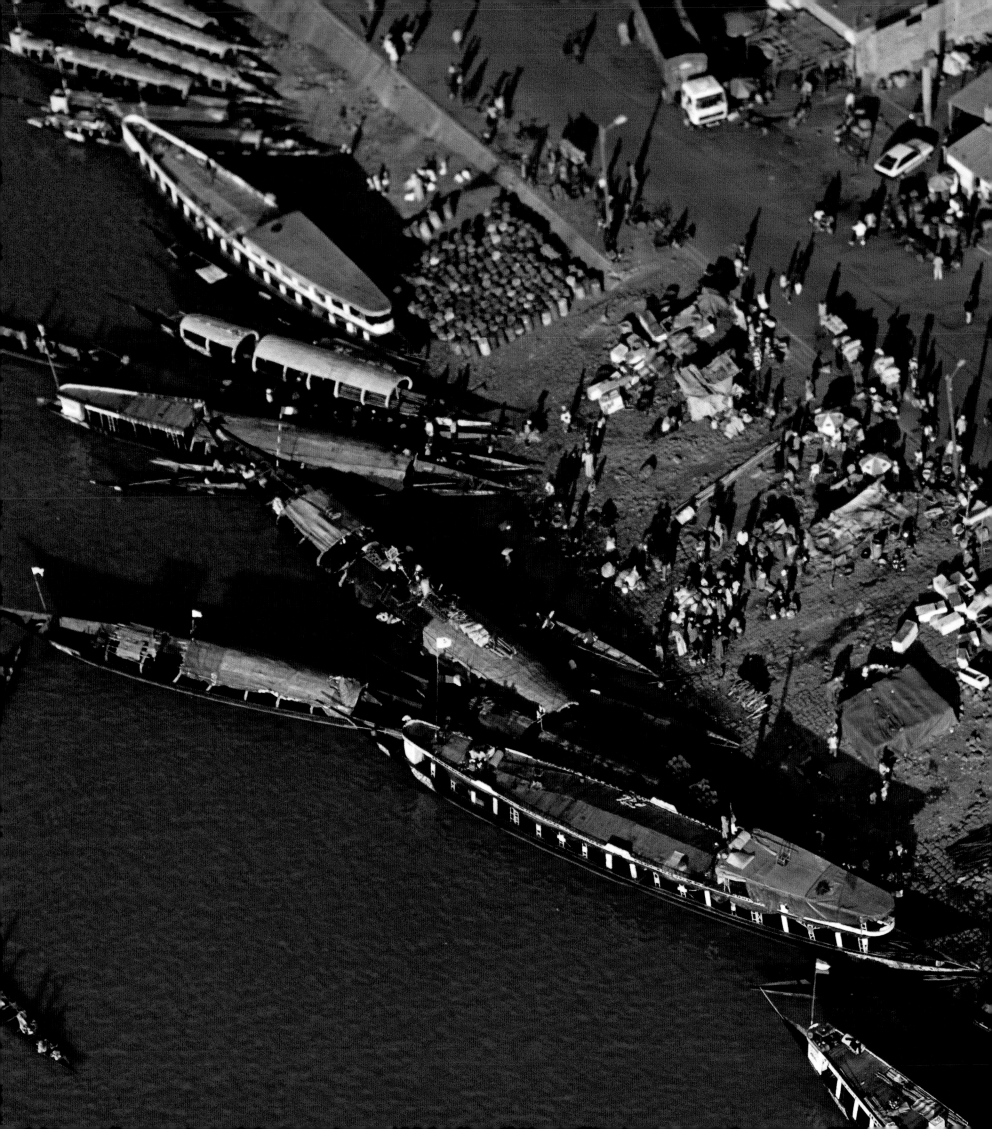

The IND's people and biodiversity directly rely on its ecosystem services for their survival. Yet poverty is rife, especially in the Mopti region where only one-third of households have access to tap water. The IND ecosystems are severely affected by erosion, poor soils, declining fisheries, and unpredictable water levels. This is worsened by the increasing human population and new infrastructure upstream, including irrigation projects and hydropower dams.

The first international conservation initiatives for the Inner Niger Delta were implemented in 1988, and its international importance was recognized under the Ramsar Convention in 2004. The current range of activities to ensure sufficient protection under this designation includes restoration of flooded forests, conflict resolution, local empowerment and ownership, alternative livelihood development, and support livestock fattening and marketing, cereal banks, rice husking, gardens, and fishpond restoration.

Beneficiaries are required to undertake various activities to conserve and restore biodiversity, such as planting trees, protecting existing forests, and digging channels to link fishponds to the river. Today, 20,000 trees have been planted, 22 hectares of flooded forests protected, and 10 hectares of *bourgou* regenerated, and one 300-meter-long channel was constructed to link a fishpond to the river Niger. Two valuable fish species that had disappeared from the pond have reappeared, and eleven species of waterbirds can now be observed.

At present, coverage of freshwater ecosystems within the global network of protected areas comes mostly from incidental inclusion in terrestrially

Left: Waterfront of Mopti, one of the biggest port towns of the Inner Niger Delta in Mali. The people of this arid region depend on the delta for many ecosystem services. Although three Ramsar sites exist here, most of the region remains unprotected. —George Steinmetz

Protected areas are a key tool for sustaining aquatic species and water resources. They are designated to limit human use and modification at particular sites, retaining representative ecosystems with their full complement of species and deriving associated goods and services for people.

valuation of ecosystem services. These initiatives have yielded many improvements for freshwater ecosystems of the IND. For example, the Bio-rights approach (van Eijk and Kumar, 2009) implemented in Mali uses microcredits to pay for environmental services (Wetlands International, 2009). It provides poor rural people with access to finances to improve their livelihoods and promote biodiversity conservation. The loans provided can be turned into partial or complete grants, depending on the effectiveness of the conservation activities carried out. Therefore, people have a strong incentive to manage and protect their environment in a sustainable way. Loans have been provided to women's groups to oriented reserves. Fresh water-focused efforts are largely limited to Ramsar sites (Wetlands of International Importance) and a modest number of reserves along lakeshores. All too often, freshwater ecosystems have gone unrepresented in conservation inventories, or have been assumed to be adequately served by terrestrial measures. Until recently, conservation planners had few guidelines for addressing the challenges presented by freshwater ecosystems. Fortunately, new conceptual advances and computerized analyses show great promise to improve our capacity to plan for the protection of rivers, lakes, and wetlands. In addition, community-based management, often cooperatives of fishers, is

proving increasingly successful in protecting resources of importance to a community that shares in the benefits of a well-managed resource.

THE MAMIRAUÁ RESERVE, AMAZON BASIN, BRAZIL

The Mamirauá Reserve encompasses an area of 11,240 km2 formed entirely by *várzea* floodplains, a mosaic of riparian forests, lakes, and channels that are annually flooded by the overflow of the nutrient-rich waters of the Amazon River. The floodplains are biologically diverse and productive ecosystems, providing the Amazon's greatest human population density with timber, fish, agriculture, and game. The goal of the Mamirauá Reserve has been to conserve *várzea* biodiversity and its benefits to people through participatory natural resource management: Exclusive rights over natural resource use within the reserve were granted to local people in exchange for their commitment to use them sustainably. The reserve was zoned into protection and sustainable use areas, scientific studies were undertaken, and educational and extension activities were carried out with local communities.

Many activities in Mamirauá have focused on fisheries, including that for the arapaima (*Arapaima gigas*), once the greatest fishery of the Amazon. Arapaima are air-breathers, surfacing to gulp air every five to fifteen minutes, and they grow to 3 m in length and 200 kg in weight. Arapaima do not migrate long distances, so they can be managed in relatively small areas by local communities. However, arapaima fisheries have been largely uncontrolled despite government regulations regarding size and seasonal limits. Arapaima populations are now thought to be widely overexploited and endangered, justifying moratoriums in three states of Brazil.

In Mamirauá, management of arapaima is based on the ability of fishers to count the individuals at the moment of their aerial breathing. Local fishers census arapaima populations each year and then, in collaboration with the Mamirauá Institute and a government agency, they use the data to determine fishing quotas. The Mamirauá Institute provides institutional and technical assistance to local fishers, the government oversees management actions and fishing quotas, and the fishers are responsible for both compliance and enforcement. Ten years of experimentation have shown that this management scheme leads to rapid recovery of arapaima populations and doubling of profits for fishers.

CHALLENGES

Freshwater ecosystems present unique challenges to the paradigm of conservation through protected areas. Traditionally, protected areas are designed to be self-contained units, which are inherently sheltered from the degrading forces around the borders. Freshwater ecosystems violate these assumptions; they are highly sensitive to human disturbances well outside of their boundaries, and they rely upon and are impacted by numerous direct and indirect connections with the surrounding landscape. Perhaps even more worrying is the fact that the medium of aquatic ecosystems—water—is itself a coveted resource that can easily be over-exploited. In much the same way that clear-cutting a forest eliminates its fundamental structure, pumping away water or altering river flows constitutes a profound reshaping of aquatic ecosystems. While society has recognized the threat posed by deforestation, water resource management is rarely viewed with the seriousness it deserves.

Rivers, lakes, and wetlands face diverse and synergistic threats associated with human activities (Dudgeon et al., 2006). These are discussed in detail in chapter 3. Disturbance of freshwater ecosystems may have very significant wider impacts. For instance, drainage of peatlands in Southeast Asia for the palm-oil industry may release huge amounts of carbon stored in the soils (Parish et al., 2008; Joosten and Wetlands International, 2009).

Maintaining connectivity—between upstream and downstream areas, rivers and their floodplains, and groundwater and surface waters—presents another major challenge for freshwater protected areas. Freshwater ecosystems are defined in part by the broad area from which they draw water. This includes drainage overland from higher to lower elevations, as well as precipitation and groundwater inputs. The resulting network of connections is a key aspect of the dynamics of organisms, energy, and nutrients in fresh water. Even well-protected river reaches can be harmed by a dam far downstream, or by upstream deforestation that alters natural flow regimes and regional climate. Lakes and wetlands are no less vulnerable to being disconnected from their watersheds. Loss of groundwater flows due to pumping or diminished recharge can be particularly problematic because these flows are essential for aquatic ecosystem health yet may originate from nearby terrestrial habitats or distant aquifers spanning huge areas. All of these threats to ecosystem connectivity jeopardize access to water-related resources, with important implications for human livelihoods. Current protected areas often encompass only small portions of a catchment, leaving protected freshwater areas vulnerable to upstream and downstream perturbations, and also diminishing the potential benefits to people and ecosystems downstream of having their water source protected.

Lateral connections with the land are also essential for fresh water. Rivers and wetlands expand and contract across their floodplains in response to precipitation patterns. Rivers fertilize floodplains, yet also benefit from inputs of organic matter, connections to outlying waters, and from expanded reproductive opportunities provided by floodplain habitats (Tochner and Stanford, 2002; Beintema et al., 2007). New research is underscoring the

dependence of lake animals on energy and nutrients arriving from surrounding forests and wetlands (Pace et al., 2004). All too often, these diverse and important lateral connections are dramatically altered through channelization, levees, dykes, and conversion of floodplains and uplands. Many protected area boundaries are actually demarcated by rivers or lakes, resulting in riparian and floodplain protection on only one bank or shore. For instance, Brazil's Jaú National Park in the Amazon, named for the Jaú River that it encompasses, is bounded by the Pauini and Carabinani rivers. Pictured Rocks National Lakeshore on Lake Superior and Gombe Stream National Park on Lake Tanganyika each protects a watershed and shoreline, but they likely afford only modest protection to the large lakes they border.

EFFECTIVENESS OF TERRESTRIAL NETWORKS

Because terrestrial reserves around the world already encompass portions of freshwater systems, we need to ask what protection they offer those systems. Studies that have evaluated the success of terrestrial networks for protecting freshwater ecosystems have found mixed outcomes. In South Africa, independent conservation prioritization exercises for aquatic and terrestrial needs revealed low overlap in priority locations, suggesting that it would be erroneous to assume that high-priority areas for terrestrial protection automatically capture freshwater priorities (Amis et al., 2009). Several national studies of fish species protection underscore this finding, revealing that incidental protection by terrestrial reserves can be incomplete, especially for species of special concern (Crivelli, 2002; Abell et al., 2007).

Analysis of Michigan's protected area network, which encompasses 21% of that state's overall land area, revealed that most wetland types were well represented within existing protected areas (Herbert et al., 2010). Such a pattern might reflect

setting aside of lands that were least-suited to development. In contrast, river riparian zones were underrepresented, and freshwater species of concern were less-well represented than terrestrial species of concern. These results serve as a potent reminder that many existing terrestrial protected areas were designated for their combination of high scenic value and low development value, rather than explicitly for biodiversity conservation or ecosystem services. Overall, it appears that freshwater resources do not receive proportional protection within reserve networks designed to protect terrestrial features.

PROTECTED AREAS FROM DIFFERENT REALMS

Protected areas cover approximately 12% of Earth's land surface. Among the 426 freshwater ecoregions of the world (Abell et al., 2008), which represent major regions possessing distinct freshwater fish communities, the extent of protected area coverage ranges from none to virtually complete. On average, 13% of each freshwater ecoregion is designated as protected—however, two-thirds of individual ecoregions have less protected area than this global average (Herbert et al., 2010). Unfortunately, these

of their protection. Lakes are included as a separate biome; as of 2003, the WDPA catalogued lake protected areas covering 7,989 km^2, or 1.54% of the world's total extent of lakes. The Ramsar Convention covers a wide variety of wetland-rich sites within terrestrial, freshwater, and marine habitats. The 1,218 inland wetland sites designated under Ramsar comprised a total of 1.39 million km^2 in 2006. By comparison, the total extent of nationally declared terrestrial protected areas in 2009 was estimated at 16.94 million km^2 (Jenkins and Joppa, 2009), excluding Ramsar sites and other internationally designated reserves. Happily, the list of Ramsar-listed wetlands continues to grow; in 2009 alone, twenty-nine new inland sites were designated, covering 56,042 km^2.

While national parks have largely been designated to protect terrestrial species and habitats, many also include substantial freshwater resources. For example, Australia's Avon Wilderness Park covers entire catchments of the Avon River headwaters, and Peru's Titicaca National Reserve was established to protect Peru's shoreline along Lake Titicaca, the world's highest-elevation navigable lake (Dudley, 2008). Along Africa's Lake Tanganyika, the only reserves are shoreline parks such as Gombe and Mahale in Tanzania, but these offer at least some protection to the nearshore waters.

Left: The Lake Titicaca frog (*Telmatobius culeus*) is endemic to the high-altitude lake for which it is named. With some specimens reaching 50cm-long, it is the largest aquatic frog in the world, and its folds of excess skin provide extra surface area to help the frog breathe at 3800 meters above sea level.
—Pete Oxford

On average, 13% of each freshwater ecoregion is designated as protected—however, two-thirds of individual ecoregions have less protected area than this global average.

numbers tell us only about terrestrial coverage within these broad geographical units, rather than specific extent of freshwater habitats protected.

Other global accounts of protected areas reveal only marginal additional evidence of freshwater protection. The World Database of Protected Areas (WDPA) largely subsumes fresh waters under terrestrial biomes, making it difficult to assess the global extent

Malawi's creation of Lake Malawi National Park in 1980 constituted the world's first freshwater underwater park, and it was designed specifically to protect the remarkable diversity of fishes found only along the rocky shores of this massive lake (Reinthal, 1993).

One type of protection gaining increased attention is the designation of rivers as "free flowing." In the United States, the National Wild and Scenic Rivers

Michigan, USA | While wetlands of many types are well represented within Michigan's extensive protected area system, river riparian habitats and freshwater species of concern are underrepresented. Hardwood forest and the Carp River, Porcupine Mountains Wilderness State Park, Michigan, USA. —Carr Clifton

The Luangwa River Valley in Zambia, protected in part by national parks and wildlife management areas, is home to an abundance of African wildlife that is strongly dependent on the flow of the river, such as the hippos (*Hippopotamus amphibius*) seen here. —Frans Lanting

Zambia

System was created in 1968. As of June 2009, 6,157 miles (9,909 km) of river had been protected as wild; an additional 6,403 miles (10,305 km) had been protected under either scenic or recreational categories (National Wild and Scenic Rivers, 2009). Canada protects free-flowing rivers under its Heritage Rivers Program; as of 2009, 9,032 km of rivers had been designated (Canadian Heritage Rivers Board, 2009). Other protected river programs exist; for instance, at the provincial level in Australia. Each program differs in terms of its restrictions and authority, but the intent is largely the same: to maintain rivers and river reaches in their relatively intact states, with a focus on minimizing threats and protecting longitudinal and lateral connectivity.

Australia's Murray-Darling Basin is a well-known example of the complexities and challenges of large-scale management of freshwater resources. The basin encompasses 1.06×10^6 km^2, and is Australia's most heavily developed river basin—primarily for irrigation (Kingsford, 2000). Despite the proclamation of many of Murray-Darling's aquatic areas as protected, degradation has continued unabated, largely due to ongoing impacts of water resource development. Natural flood frequencies of large wetlands, such as the Macquarie Marshes, have been considerably reduced. These failings have shaped the debate over the basin's last free-flowing river, the Paroo.

The Paroo River is the most westerly in the Murray-Darling Basin and extends more than 600 km, bisected by two states: Queensland (QLD) and New South Wales (NSW). The waters of the Paroo River inundate approximately 8,000 km^2 of floodplain habitats during floods. They also support tourism, pastoralism, fishing, and beekeeping for Aboriginal people. In 1979, the Nocoleche Nature Reserve (740 km^2) was declared a protected area in the mid-reaches of the river in NSW. Currawinya Lakes National Park was created in 1991 in QLD (1,513 km^2), covering two lakes in the Paroo River catchment (Ramsar-listed in 1996). Despite protected area status, government support

for the development of irrigation systems became an acute threat to the Paroo River's flow regime in the mid-1990s. In response to this, the QLD and NSW governments agreed to protect all the flows of the Paroo River in 2003, and plans now prohibit water resource development apart from minimal use for towns and tourism. Further protection of the river to maintain a free-flowing status helped inspire recent designation of the Paroo-Darling National Park (1,513 km^2), which was declared in 2000 and includes the lower lakes of the Paroo River. The Paroo-Darling National Park was Ramsar-listed in 2008, along with Nocoleche Nature Reserve.

The World Commission on Protected Areas is actively working to better include freshwater systems in protected area assessments and to enhance management of freshwater resources within protected areas. The pace of establishing new reserves is slowing in most regions, making improved management of existing protected areas ever-more important. Additional needs include accounting for aquatic connections between protected and unprotected areas.

MANAGEMENT AND DESIGN OF PROTECTED AREAS

Because freshwater systems benefit from conservation of natural landscapes in their catchments, fresh waters within existing protected areas may already receive some degree of protection. However, there are limits to the freshwater conservation potential of many existing protected areas. Some of these limits are "hard." For instance, a small reserve situated far downstream within a large catchment may be unable to improve the integrity of a highly disturbed river flowing through it. Threats originating outside a reserve, such as large-scale water withdrawals upstream, may simply overcome whatever benefits are offered by protected status, contributing to continued decline despite good intentions (Kingsford and Thomas, 1995).

Other limits might be considered "soft," because management practices can address them. Many existing protected areas contain flow management structures, including dams. A dammed river may never be "natural," but dam releases can govern downstream flows. Dudley (2009) lists many options for improving the management of existing protected areas, including protecting or restoring connectivity by removing barriers, reconnecting rivers with floodplains, and ensuring that roads and associated infrastructure are not fragmenting stream systems; protecting native fauna by prohibiting overfishing and the stocking or spread of introduced species; restricting motorized watercraft and discharge from boats; managing point-

is South Africa's flagship park, spanning two million hectares and adjacent to large conservation areas in neighboring nations. The park is known internationally for big-game viewing in the natural environment. Five major rivers flow through KNP, all of which arise in mountain headlands to the west and enter the park after flowing through a mix of seminatural, agricultural, industrial, and residential settings, exiting the park into Mozambique and discharging into the Indian Ocean. Within KNP, these rivers and their riparia sustain more than fifty fish species and more than 500 bird species, a third of which depend on riparian or aquatic habitats for their existence. The rivers are also an integral part of the tourist experience for park visitors.

Freshwater protected areas need to be custom-designed to fully overcome the challenges of water extraction, cumulative threats, and lack of ecosystem connectivity.

source discharges from recreational facilities; and protecting or restoring adjacent vegetation. A first step in making existing protected areas "freshwater–friendly" is simply building freshwater objectives into management plans. In many regions, this will require developing new management structures that can span political jurisdictions and economic sectors in order to address the broad spatial scales and diverse threats of freshwater ecosystems. Only such bodies, empowered by adequate funding and authority, can overcome the tragedy of the commons that currently applies in most large river basins and lakes. As it stands in most large freshwater ecosystems, no single agency has the vision or power to manage at the needed scale.

South Africa's Kruger National Park (KNP) has effectively included freshwater objectives into its management, connecting upstream and downstream needs within and outside of the park to address development and conservation needs. With its earliest component proclaimed 110 years ago, Kruger

Although the rivers that flow through KNP provide a range of ecosystem services to human populations upstream and downstream of the park, most are also affected by heavy water withdrawals and water-quality degradation. As early as the 1970s, park managers began to implement proactive interventions such as in-park dams to maintain sufficient water levels in this semiarid environment, and a pump scheme to offset flow losses in the highly biodiverse Sabie River. The early recognition that upstream activities were degrading habitat conditions within the park eventually led to the formation of the Kruger National Park Rivers Research Programme—a multidisciplinary effort to encourage science-based river management involving universities, government agencies, and resource users. KNP now plays a role, often central, in aquatic research and management that includes joint future visioning, flow prescriptions, operating rules for dams, pollution control, quota permitting, interception taxation, alien-plant control in rivers, and overall catchment management. Some

Following spread: The Little Colorado River is protected as it flows through Grand Canyon National Park in Arizona, USA. Despite being wilder than the larger, flow-controlled Colorado River with which it joins, the Little Colorado has been impacted upstream of the park boundary by development, damming, and even a nuclear accident. —Jack Dykinga

Malaysia | The protection of headwaters regions around the globe, such as those in Lambir Hills National Park, Malaysia, set the foundation for safeguarding the health of downstream freshwater ecosystems. —Tim Laman

The headwaters of the Flathead River in British Columbia, Canada, used as an international benchmark for water quality, are home to what may be the last un-hybridized populations of west slope cutthroat trout (*Oncorhynchus clarkii lewisi*). A recent mining ban and a U.S.-Canadian conservation agreement promises preservation of this pristine watershed. —Michael Ready

British Columbia, Canada

measurable improvements have resulted from these water-oriented interventions. For instance, apart from one recent occasion, flows of the region's perennial rivers have become more continuous. Flow patterns have particularly improved in the Letaba River, and new agreements give reason for optimism despite some recent troubling flow trends in catchments that are subject to severe development pressure around the park. Management actions appear to have prevented most losses of aquatic species from KNP, although recent crocodile deaths in the Olifants River are occurring despite flow- and water-quality improvements. Overall, active management of KNP for freshwater resources has certainly helped counter the growing pressure from development. Continuing to build on these successes in integrated water resource management benefits both the biota of KNP and the regional human population by enhancing the quality and quantity of water downstream of the park.

Freshwater protected areas need to be custom-designed to fully overcome the challenges of water extraction, cumulative threats, and lack of ecosystem connectivity. This process can draw upon many of the basic lessons from the well-developed practice of terrestrial planning. The fundamental goals for any reserve are to protect species and biodiversity, represent ecosystem diversity, complement existing reserves, and protect irreplaceable resources specific to the area (Margules and Pressey, 2000). Computerized analysis enables conservationists to compare alternative sites for new protected areas in order to maximize representativeness, complementarity, and irreplacibility. Connections between reserves, levels of threat to reserves, and economic costs can also be factored in (Sarkar et al., 2006). However, applying these methods to most freshwater systems is hampered by shortcomings in mapping of aquatic species diversity, in understanding of the extent of connectivity, and in rules of thumb about how human activities at reserve edges propagate inward and downstream.

The scarcity of sufficient surveys to map species distributions is an obvious impediment to protecting freshwater biodiversity. In well-studied regions, some species-level information for birds, fishes, aquatic plants, and a few invertebrate groups may be available, as well as genus-level information on aquatic insects. These data may be sufficient to develop conservation plans based on biodiversity representation, especially if mathematical models can be used to predict species distributions from a limited number of known locations (Sowa et al., 2005; Linke et al., 2009; Esselman and Allan, 2010). Alternatively, incomplete knowledge can be circumvented by targeting protection of a set amount (e.g., 20%) of a particular habitat type or other surrogate for freshwater biodiversity (Nel et al., 2007; Roux et al., 2008). In remote areas where only satellite imagery is available, classifications of river types using landscape features (river size, elevation, contributing geology, etc.) have been used as a proxy for biodiversity patterns (Thieme et al., 2007). Though this mix of approaches is not ideal, it nonetheless enables conservationists to more effectively design protected area networks for freshwater biodiversity than has been possible previously.

Rivers are especially challenging for designating protected areas owing to their linear geometry and because their integrity relies on natural connections between upstream and downstream reaches. Fortunately, recent innovations in computer modeling offer ways to handle the geometric constraints of waterways, with new reserve design models allowing planners to focus on connectivity specifically within river-channel networks. As these computerized approaches continue to progress, we hope to see connectivity with floodplains and groundwater incorporated, as well as more realistic representation of the needs of species—such as salmon—that move long distances in the river channel.

PLACE-BASED TOOLS FOR PROTECTING FRESHWATER ECOSYSTEMS

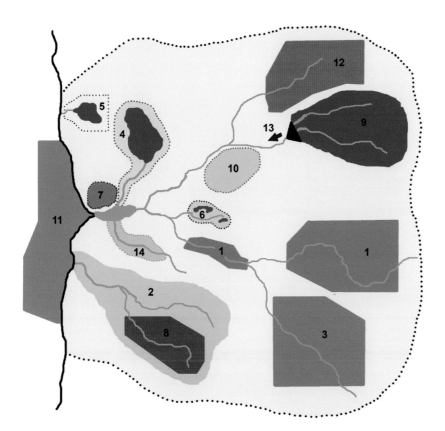

1. National Park / Wildlife Reserve

2. Wild / Heritage River

3. Private Protected Area / Conservancy

4. Ramsar Wetland

5. Wetland Protection Zoning

6. Fisheries / Aquatic Reserve

7. Urban Land Use Zoning

8. Community Conserved Area

9. Water Supply Catchment

10. Aquifer Recharge Area

11. Marine Park Reserve

12. Certified Forest Area

13. Environmental Flow

14. Floodplain / Riparian Reserve

Figure 4.1. A visualization of place-based protection for fresh water, illustrating a number of protective actions that may be either co-located with the target of interest, or situated with greatest effectiveness to mitigate threats emanating from upstream, downstream, or lateral to the river system. Modified with permission of Stuart Blanch and Robin Abell.

A NEW CONCEPTUAL FRAMEWORK

Perhaps too often, growing needs for freshwater protection have led conservationists to advocate for protection of entire catchments. Unfortunately, such requests are generally impractical due to area requirements and conflicts with human uses, creating an unproductive stalemate. As an alternative, Abell et al. (2007) proposed a multiple-use zoning framework in which freshwater focal areas are embedded in critical management zones, which in turn are embedded in catchment management zones. For example, the focal area might be critical habitat for a target migratory species, and the associated critical management zones

critical organic matter inputs to a river; an aquifer recharge area might prevent pollution of groundwater that ultimately upwells into the river; and a dam on the main channel might be operated to provide adequate flows to a downstream, protected area. Collectively, applying these strategies across a single landscape is likely to have far greater impact than any one approach in isolation. Indeed, even without the designation of protected areas, these and related strategies can contribute to maintaining the integrity of rivers, lakes, and wetlands. What protected areas add, importantly, is a geographic focal point around which these strategies can be designed and deployed, drawing upon legal tools and agency responsibilities for resource protection (Gilman et al., 2004).

Left: Given the high connectivity within water systems from source to sea, the protection of fresh waters can significantly benefit the health of marine ecosystems. In Fiji, an innovative ridge-to-reef approach seeks to ensure that links between healthy catchments and healthy reefs remain intact.
—Michele Westmorland

The National Protected Area Committee has now identified high connectivity, "ridge-to-reef" areas for inclusion in the national network of protected areas, including potential Ramsar sites.

could be a barrier-free downstream corridor for that species, or an upstream riparian protection strategy to minimize disturbance from land-use activities. These more narrowly focused actions are embedded within integrative catchment management strategies that balance nature protection with human uses. Current initiatives in South Africa are in fact beginning to apply this framework within certain catchments, as does a recent design of protected areas for freshwater fishes in Belize (Esselman and Allan, 2010).

This zoning framework emphasizes the need to implement freshwater conservation strategies outside as well as within formally designated protected areas. Because freshwater ecosystems integrate disturbances across their catchments, a broad suite of protected area strategies can be pursued at different but complementary spatial scales (see fig. 4.1). For instance, a certified-sustainable forest plantation might minimize hydrologic alterations and provide

Protected-area staff can also serve a "watchdog" role through sustained monitoring of aquatic ecosystem conditions in relation to shifts in land use and activities both outside and inside boundaries of protection.

Fiji in the Pacific Islands illustrates how large-scale management is needed to allow for multiple uses including species conservation. Several Pacific Islands were recently recognized to be global priorities for freshwater conservation based on the high density of endemic species (Abell et al., 2008). In the ecological context of oceanic high islands, freshwater faunas have developed highly migratory life history traits and have a greater level of connectivity to the ocean and estuarine environments than faunas of larger continental landmasses. Research has clearly demonstrated strong links between catchment land clearing, nonnative species introductions, and loss of migratory pathways for freshwater fishes (Jenkins et al., 2010).

In Fiji, a collective of nongovernmental organizations (NGOs) and national government agencies is implementing a multipronged management approach that combines landscape and seascape conservation. At the national scale, spatial data were used to identify priority areas for conservation that connect forests, hydrologic networks, and coral reefs. The National Protected Area Committee has now identified high connectivity, "ridge-to-reef" areas for inclusion in the national network of protected areas, including potential Ramsar sites. In addition, several degraded catchments have been identified as priorities for reforestation and riparian restoration. At the local level, the Kubulau District of Vanua Levu has become the first district in the country to devise and implement a comprehensive ecosystem management plan. This plan extends from headwaters out to far offshore reefs, reflecting the natural scale of ecological connections. Included in the plan are protected areas for forested headwaters, riparian zone management, mangrove protected areas, marine protected areas, and prohibitions on introducing nonnative faunas. The ten local villages implementing the plan have already experienced increases in subsistence fisheries while conserving their forest, freshwater, estuarine, and coral reef biodiversity. This example from Fiji highlights the benefits of cross-sector collaborations and ecosystem-based approaches for conserving freshwater biodiversity and ecosystem services for people.

In conclusion, under the Convention on Biological Diversity, countries are committed to protecting 10% of representative terrestrial, marine, and freshwater ecosystems (IUCN, 2008). This is particularly challenging for fresh waters due to inadequate knowledge of the extent of existing protection, data shortfalls, challenges of protecting flow regimes, and the need for analytic approaches that take into account the connectivity and sensitivity of freshwater ecosystems. Although fresh waters benefit from terrestrial protected areas, a greater emphasis on freshwater-specific strategies is needed. Ultimately, this requires designing and managing protected areas in ways that account for the interconnections among terrestrial, freshwater, and marine environments. Given the absolute dependence of both humanity and biodiversity on water, protected areas offer an excellent starting point for enhancing the sustainability of freshwater resource use and conservation.

Right: Tolmer Falls in the rainy season. Litchfield National Park, Northern Territory, Australia. —Theo Allofs

Following spread: Pinacate Biosphere Reserve in Mexico's Sonoran Desert features an impressive diversity of plants, birds, mammals, and reptiles. It even counts among its residents freshwater species such as a small endangered pupfish (*Cyprinodon eremus*) and the Sonora mud turtle (*Kinosternon sonoriensis longifemorale*), both well adapted to survival in the scarce fresh water of this arid ecosystem. —Claudio Contreras-Koob

FIVE
FRESHWATER
ECOSYSTEM
SERVICES

FRESHWATER ECOSYSTEM SERVICES:
ESSENTIAL FOR HUMAN WELL-BEING

Tracy A. Farrell, David Batker, Lucy Emerton, Will Turner

reshwater ecosystems cover just 12.8 million square kilometers of the planet's surface—less than one-quarter of one percent—but they are home to some of the greatest concentrations of species and provide services without which life would not be possible (WWF, 2009). These systems are unfortunately under great threat. More than half of our planet's wetlands have been lost, and freshwater biodiversity declined by 35% from 1970 to 2005, a rate much higher than that occurring in either the forest or marine biomes (MEA, 2005a; Loh, 2008). With increasing degradation and loss of freshwater ecosystems, loss of related services are also likely to occur. If we continue our current "business-as-usual" development trajectory, by 2050 we could lose the 11% of the natural areas we have left that are critical for securing the provision of ecosystem services (TEEB, 2008). Current trends need to be reversed by correcting market failures and pursuing a new development paradigm where freshwater ecosystems are valued for the services they provide.

GOODS AND SERVICES FROM FRESHWATER ECOSYSTEMS

Ecosystem services are the ecological conditions and processes that regulate and provide for human well-being (Daily, 1997). Healthy freshwater ecosystems are essential for human societies and economies to survive, prosper, and grow (Phillips et al., 2002; Emerton and Bos, 2004; Emerton, 2005). They are especially important for the world's poor, who are often totally dependent upon them for subsistence and income, and cannot access technological alternatives such as piped-in water or wastewater treatment facilities (MEA, 2005b). Fresh water is perhaps the most basic and obvious service provided by ecosystems to meet human needs. Humanity consumes 4,000 km3 of fresh water each year to meet domestic, industrial, and energy production (cooling) needs. Fresh water is also needed for food. Another 6,400 km3 of it is consumed annually for agriculture (Margat and Andréassian, 2008). Inland fisheries are a major source of protein for a billion people, yielding 7.7 million metric tons of fish in 1997—which may reflect less than half of actual capture (LePrieur et al., 2008). Harvest of freshwater species for food also includes turtles, frogs, snails, and crayfish (Revenga and Kura, 2003; Bogan, 2008; Strong et al., 2008).

Globally, inland fisheries and aquaculture represent about 25% (34 million metric tons) of reported world fisheries production in 2003 (FAO, 2004). Inland fisheries and aquaculture are an important part of the economy of many countries (Neiland et al., 2000; Finlayson et al., 2006; Dugan et al., 2007). Fishing and related

Opening spread: Traditional fishers train cormorants to dive for fish attracted to the light of a lantern. Li River, Guangxi, south-central China.
—Art Wolfe

Previous spread: The people of Inle Lake, Burma (Myanmar), live on the water in stilt houses and tend floating gardens made from natural peat bogs.
—Karen Kasmauski

Left: Kaieteur Falls on the Potaro River in Guyana is one of the most beautiful waterfalls in the world and also one of the most powerful, with a single-drop height of 226 meters and average volume of 663 cubic meters per second. The recently expanded Kaieteur National Park is beginning to be recognized for its potential as a world-class ecotourism destination.
—Pete Oxford

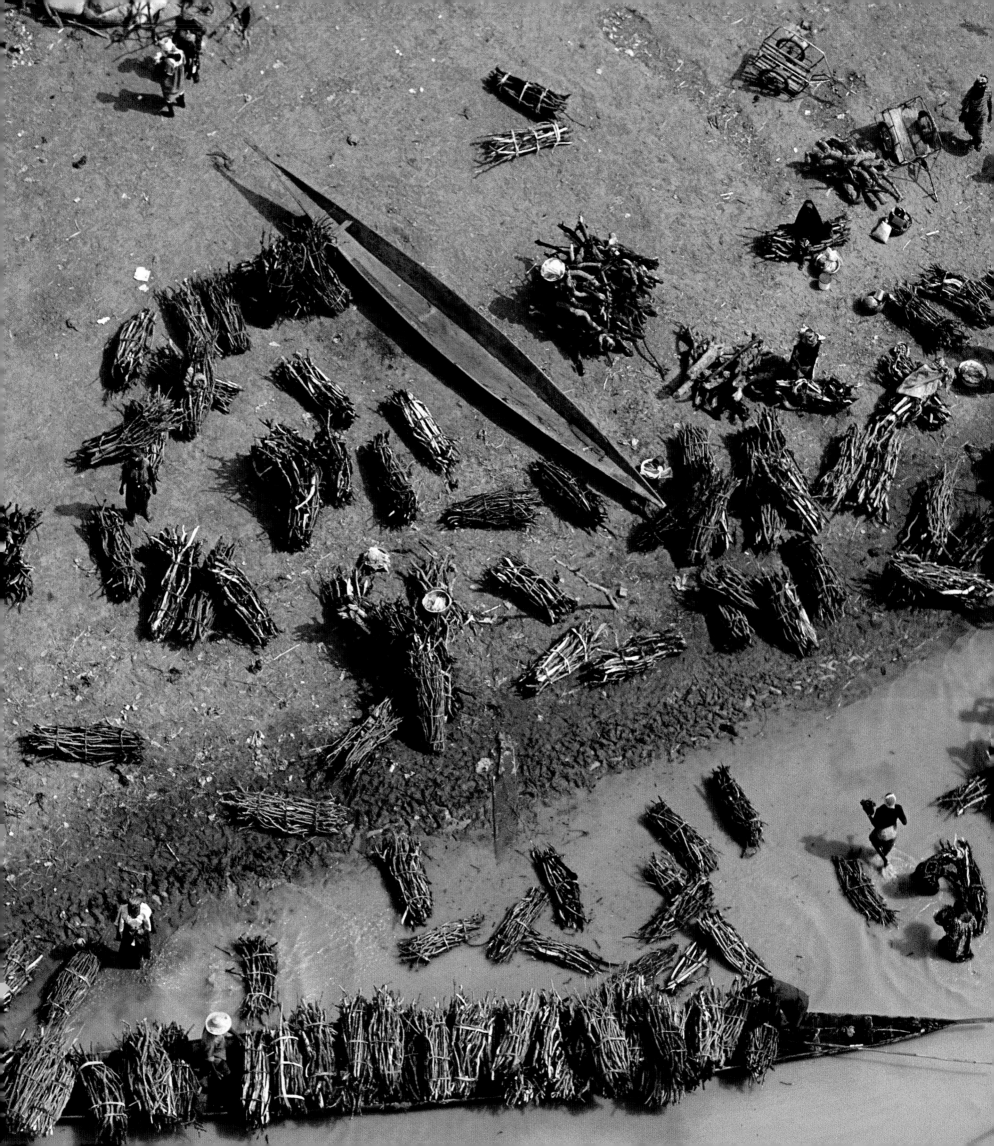

activities are the primary source of income for about one-third of the people living around Tonle Sap, a lake in Cambodia, and a secondary source of income for over half of those people (Baran, 2005). In 2005, worldwide production of the giant freshwater prawn, *Macrobrachium rosenbergii*, exceeded 205,000 metric tons and was valued at US$896,263,000 (Wowor and Ng, 2007).

Freshwater fishes, decapods, crustaceans, and plants contribute toward the aquarium trade, which is an important income source; more than one billion ornamental fishes are traded worldwide, including 4,000 freshwater species (Whittington and Chong, 2007). Some estimates in the early 2000s showed that Sri Lanka earned US$8 million per year from ornamental fish and plant exports (Wijesekara and Yakupitiyage, 2001). Freshwater mollusks are also used for the production of most of the world's cultured pearls (Revenga and Kura, 2003). Crocodiles, whether farmed, ranched, or wild, remain significant sources of leather and meat.

The variety of benefits provided by freshwater ecosystems is astounding, encompassing water for drinking, washing, aquatic organisms (used for food and medicine), agricultural production, transportation, and industrial processes, as well as energy and electricity generation (MEA, 2005a). Freshwater ecosystems deliver provisioning services, as mentioned above, and also deliver regulating, cultural, and supporting services (see table 5.1).

"Regulating services" include water-quality maintenance such as purification and filtration, delivery of nutrient-rich sediments to floodplains, flood control, and storm protection (Baron et al., 2002; Postel and Richter, 2003; Wallace et al., 2003; Emerton and Bos, 2004; MEA, 2005b). Intact wetlands and floodplains are particularly valuable for human livelihoods; they provide food and purify water, and they reduce climate change risk, acting as critical buffers against sea-level rise and storm surges (IIED, 2007).

Recreational, scenic, and spiritual or cultural values are less-direct services provided by freshwater ecosystems, but they are no less important for human well-being. On average, 35 to 60 million people in the United States spend roughly $40 billion annually on recreational fishing (Helfman, 2007). In Canada, Mexico, and the United States, more than 60 million people watch migratory birds, and another 3.2 million hunt ducks, geese, and other game birds—spending more than US$20 billion annually (Ramsar, 2001). Cultural values include greater connectivity to local cultures and traditions, spiritual values, human happiness, increased productivity, and improved social relations (MEA, 2005b).

Supporting services include the hydrologic cycle and nutrient cycling, the latter of which plays a role in floodplain fertility, primary production, predator/prey relationships and ecosystem resilience. These services are often difficult to quantify, but cannot be ignored; they underpin the delivery of all of the other services (MEA, 2005b). Freshwater mussels increase available fine particulate matter (both organic and inorganic) on substrates (Howard and Cuffey, 2006) and capture bacteria from rivers and streams (Silverman et al., 1997). Another study found that the total economic value of insect pollination worldwide amounted to $US188 billion, representing 9.4% of the value of world agricultural production used for human food in 2005 (Gallai et al, 2007).

The services delivered depend upon the freshwater ecosystem type (see table 5.1). Lakes, rivers, marshes, and coastal regions (to a depth of 6 meters at low tide) cover more than 12.8 million km2—an area 33% larger than the United States and 50% larger than Brazil—and deliver a full complement of services, but lesser known systems, such as underground caves and even snow and ice, are also part of service delivery (MEA, 2005a).

Agricultural and aquacultural systems cover 25% of Earth's land surface; rice fields alone cover about 1.3 million km2 (90% of which are in Asia) (MEA, 2005a;

Left: The forests, rivers, and lakes of Alaska's Kenai Peninsula produce large populations of chinook, coho, and pink salmon; steelhead trout; and Dolly Varden char, which support both commercial fishing and the local tourist industry. Hazel Lake, Kenai Mountains, Alaska. —Galen Rowell

	Agricultural lands	Peat Swamps	Delta	Estuary	Forest	Wetland	Riparian Buffer	Lakes/Rivers	Perennial Ice/Snow	Urban waters	Aquifers
Provisioning											
Water Supply		X	X	X	x	x	X	x	x	X	x
Food	x	X	x	x	X	X	X	x		X	
Raw Materials	X	X	X	X	x	X	X	X			
Medicinal Resources	X	X	X	X	X	X	X	X			
Regulating											
Gas & Climate Regulation	X	X	X	X	X	X	x	X	X		
Disturbance Regulation		X	X		X	X	X	X		X	X
Soil Erosion Control	X		X		X	X	x	X	X	X	
Water Regulation	X	X	X	X	X	X	x	X	X	X	X
Biological Control					x	x					
Water Quality & Waste Processing	X	X	X	X	x	x	x	X		X	X
Soil Formation	X	X	X	X	X	X		X			
Supporting											
Nutrient Cycling	X	X	X	x	X	X	X	X		X	
Biodiversity & Habitat	X	X	X	X	x	x	X	x	X	X	
Primary Productivity	X	X	X	X	X	X	X	X		X	
Pollination	x		X		X	X	x				
Cultural											
Esthetic	x	X	X	X	x	x	X	X	X	X	
Recreational & Touristic		X	X	X	x	x	X	x		x	
Scientific & Educational	X	X	X	X	X	X	X	X	X	X	X
Spiritual & Religious	X		X	X	X	X	X	X	X		

Table 5.1 shows the ecosystem services provided by freshwater systems. Many critical valuation studies have not been completed. Green highlights show ecosystem service and freshwater system combinations for which economic values are available.

TEEB, 2008). These systems depend on water, and impact the supply of it and delivery of other ecosystem services such as native fisheries production and water purification.

Peatlands are any type of wetland in which decayed plant matter or peat accumulates. Peatlands provide food and raw materials, and support primary productivity and nutrient cycling. They cover approximately 4 million km2 of the planet and are found in at least 173 countries, although the vast majority are in Canada (37%) and Russia (30%) (MEA, 2005a). Peatlands are also very important for regulating our climate; they hold around 1.5% of the total estimated global carbon storage and 25% to 30% of the amount of carbon contained in terrestrial vegetation and soils (MEA, 2005a).

Deltaic and estuarine systems support rich biodiversity, sustain inland and coastal fisheries, and protect coastal communities from flooding and hurricanes/typhoons. There are around 1,200 major estuaries covering approximately 500,000 km2 across the planet, with mangrove forests covering around 160,000 to 180,000 km2 in tropical and subtropical areas (MEA, 2005a). Coastal wetlands, in particular, can help protect human settlements from large waves related to hurricanes and storm surges; protect coastal aquifers limiting inland saltwater intrusions; offer refuge for species; help stabilize soils and habitat; and buffer against changes in salinity of estuaries or altered tidal ranges. Floodplains ensure natural replenishment of sediments, rebuilding deltas, improving agricultural fertility, and minimizing saltwater intrusions into inland waters. They also redistribute nutrients into coastal waters.

Forests and upland vegetation provide food and medicine, and can help reduce the magnitude of certain peak-flow flood events, minimizing soil erosion/ soil loss and stabilizing and minimizing landslides. Almost 40 million km2 of forest cover Earth's surface—roughly 30% of the planet's total land area (FAO, 2006). The extent to which forest cover-loss contributes to flooding depends upon the steepness of slope, magnitude of storm event, velocity of water flows, type of forest cover, and extent to which the area has been cleared (Bradshaw et al., 2009). Forests may also play a significant role in water recharge and in generating rainfall. Sheil and Murdiyarso (2009) examined atmospheric pressure differences along the interior to the coast in the Amazon and Congo river basins, and suggested that intact forest cover in these regions contributes to their high rainfall. In the lowlands, river floodplains serve as natural safety nets to contain the impacts of soil erosion, and allow for soil fertility and agricultural growth (MEA, 2005a).

Wetlands in general are some of the most studied and valued freshwater ecosystems. Several economically important plants are harvested from wetlands, including phragmites reeds, lotus root, wild rice, and water chestnut (Li et al., 2000). More than 2.7 billion people rely on rice, a wetland grain, as a major food source (Chambers et al., 2008). Wetlands provide storm protection; one study in Louisiana (Costanza et al., 2008) showed values of more than $10,000 per hectare, per year for hurricane protection. Wetlands sequester carbon and help regulate its release into the biosphere. Wetlands also filter pollutants such as excessive nitrogen and phosphorous, which might otherwise result in eutrophication of lakes and coastal areas. (Some wetlands have been found to reduce the nitrate concentrations by more than 80% [MEA, 2005a]). Wetlands are also valuable in urban environments. For example, Conservation International restored the structure and function of six protected area wetlands in Bogota, Colombia, enhancing flood mitigation, water purification, and scenic areas for recreation and environmental education, and conserving biodiversity.

Vast networks of **rivers and their tributaries** deliver water for drinking and washing, energy production, and transportation. These networks feed into the 5- to 15 million lakes that cover 500 km2 of our planet, generating recreational and other benefits (MEA, 2005a). Forests, rivers, wetlands, and lakes are vital to flood protection, and their services to people and wildlife depend heavily on the condition of the floodplain. It is widely recognized, for example, that in addition to regulated low-flow conditions, higher flows and even floods are essential to the ecological health and dynamism of river, floodplain, and estuarine ecosystems (Bunn and Arthington, 2002). Allowing floodwaters to spread out and dissipate provides far greater flood protection for people outside the inundated floodplain, and also recharges the groundwater. In addition, river flows allow for greater natural sediment deposits, building wetlands and land and permitting nutrient cycling and soil replenishment. Rivers also provide waste processing and disposal, transporting excess organic material for redeposition downstream or into the ocean-feeding coastal and marine ecosystems. Finally, this constant hydrological flux provides variable ecological conditions that can help control the populations of aquatic species that are vectors for disease.

Perennial snow and ice represent about 2% of the planet's water (fresh water and marine) and provide another set of vital services. Snow pack is absolutely crucial for maintaining dry-season water supplies and for reducing floods and recharging aquifers. Urban water represents less than 1% of global runoff, but supplies water to more than 4 billion people (Vörösmarty et al., 2005). People tend to live in areas with locally sustainable water supplies or river corridor flows, making these waters—even though they are likely to be polluted or degraded—important for human habitation (Meybeck et al., 2001).

Finally, **underground aquifers** should not be overlooked as freshwater systems, as they are absolutely vital for providing water and for maintaining springs, low-flow waters, and other benefits. This is particularly true in places where surface water has been allocated elsewhere or polluted.

DISTRIBUTION AND AVAILABILITY OF FRESHWATER ECOSYSTEM SERVICES

Water moves between all parts of Earth in the form of vapor, liquid, and solid, passing throughout the broader biophysical environment (atmospheric, marine, terrestrial, aquatic, and subterranean) (MEA, 2005a). It is this hydrologic cycle that sustains and regulates inland freshwater ecosystems and ensures service delivery. Freshwater access and availability differs in time and space, governed by evaporative, recharge, and runoff processes.

The extent to which a given ecosystem provides global runoff is usually similar to the fraction of precipitation received. Forests receive slightly more than half of global precipitation and yield about half of the total global runoff, while mountains represent one-quarter of both global precipitation and runoff. Cultivated and island systems are the next-most important source areas, each constituting about 15% of global runoff (although water quality is typically lower in agricultural and urban developed systems). Dryland ecosystems, despite their large area, contribute less than 10% to the renewable water supply, due to high evapotranspiration (Vörösmarty et al., 2005).

The volume of clean water flowing from a particular area can be estimated by adjusting the precipitation falling on that area with a coefficient that quantifies the ability of various land covers to deliver precipitation downstream *in a clean state*. For example, although wetlands and many forests contribute substantially to evaporation and evapotranspiration, they are among the most effective land cover types in removing sediments for mitigating other factors that reduce quality (coefficient of 1.0, which is highest quality, given the scale is zero to 1.0). On the other hand, agricultural lands and artificial surfaces deliver a high proportion of precipitation downstream (coefficient of 0.9), often very quickly, but generally contribute to reduced water quality (coefficient of 0.1). Figure

5.1a maps the volume of clean water provided by natural habitats worldwide, based on precipitation capture and land cover data depicting likely quality of the water as it flows downstream. These "potential freshwater services" often act as a supporting service for downstream ecosystems, and as a storehouse of services for future use or to buffer human communities against future change.

It is often the case that we assign more value to fresh water if it is more readily available to support human activities. Thus, a key step is to modify the prior maps of "potential services," weighting them according to the presence of human demand downstream. This step introduces calculations relating the water delivered by upstream habitats to the demand for various human uses downstream. The fresh water provided by upstream habitats generally supports the needs of multiple human communities downstream. Downstream communities, in turn, often obtain water that originates from multiple alternative upstream sources. Taking hydrological drainage direction into consideration enables us to map "realized freshwater services," assigning value to habitats in direct proportion to their role in supplying clean fresh water used by certain downstream beneficiaries. Figure 5.1b maps the volume of clean water provided by natural habitats that contributes to downstream demand, in this case consumption by total human population downstream. This map extends "potential services" to estimate the services that are actually realized, accounting for the complex spatial flows between source habitats and downstream beneficiaries, and thus shows substantial variation based on human population density and hydrological flow directions.

The initial results of these studies provide coarse estimates of freshwater service flows. Brazil has the greatest volume of potential services, largely due to the Amazon basin's high precipitation and water flow volume, with Russia and Canada each delivering about half of that amount. At a national scale, realized freshwater services are greatest in China, largely

The Ganges River flows from glacial Himalayan headwaters and provides services for one of the greatest concentrations of people on Earth. Many Hindus consider life incomplete without having bathed at least once in the river.
—Art Wolfe

Ganges River, India

Virginia, USA | The Dragon Run in Virginia is a pristine cypress swamp that filters an entire watershed as it flows to the Chesapeake Bay, one of the North Atlantic's most important estuaries. The Dragon Run is home to fifty-five species of fishes, and is used as an important spawning ground for several anadromous species including American shad, alewife herring, and striped bass. —Justin Black

The Adams River in central British Columbia is host to one of the greatest salmon migrations in the world. A population peak occurs every four years when millions of sockeye (*Oncorhynchus nerka*) converge in this small area to spawn and die. Fish caught and scavenged by bear, eagles, and other animals during the migration end up returning essential nutrients to the surrounding forest. —Garth Lenz

British Columbia, Canada

Figure 5.1. (a) Potential (above) and (b) realized (below) freshwater services maps.

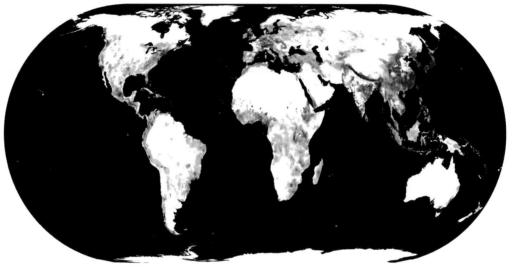

due to the important role that the Himalayas play in delivering water to more than a billion people directly dependent upon them downstream. India, the United States, and Indonesia, combined, deliver amounts similar to those in China. This initial analysis indicates a high degree of concordance between regions of great importance for delivery of clean water and regions of high priority for biodiversity conservation. The Biodiversity Hotspots (Myers et al., 2000; Mittermeier et al., 2004) and High-Biodiversity Wilderness Areas (Mittermeier et al., 2003), for example, which, combined, cover only 23% of Earth's surface, are the origin of a disproportionate amount of both potential

services (65.3% of the global total) and realized services (61.8%) in figure 5.1. These initial results are encouraging, suggesting that win-win situations exist in which many of the same actions to protect natural habitats contribute simultaneously to sustaining both biodiversity and the freshwater ecosystem services upon which we all depend. More work is needed; these models do not account for subsurface hydrological flows, for intra-annual variability including drought and flood events, and for longer-term trends such as climate change. They also do not capture discontinuities such as dams and other threats that interrupt service flows.

RELATIONSHIPS BETWEEN FRESHWATER ECOSYSTEMS, SERVICE FLOWS, AND THREATS

A strong consensus exists within the scientific community that, if we are to secure the delivery of ecosystem goods and services to society, we need to maintain some semblance of natural flows to sustain the ecological health of freshwater ecosystems (Poff et al., 1997; Postel and Richter, 2003; Richter, 2009). Yet this is not the direction we are pursuing. Development agencies have adopted rules of thumb that leave as little as 10% of water within rivers for environmental flows, while ecologists suggest that this number needs to be as high as 80% (Hirji and Davis, 2009). Population and unsustainable economic growth are driving freshwater ecosystem degradation and loss of natural flows. They result in infrastructure development, land conversion, water withdrawal, eutrophication and pollution, overharvesting and overexploitation, and the introduction of invasive alien species (MEA, 2005a). Global climate change is expected to exacerbate this loss and degradation, and to increase the incidence of vector-borne and waterborne diseases in many regions (Bates, 2008). Threats are covered in more detail in chapter 3.

Ecohydrological dynamics govern natural flows, and the extent to which services are delivered depends on threats to those flows. Rivers and streams depend on the magnitude, frequency, duration, timing, and rate of change of hydrologic conditions—yet dams block fish migrations, increase water temperature, degrade habitat, and disrupt seasonal triggers for aquatic species reproduction. Natural lakes are governed by lake depth, turnover, trophic status, and human activities. Dams, point and nonpoint source pollution, overfishing, and invasives threaten aquatic resources, food, and medicine, and sense of place/ spiritual values. Wetlands and floodplains contain vegetation adapted to inundation and desiccation. Service delivery is highly dependent on connectivity to other systems, but dams, dikes, and draining eliminate natural flood control and filtration, release methane and carbon, increase invasives, and ruin habitat for fish and waterfowl. Coastal systems are influenced by the quantity, quality, and timing of freshwater inputs and the daily and seasonal influence of tides, salinity, temperature, turbidity, and energy flux. Mangrove clearing, runoff, and pollution disrupt pH balances and species reproduction. Underground systems supply drinking water and irrigation, help retain soil, remove pollutants, and recharge surface water—all of which are dependent upon runoff filtering into soils, soil retention, and dry-season water flows. Dams impact aquifer replenishment and agriculture impacts groundwater quality and quantity (Braga, 1999; Postel and Richter, 2003; MEA, 2005a).

Growing pressures from human development and climate change increase the likelihood of potentially abrupt changes in ecosystems—changes that can be large in magnitude and difficult, expensive, or impossible to reverse. If natural flows are maintained, then freshwater ecosystems are healthier and provide valuable benefits in perpetuity. These ecosystems also require very little maintenance, compared to built infrastructure that would be required to replace these benefits—for example, a desalinization plant or levees for flood control. In addition, forests, wetlands, lakes, or rivers within a watershed provide a suite of ecosystem services as local as fish on the plate for local fishers or as distant as global climate stabilization. If freshwater ecosystems are damaged or destroyed, their loss may be irreplaceable or require tremendous investments that recover only a single service, such as flood protection. Although all people depend on fresh water, and it is necessary for our economy, we also have enormous species diversity to protect. It is clear that we have not yet sufficiently mainstreamed freshwater ecosystems and their protection into development decision making. A major reason for this is the inadequate economic valuation attributed to freshwater ecosystem services, which we describe next.

VALUATION OF FRESHWATER ECOSYSTEM SERVICES

Goods, such as fishes, fresh water, food, and fiber, are relatively easy to value economically because they are measured in physical quantities over time; tons of fish caught in a year, for instance, or cubic feet of potable water per second. Services, such as water quality, flood control, aesthetic value, and nutrient cycling, are benefits that cannot be easily measured by physical amounts over time. In some cases these services, by their very nature, cannot be privatized; they are "public goods and services." Flood protection is one of many services that is "public"; that is, you cannot exclude a single landowner from flood protection if he or she does not pay. If landowners live downstream of a wetland, or behind the levee, they get flood protection—even if they don't pay for it.

Of the 192 possible combinations of ecosystems types and the ecosystem services they provide, only sixty-one of these have been valued (Batker, 2010), demonstrating the need for many more studies. Biodiversity is unique; it is a critical part of the natural infrastructure, providing goods and services. A biodiverse freshwater system has qualities of resiliency and sustainability that "built capital" lacks and that systems with less biodiversity may lack. Climate change is introducing tremendous concern about how brittle both built and natural systems will be in the coming decades. The diversity of life within an ecosystem constitutes much of the physical structure that produces both goods and services—many of these services are very difficult to quantify and value economically.

In spite of these challenges, the economic value of ecosystem services can be immense. For example, a recent study of Ulaanbaatar, the capital city of Mongolia, revealed that conservation of the Upper Tuul watershed ecosystem above the city would generate additional water benefits of US$15 a year for every US$1 invested. In twenty-five years' time, the goods and services generated would be worth US$37 million a year more than would be the case if the Upper Tuul watershed were not protected (Emerton et al., 2009).

Over the last two decades, the application of a more inclusive "total economic value framework" has provided a set of conceptual and methodological tools that allow ecosystem values to be more easily and accurately assessed (Pearce, 1992). Instead of focusing only on direct commercial values, this framework encompasses subsistence and non-market values, ecological functions, and non-use benefits. This more holistic approach essentially involves considering the value of the complete range of characteristics of an ecosystem as an integrated system—resource stocks or assets, flows of environmental services, and the attributes of the ecosystem as a whole (Barbier, 1994).

Over the last decade, payment for ecosystem services (PES) has become an increasingly common way of raising revenues for the government authorities who are responsible for protected areas, and generating income for the people who live in and use ecosystems that deliver key freshwater services. For example, the city of Cuenca, in the southern Ecuadorian Andes, levies surcharges by the municipal water authority on water bills and industrial water charges, and then transfers those levies to the Municipal Corporation of Cajas National Park (the watershed for the town) (Espinosa, 2005). Around the buffer zone of La Peñablanca Protected Landscape in the Philippines, poor local villagers reached agreement with a local tour operator to share a proportion of tourism revenues with the local community as payment for planting trees and developing sustainable farming techniques that sustain the landscape quality, attracting tourists (REECS, 2008).

PES schemes have also engaged hydropower facilities, farmers, and water-dependent manufacturing industries. In Costa Rica, for example, La Esperanza

Left: Alpacas (*Vicugna pacos*) in Las Cajas National Park near Cuenca, Ecuador. The park is the watershed for the city of Cuenca, and its management is funded by taxes levied on residential and commercial water use downstream. —Pete Oxford

Hydropower Project contracted with the Monteverde Conservation League to maintain forest cover for much of the hydropower plant's upper catchment. The payment increases through the first five years of the contract, from $.03 to $.10 per km^2 per year, and from the fifth year onward settles at $.10 per km2 per year; a formula based on power produced and the tariff at which the power is sold. This PES scheme funds 10% to 25% of the League's annual budget (Rojas and Aylward, 2002). Perrier Vittel S. A., the world's largest bottler of natural mineral water, acquired property and compensated farmers to reduce nitrates and pesticides and restore natural water purification in a subbasin of the Rhine-Meuse watershed in northeastern France. Thus far, Vittel has paid almost $25 million and improved conservation on more than 100 km^2 of farmland (Perrot-Maître and Davis, 2001). Large-scale agricultural water users in the Cauca River Valley, Colombia, contribute funds into a voluntary PES, used to protect and regenerate native forests and provide technical assistance, training, and environmental education-enhancing conservation measures on more than 10,000 km^2 of land (Echavarría, 2002).

Successful PES schemes have been implemented on the basis of sound science, financial appraisal, negotiation, and stakeholder participation, and on a solid legal basis that protects the rights of both buyers and sellers of ecosystem services. There must also be a clear demand and willingness to pay among users.

MAINTAINING ECOSYSTEM SERVICES FOR THE FUTURE

Freshwater ecosystem goods and services are a blessing, a bargain, and a good investment opportunity. Attributing market value and avoiding perverse production subsidies that disincentivize ecosystem protection are at the crux of maintaining the vital freshwater ecosystems that provide these services. Threats, including nutrient loading, water withdrawals in places incapable of sustaining them and climate change, must also be addressed. Good governance of freshwater resources includes recognition that the mix of species that comprises freshwater ecosystems require the resource of fresh water just as humans do; that is, freshwater ecosystems themselves are an important freshwater user and stakeholder. This governance of fresh water also requires transparency and accountability of government and private-sector decision making.

Development activities can unintentionally result in service trade-offs, such as agricultural production for water quality, or land use for biodiversity. Adverse trade-offs can also occur between services, such as electricity production for fisheries—a situation that, like many others, requires consideration of service flows across political boundaries. Land and water use and management activities, examined together—particularly when working toward goals of healthy ecosystems—can ensure diverse species populations and clean and sufficient supplies of fresh water to meet the multiple needs of people (CAoWMiA, 2007). Several factors can help solve freshwater conservation and economic development problems; these include better valuation of the economic benefits that freshwater systems provide, understanding where services are provisioned, identifiying who are the benefactors and who are the damagers of freshwater systems and their services, and how economic incentives can be changed to reflect this. Useful management approaches include integrated river basin management and strategic environmental assessments for regionwide planning of development activities. These approaches support both conservation and the achievement of the Millennium Development Goals for tackling human well-being and environmental sustainability.

Mali, Africa | Mali nomad boys drinking from and playing in a lake at the peak of the summer dry season. Water is delivered to these natural reservoirs by seasonal flood cycles of the Niger River. —Karen Kasmauski

A team of recreational spelunkers drop into the 50-meter-deep Neversink Pit in Alabama, USA, a wet limestone sinkhole that harbors a rare species of fern. The cave has recently been bought by a local group of cavers to preserve it for future generations. —George Steinmetz

Alabama, USA

SIX
FRESH WATER FOR THE FUTURE

FRESH WATER FOR THE FUTURE
POLICY TO SECURE AN ESSENTIAL SERVICE FOR ALL

D. Mark Smith

I n looking forward to 2050 and imagining the river basins of the future, what do we want from our rivers, lakes, and wetlands? What are our priorities in organizing and managing the tapestry of forests, farming, towns, and cities that give river basins their character and shape the goods and services we receive from them? How can we secure fresh water for both people and nature?

Depending on your perspective, the answers to these questions might seem quite straightforward. All people must have access to a reliable and safe freshwater supply. People need to have fresh water and energy to drive economic growth. Biodiversity must be conserved, for its own sake and because of its role in ecosystem function and in supplying ecosystem services. The difficulties arise when combining these aims. Satisfying human and economic needs for fresh water will have to be achieved while reversing the desiccation, pollution, and loss of natural flows; impacts that have made freshwater ecosystems the most threatened and degraded worldwide (MEA, 2005). Bearing all this in mind, managing our river basins and creating fresh water–secure futures is a complicated task.

Per-capita demand for fresh water is rising as prosperity increases. By 2025, there could be 3 billion people living in water-stressed countries, compared to 700 million in 2006 (UNDP, 2006). Climate change-induced droughts, floods, glacier melt, and sea-level rise are serious concerns. Engineering more infrastructure has been promoted to lower these and other risks. As demand for irrigation and electricity rises, there are also widespread and renewed calls to build more water-storage facilities, including more hydropower dams. Under one set of choices for the future, the impetus to modify and engineer river basins—to regulate and control when and where water flows in rivers, wetlands, and floodplains—is strengthening. There is another set of choices we could make, however, in which we restore and protect these systems as part of nature's infrastructure, making the resilience of river basins and freshwater ecosystems an intrinsic part of our future water and energy security.

Any choice over the future of our fresh waters must live within water realities. Freshwater flows are used and re-used. Some uses mean that fresh water is lost, as is the case when irrigation water evaporates. Fresh water can be exchanged from one use to another (between people, or between people and nature) as it flows from up- to downstream. Pollution changes where water can be used and for what benefits, and limits options for use downstream. The priorities one person or group gives to freshwater use or flow regulation are interconnected with and interdependent on the priorities of others. Within these interdependencies, it is easy for freshwater use to benefit some people over others, or to benefit the needs of people over nature. For biodiversity, the message is that we will have to solve people's freshwater problems to ensure that there is enough fresh water for nature.

Previous spread: Runoff from open-air iron mining operations clearly illustrates the unintended consequences of resource extraction. Serra dos Carajas, Brazil. —Daniel Beltrá

Left: Global climate change is melting many of our world's glaciers, broadening the need for protection and policies beyond the scale of parks. Meltwater channel on a glacier in Wrangell-St. Elias National Park, Alaska, USA. —Frans Lanting

In any river basins of the future that we imagine, the fates of both people and nature will be inseparable. If nature is overlooked, the flows of fresh water to and from ecosystems that sustain ecosystem function and services are easily degraded or lost. Cutting off the annual pulse of floodwaters from wetlands downstream from dams, for example, can destroy fisheries, leaving people with less protein in their diet and poorer health. Draining wetlands or changing land uses reduces infiltration of groundwater and nature's ability to remove pollution, raising costs for water treatment downstream. In degraded watersheds, nature stores less water and is less effective in holding back sediment, leading to reduced hydropower generation. Without fresh water for nature, loss of ecosystem services has real costs that must be counted in terms of health, food security, livelihoods, and jobs (Emerton and Bos, 2004).

Organizing water futures that will serve the needs of people as well as nature is a complex puzzle. The framework to do this—Integrated Water Resources Management, or IWRM—exists and has long been known to water planners and managers as a way of balancing competing uses and enhancing water governance (GWP/INBO, 2009). IWRM is complicated but can be implemented with effective laws, policies, and institutions in place. It must also incorporate the needs of nature. IWRM provides a guiding framework for action, but its successful implementation requires social change and several years (or even decades) to achieve.

POLICY AND GOVERNANCE IN A CHANGING WORLD

When looking at the problem of fresh water—whether from a supply, economic, or biodiversity perspective—most often we know what to do. For one thing, we need to deliver safe fresh water to reduce poverty; thus, investment in appropriate infrastructure and maintenance is necessary. For another, we need to cope with freshwater scarcity by using it efficiently,

adaptively, and within the limits of its availability. And, critically, we need to conserve freshwater biodiversity by allocating water to nature, protecting habitats, and restoring connectivity and the natural rhythm of river flows.

Climate change, however, means that knowing what to do is no longer as clear. The hydrology of many river basins will change (Bates et al., 2008). Drier climates are projected this century in some parts of the world, such as North Africa and Central America, and wetter climates in others, including East Asia and equatorial Africa. Precipitation is projected to be more variable, with higher intensities and longer dry spells. It may fall less often as snow, and be stored less in snow packs. Extreme events, including drought, floods, and storms, are projected to be more frequent. The volume and timing of runoff in rivers will change. By 2050, annual average river runoff is projected to decrease by 10% to 30% in the drier parts of the world, while increasing by 10% to 40% in wetter areas (IPCC, 2007). Add to this the expected inundation of low-lying coasts, and some river basins we know today may become different places, with very different freshwater regimes and risks. We can no longer rely on historical hydrological knowledge and data as bases for the way we manage fresh water. The old assumptions about drought and flood, runoff, and river flow can no longer be trusted. The implications for freshwater security, whether for cities, farms, or river basins, will be profound in some locations.

Climate change is just one facet of global change impacting freshwater resources and their management. By 2050, Earth will have to support an additional 2 billion people. This is 140,000 more people per day needing food, clothing, housing, livelihoods, jobs—and fresh water—in order to live and to ensure the ecological and economic productivity that will sustain them. An urbanizing world means that most of this population growth is expected in towns and cities, putting pressure on freshwater infrastructure in cities and the ecosystems and infrastructure of the basins that supply the cities' fresh water. Rapid economic growth is expanding prosperity and shifting consumption patterns in places such as China, India, and Brazil, driving up natural resource use per capita. Globalization means that crop failure in Australia can trigger a spike in food prices and street demonstrations on the other side of the world. The "triple crisis" of 2007–2009, involving the global financial system, food security, and energy markets, created hardship for hundreds of millions and possibly gave a foretaste of things to come.

As global change unfolds, pressure on freshwater resources is intensifying. Evidence of this abounds. China is investing billions in the South-to-North Water Diversion Project, which will divert water from the Yangtze River to the drier but more populated north. In the Mekong basin, eight hydropower dams are planned on the river's main stem to meet rising energy demand from economic expansion. Groundwater pumping for irrigation is lowering water tables in Rajasthan, Punjab, and Haryana states in India (Rodell et al., 2009). Shrinkage of the Ogallala aquifer in the midwestern United States is putting future food security for hundreds of millions of people at risk (National Geographic, 2010). In the Zarqa River in Jordan, decades of dumping solid waste, industrial effluent, and untreated sewage has turned the river from a national aquatic icon into a foul gutter. In the East African drylands, a four-year drought is causing hunger, migration, and collapsed wealth as livestock herds dwindle.

Global change and the surprises and uncertainties it brings only amplifies the need for effective policies and institutions to manage fresh water. There are few places in the world where "business as usual" is going to be good enough to meet this challenge. People and politicians in wealthy, industrialized, and emerging or developing countries alike have to be motivated to put in place reforms of water governance—of water policies, laws, and institutions—that will catalyze and promote innovation and smart solutions.

EMPOWERING PEOPLE FOR BETTER MANAGEMENT

Effective governance of fresh water will be the key to securing our future. Innovative and smarter solutions come from empowering people to make choices about how to manage their fresh water, in contrast to traditional, top-down "command-and-control" approaches. The town of Attapeu (Samakhi Xai) in Lao PDR provides an example for how this is true. Empowerment, through learning and institutional change at local level, led villagers to work together to monitor health, family nutrition, and the local environment. With new knowledge and shared understanding, villagers changed decision making about fresh water, food, and hygiene. Resulting improvements to the water supply cut waterborne disease, and villagers decided to establish fish conservation zones in nearby wetlands, leading to better fish catches, less malnutrition, and healthier wetlands.

Experience shows that when freshwater management is entrusted to technocrats in government institutions, decisions tend to be based on a narrow set of priorities. Some priorities for fresh water end up privileged, and others, overlooked. Planning and investment in infrastructure for hydropower or irrigation, for example, may not consider alternatives adequately because of a lack of understanding of links between upstream and downstream impacts, or of the costs and benefits of damage to ecosystem services. Favoring irrigation for agriculture and dam building over fresh water for ecosystem needs, for example, may jeopardize fisheries production and biodiversity downstream, impacting the livelihoods, food security, and well-being of the communities that lose out. Under a "command-and-control" style of freshwater management, policies and incentives to improve efficiency, or to invest in nature as a provider of services such as freshwater storage and purification and flood regulation, are usually weak. The result is that fresh water is allocated beyond the amount actually available, and/or it becomes easily polluted.

A cave on the Jordanian shore of the Dead Sea, where splashing waves have left a thick layer of salt crystals and stalactites. Once submerged, this cave became exposed due to lake-level declines caused by upstream diversions of fresh water for agriculture. —George Steinmetz

Dead Sea, Jordan

Including people in decision making is critical, because everyone has a stake in freshwater use and allocation. Choices about how fresh water is used and managed are made in households and by community user groups, as well as by irrigation board offices, power companies, corporate boards, river basin commissions, and freshwater ministries, and at intergovernmental negotiating tables and by governors, prime ministers, and presidents. Priorities for individual stakeholders differ and depend on scale. Farmers sharing fresh water along an irrigation furrow on the slopes of Mount Kilimanjaro may care about the farmer at the bottom of the furrow getting her fair share of water as well as an abundant community harvest, but adequate flow of fresh water into reservoirs of hydropower dams downstream is not important for these farmers. For dam operators or water ministry officials, on the other hand, low flows downstream equate to power outages in cities and factories and, ultimately, to lower national income. Without knowledge, incentives, and guidance, neither constituency may care about water for wetlands. For all these reasons, making freshwater management and allocation decisions that benefit multiple uses and needs requires finding effective ways of working with diverse stakeholders and across scales, from households to international basin agencies.

Effective governance of fresh water builds a framework for coordination, with transparent roles and responsibilities that are appropriate at different levels. People are empowered to have a voice in the decisions that affect them, with space for nature's advocates to make sure that the freshwater needs of ecosystems and the services they provide are represented and incorporated into planning and decision making. Institutions, laws, and regulations that apply at each level need to be set up to allocate roles and responsibilities that ensure that this is the case. Consider the Komadugu Yobe river basin in northern Nigeria, part of the Lake Chad basin. Poverty and frequent drought, dams, abstraction, and regional climate change have shrunk the river and replaced the natural cycle of seasonal flows with year-round low flows. Ecosystems along the river are badly degraded, including the Ramsar-listed Hadejia-Nguru

wetlands. Growing conflict among fishing, farming, and pastoralist communities due to freshwater scarcity and environmental degradation wound up increasing political tension among the six federal Nigerian states sharing the basin.

A new dialogue among basin states emerged in 2005 thanks to sharing of data from hydrological, environmental, social, and economic assessments of the basin. Dialogue made clear the absence of coherent and coordinated basin-management institutions. State Integrated Water Resources Management committees were formed to coordinate freshwater resource management, and a "Water Charter" for the basin was developed. This laid out a framework for governance and institutional reform for the basin based on clarifying the roles and responsibilities of governments, communities, dam operators, and wetland managers, among other key stakeholders. Actions required for basin restoration and sustainable development of freshwater resources were defined through a multi-stakeholder negotiation process to create a catchment management plan. By 2006, local-scale river-restoration pilot projects were underway, water conflicts reaching court had been reduced by 90%, and a joint trust fund to finance restoration of the river had been agreed to by the federal and state governments.

Roles and responsibilities are distinctly different at global, national, and local levels. At the global level, international agreements set out higher-level principles and shared commitments, including the Ramsar Convention on Wetlands, the Dublin Statement of 1992, and the Ministerial Declarations of the World Water Forums. At the national level, policies, laws, and institutions create authority for decisions made at lower levels, establishing accountability and enabling action by stakeholders as part of an empowering architecture for governing fresh water. This architecture resists "command and control," and enables freshwater managers to respond to local priorities and adapt to change in whatever form it may take.

Each country must adapt freshwater management principles to meet its specific needs, but an empowering

FRESH WATER

Beavertail cactus (*Opuntia basilaris*) in the lower
canyons of the Rio Grande National Wild
and Scenic River, Texas, USA-Mexico border.
Transboundary management of freshwater
ecosystems is complex but critical. —Carr Clifton

Rio Grande, Texas

architecture for governance does translate into implementation, as illustrated by the case of South Africa. At the global level, the Dublin Statement of 1992 urged governments to ensure sustainable freshwater futures based on effective management of fresh water as a finite resource, participation of stakeholders, gender equity, and recognition of the economic value of fresh water (ICWE, 1992). Reflecting these principles, the National Water Policy of South Africa was adopted in 1997 and led to the creation of a new national freshwater law finalized in 1998. Key pillars include the "reserve," which sets basic human needs as the first priority for freshwater allocation and protection of aquatic ecosystems as the second. Management of freshwater resources is delegated to catchment management agencies. These agencies set strategy and coordinate implementation within the requirements of freshwater law—including for an ecological reserve—but, according to local priorities, seek the participation of multi-stakeholder advisory committees and local water user associations when drawing up agreements (Iza and Stein, 2009).

Freshwater governance must also address the more than 260 river basins that cross national boundaries. Without coordination of transboundary water management, fresh water readily becomes a source of tension among states. Pollution or diversion of fresh water by upstream neighbors impacts downstream nations. Without coordination, freshwater resources are easily degraded, with damaging effects on ecosystems and biodiversity. To fill this gap, international river basin organizations have been formed in many transboundary river and lake basins around the world. Examples include the Mekong River Commission, the Volta Basin Authority in West Africa, and the Parana-Paraguay Plata Intergovernmental Coordination Committee (Sadoff et al., 2008). These institutions take many forms and have a variety of mandates, but they generally aim to build trust, coordination, and sharing of benefits from freshwater resources among the countries that share a basin. However, there are no such cooperative management arrangements in place for some 60% of international watercourses. The UN Watercourses Convention of 1997 attempted to address this by providing a global legal umbrella that sets out the rights and legal obligations of countries sharing international watercourses—but it has not yet been ratified by sufficient numbers of countries to bring it into force. This has left many river basins and important aquatic ecosystems vulnerable to unilateral actions of one basin country.

PATHWAYS TO A GREATER SECURITY

Achieving freshwater security by 2050—while feeding 9 billion people, adapting to climate change, ensuring energy security, and sustaining poverty reduction and growth—will change river basins. What we will need are resilient river basins capable of withstanding and recovering from shocks and stresses. Empowering people to find and innovate workable, sustainable solutions will be one key component to making river basins resilient.

What does a resilient river basin look like? Experience from managing river basins, including practical lessons from rivers such as the Komadugu Yobe, Pangani, Mekong, and others gives us many clues. In a resilient river basin, forests, soils, wetlands, and floodplains are part of the natural infrastructure that stores water, regulates flows, and moderates the hydrograph. Projects that develop natural infrastructure or combine it with built infrastructure can maximize efficiency, reduce fragmentation of rivers, and meet the flow requirements of ecosystems. Through better management of freshwater ecosystems, a more diverse economy exists and people have options for their livelihoods—a situation that provides people with choices when responding to change. People are also empowered to take action through a governance architecture that promotes self-organization. Basin institutions need to be adaptive, through learning and access to new knowledge, information, and skills.

Consider institutional strengthening and freshwater allocation in the Pangani River basin in Tanzania. Over-allocation of water and projected drought has intensified water scarcity, putting 3.4 million people at risk. A national water policy exists based on the principles of IWRM, which the Pangani Basin Water Office has used to pioneer water allocation based on "'environmental flows." Water is allocated within the limits of its availability, and determined by negotiation among stakeholders to accommodate different uses and sustain ecosystem services (Dyson et al., 2008). Institutional strengthening has enabled coordination of decision making over water allocation on scales from local to basinwide, as well as empowered diverse stakeholders to participate in the discovery of options, learning, and joint action. Through this process, stakeholders are generating scenarios for development of the basin that incorporate allocation of water to ecosystems, including wetlands and estuary habitats, that will sustain ecosystem services vital for their livelihoods. Stakeholders and the Basin Water Office are learning to use information and planning tools to build water security, sustain ecosystems, and reduce vulnerability to climate change.

In a resilient river basin, both nature and resilient people are necessary and inseparable. Biodiversity and ecosystem services are the basis for ecological resilience. As a result, in a resilient river, biodiversity conservation aligns with, rather than opposes, priority economic and social issues. Freshwater policies, laws, and institutions are set up to enable innovation and adaptive solutions to local priorities that build freshwater security while reinforcing social resilience.

Policy makers need a practical framework around which they can chart pathways toward more resilient future river basins. Four guiding principles can serve as the basis for starting to build resilience into river basin development and freshwater resource management:

1. *Diversity*—of the economy, livelihoods, and nature, because people are more able to cope with shocks and stresses where there are diverse livelihood options and economies, and where biodiversity ensures a reliable supply of ecosystem services.
2. *Sustainable technologies and infrastructure*—where the design and operation of water infrastructure avoids damage to natural systems, and integrates and makes use of ecosystem services to support freshwater security.
3. *Self-organization*—to empower people to take action and adapt, through multi-stakeholder participation in governance and in enabling institutions.
4. *Learning*—through the provision of better information and capacity building, for both individuals and institutions, to strengthen adaptation and catalyze innovation.

THE TIME IS NOW

When we look forward to the river basins of the future, 2050 is just one date picked from among many. All the same, forty years hence is an important horizon. Choices made now about infrastructure investments and design will be operating in 2050. Today's choices about how fresh water flows and is stored and cleaned, by built infrastructure and healthy ecosystems, will be the reality in 2050. What we do now in reforming and reinventing freshwater policies and the choices we make over fresh water will help to shape our success or failure in meeting the challenges of a changing climate, food security for 9 billion people, and protecting biodiversity during an era of rapid global change.

Progress depends on motivating people and politicians to change—and on empowering people to take action. Our knowledge of what actions are needed to solve freshwater problems is well developed. To safeguard biodiversity, we must ensure that people's freshwater problems are solved in ways that incorporate nature's needs for fresh water. An architecture of policies, laws, and institutions that empower people to allocate freshwater resources wisely will bring us success. In this vision, river basins provide freshwater security, and people and nature are resilient to change. Now is the time to begin. The abundance, availability, and beauty of our freshwater ecosystems depend on it.

These Kayapó children from the village of Kubekrakej, in the southeastern Amazon region of Brazil, play in a waterfall in the Riozinho, a tributary of the mighty Rio Xingú. —Cristina G. Mittermeier

Amazon, Brazil

Mali | Lakes evaporate at the height of the dry season in Mali. Here, a health worker lifts slabs of mud to look for moisture as winds whip across the lakebed. —Karen Kasmauski

The Greenland ice sheet, 110,000 years old and the world's second-largest ice cap after Antarctica, is on pace to disappear and raise sea level by seven meters within the next two centuries unless humans act quickly to address climate change. Glacial meltwater cuts channels and tunnels that drain and destabilize the glacier. —Chris Linder

Greenland

APPENDIX

APPENDIX

SOME EXAMPLES OF COMMON ENGAGEMENT FOR CONSERVING THE WORLD'S WETLANDS

Dennis Landenbergue, Dwight Peck

RAMSAR CONVENTION AND WWF

The year 2011 marks a significant anniversary in the world of environmental conservation; the Ramsar Convention and WWF will celebrate their fortieth and fiftieth birthdays, respectively. This provides an occasion to celebrate a remarkable relationship of cooperation and mutual support that has continued throughout the life of the modern environmental movement and protected millions of hectares of wetlands.

Wetlands are areas where water is the primary factor controlling the environment and the associated plant and animal life. They occur where the water table is at or near the surface of the land, or where the land is covered by shallow water. Under the text of the Ramsar Convention, wetlands are defined as "areas of marsh, fen, peatland or water, whether natural or artificial, permanent or temporary, with water that is static or flowing, fresh, brackish or salt, including areas of marine water the depth of which at low tide does not exceed six meters." The Ramsar definition specifically includes marine and coastal, estuarine, lacustrine, riverine, and palustrine or marshy wetlands (and thus differs to some extent from that used in this book through its inclusion of coastal marine systems), as well as groundwater and human-made wetlands such as rice paddies, shrimp ponds, and reservoirs. The definition embraces virtually all aspects of freshwater management and conservation.

Wetlands are among the world's most productive environments. They are cradles of biological diversity, providing the water and primary productivity upon which countless species of plants and animals depend for survival. They support high concentrations of birds, mammals, reptiles, amphibians, fishes, and invertebrate species. Wetlands are also important storehouses of plant genetic material.

The multiple roles of wetland ecosystems and their value to humanity—the "ecosystem services" they provide—have been increasingly understood and documented in recent years. This has led to large expenditures to restore lost or degraded hydrological and biological functions of wetlands. The ability of wetlands to adapt to changing conditions and accelerating rates of change will be crucial to human communities and wildlife everywhere as the full impact of climate change on our ecosystem lifelines is felt.

In addition, wetlands have special attributes as part of the cultural heritage of humanity—they are related to religious and cosmological beliefs and spiritual values, constitute a source of aesthetic and artistic inspiration, yield invaluable archaeological evidence from the remote past, provide wildlife sanctuaries, and form the basis

Previous spread: Sandhill cranes (*Grus canadensis*) and snow geese (*Chen caerulescens*) migrating through the Rio Grande flyway, Bosque del Apache National Wildlife Refuge, New Mexico, USA. — Jack Dykinga

Left: Jabirú storks (*Mycteria jabiru*), Pantanal, Brazil. —Staffan Widstrand

of important local social, economic, and cultural traditions.

HISTORY OF WWF

"The Launching of a New Ark" was the first WWF report. It stated, "During the 1950s it had become increasingly evident that the impact of human progress and development on the natural world had produced what amounted to a state of emergency

HRH Prince Bernhard, who was the first president of WWF's international board of trustees. Under the direction of Fritz Vollmar, a small WWF secretariat team was hosted in IUCN's headquarters, which was then in Morges, Switzerland. WWF quickly became a leader in raising public awareness about the urgency of environmental issues, in environmental policy making, and in project implementation on the ground. WWF currently operates through a network of ninety offices in more than forty countries, with its central secretariat WWF International still located in

Wetlands are among the world's most productive environments. They are cradles of biological diversity, providing the water and primary productivity upon which countless species of plants and animals depend for survival.

for wildlife. Powerful arguments—ethical, aesthetic, scientific, and economic—seem to place a direct moral responsibility on mankind to take the long view and to conserve this natural heritage wisely."

Recognition began to spread across the world that environmental loss and degradation were accelerating and required concerted legal and public action. To address this concern, Peter Scott of the International Union for Conservation of Nature (IUCN); Julian Huxley, one of the founders of UNESCO; Max Nicholson of the British Nature Conservancy; and Guy Mountfort, an ornithologist and businessman, created WWF. Its purpose was to conserve the world's wildlife, ensure the sustainable use of natural resources, and promote the reduction of pollution and wasteful consumption.

On September 11, 1961, WWF was legally constituted under Swiss law at Zurich, and registered as a tax-exempt charitable foundation on October 16, 1961. The new fund was set up with strong support from HRH Prince Philip, Duke of Edinburgh, and from

IUCN headquarters, which has now moved to Gland, Switzerland.

WWF worked with the Spanish government to purchase sections of the marshes of the Coto de Doñana in Andalucía, the agency's first big project and one of the greatest wetland complexes in the world. This was thanks to Dr. Luc Hoffmann, a WWF founding father (and author of the foreword to this book), who is now one of WWF's two vice president emeriti (the other being Prince Philip). Doñana is now a National Park, a UNESCO World Heritage Site, and a Wetland of International Importance under the Ramsar Convention on Wetlands.

HISTORY OF THE RAMSAR CONVENTION ON WETLANDS

It was during a 1962 conference on Project MAR (from "marshes," "marécages," "marismas"), which focused on wetland reclamation and degradation in Europe, that an international convention on wetlands was first suggested. The MAR Conference was organized by Luc Hoffmann with IUCN; participating organizations included the International Waterfowl and Wetlands Research Bureau (IWRB, now Wetlands International), and the International Council for Bird Preservation (ICBP; now BirdLife International).

Over the next eight years, wetland convention text was negotiated through a series of international technical meetings (St. Andrews, 1963; Noordwijk, 1966; Leningrad, 1968; Morges, 1968; Vienna, 1969; Moscow, 1969; Espoo, 1970). These were held mainly under the auspices of IWRB, guided by Professor G. V. T. Matthews, and led by the Government of the Netherlands. The initial text emphasized conserving waterfowl through establishing a network of refuges. The late Cyrille de Klemm, a legal expert, suggested that the text reflect conservation of wetland habitats rather than species.

Eskander Firouz, the director of Iran's Game and Fish Department, organized an international meeting at which the text of the Convention was agreed to on February 2, 1971. It was signed by the delegates from eighteen nations the next day. The Convention entered into force in December 1975, upon receipt of the seventh instrument of accession to ratify the Convention. After its adoption, the Ramsar Convention was amended by a new treaty in December 1982 and by a series of "Regina Amendments" in 1987, which created a secretariat and budget process.

Ramsar is the first of the modern global inter-governmental treaties on the conservation and sustainable use of natural resources. Although its provisions are relatively straightforward and general compared to more recent treaties, the text of the Convention was ahead of its time in that it strongly emphasized the interdependence of people and wetlands, and the critical roles that wetlands play in the hydrological cycle and in sustainable water management. Over the years, the Conference of the Contracting Parties has further developed and interpreted the basic tenets of the treaty text and

succeeded in keeping the work of the Convention in line with changing world perceptions, priorities, and trends in environmental thinking.

The official name of the treaty, "Convention on Wetlands of International Importance especially as Waterfowl Habitat", reflects the original convention emphasis on the conservation and "wise use" (see below) of wetlands primarily as habitat for waterbirds. Over the years, the Convention has broadened its scope to cover all aspects of wetland conservation and wise use, recognizing wetlands as ecosystems that are extremely important for biodiversity conservation and for the well-being of human communities, thus fulfilling the full scope of the Convention text.

The mission of the Ramsar Convention, adopted by the Parties in 1999 and refined in 2002, is "the conservation and wise use of all wetlands through local and national actions and international cooperation, as a contribution toward achieving sustainable development throughout the world." As of April 2010, the Convention had 159 Contracting Parties, or member states, from all parts of the world. Although the central message calls for the sustainable use of all wetlands, the "flagship" of the Convention is the List of Wetlands of International Importance (the "Ramsar List"). Presently, 1,888 wetlands covering 1.85 million km2 are on the list to receive the special protected status known as "Ramsar site."

The United Nations Educational, Scientific and Cultural Organization (UNESCO) serves as the depositary for the Convention, but the Ramsar Convention is not part of the United Nations and UNESCO system of environment conventions and agreements. The Convention is responsible only to its Conference of the Contracting Parties (COP), and its day-to-day administration has been entrusted to a secretariat under the authority of a Standing Committee elected by the COP.

FRESH WATER

Drijen Lake at dusk in Hutovo Blato Nature
Park, a Ramsar site and Important Bird Area
(IBA), Bosnia-Herzegovina. The park provides
important habitat for 240 migratory bird species.
—Elio della Ferrera/Wild Wonders of Europe

Bosnia-Herzegovina

AN INTERGOVERNMENTAL CONVENTION ON WETLANDS

The Ramsar Convention on Wetlands was developed as a means to call international attention to the rate at which wetland habitats were disappearing, in part due to a lack of understanding of their important functions, values, goods, and services. Governments that join the Convention are expressing their willingness to make a commitment to help reverse our history of wetland loss and degradation.

In addition, many wetlands cross the boundaries of two or more states, or are part of river basins that include more than one state. The health of these and other wetlands is dependent upon the quality and quantity of the transboundary water supply from rivers, streams, lakes, or underground aquifers. Human impacts on water sources, such as agricultural, industrial, or domestic pollution, may occur at considerable distances from wetland areas, often beyond the borders of the states affected. Wetland habitats can be degraded or even destroyed, and the health and livelihood of local people put at risk. Many of the wetland faunas—for example, some fish species, many waterbirds, insects such as butterflies and dragonflies, and mammals such as otters—travel over large distances; therefore, their conservation and management also require international cooperation.

In sum, wetlands constitute a resource of great economic, cultural, scientific, and recreational value to human life; wetlands and people are ultimately interdependent. As such, the progressive encroachment on and loss of wetlands needs to be stemmed, and measures must be taken to conserve and make wise use of wetland resources. To achieve this at a global level requires cooperative, intergovernmental action. The Ramsar Convention on Wetlands provides the framework for such international, as well as national and local, action.

THE "WISE USE" OF WETLANDS

Under Article 3.1 of the Convention, Parties agree to "formulate and implement their planning so as to promote the conservation of the wetlands included in the List, and as far as possible the wise use of wetlands in their territory." Through this concept of "wise use," which was pioneering when the Convention was drafted, the Convention continues to emphasize that human use on a sustainable basis is entirely compatible with Ramsar principles and wetland conservation in general. The Ramsar wise-use concept applies to all wetlands and water resources in a Contracting Party's territory, not only to those sites designated as Wetlands of International Importance. Its application is crucial to ensuring that wetlands can continue to fulfill their vital role in supporting maintenance of biological diversity and human well-being.

As this term "wise use" gained currency within the Ramsar community and was used elsewhere for different purposes, the Conference of the Parties recognized the need for greater precision. It adopted a clear definition in 1987, subsequently updated in 2005: "Wise use of wetlands is the maintenance of their ecological character, achieved through the implementation of ecosystem approaches, within the context of sustainable development." This established a congruency between "wise use" and the terminology of the World Conservation Strategy, developed by WWF, IUCN, and UNEP in 1980 to link human well-being and our dependence on nature as integral parts of a whole.

THE OBLIGATIONS OF RAMSAR PARTIES

States that join the Convention commit to the "Three Pillars" of the Convention. Parties designate at least one wetland at the time of accession for inclusion in the List of Wetlands of International Importance and promote its conservation, and "designate suitable wetlands within its territory" to add to the List.

Parties also commit "to arrange to be informed at the earliest possible time if the ecological character of any wetland in its territory and included in the List has changed, is changing, or is likely to change as the result of technological developments, pollution, or other human interference." Information on such changes must be immediately shared with the Ramsar Secretariat.

There is also a general obligation for the Contracting Parties to include wetland conservation considerations in their national land-use planning, promoting "the wise use of wetlands in their territory." And thirdly, they have also agreed to consult with other Contracting Parties about implementation of the Convention, especially in regard to transboundary wetlands, shared water systems, and shared species.

The Ramsar Convention is not a regulatory regime and has no punitive sanctions or stipulated violations for defaulting on treaty commitments. However, failure to meet the treaty's commitments could lead to political and diplomatic discomfort in high-profile international fora, unfavorable media attention, reduced access to international funding for wetland conservation, and lost opportunity to be part of a robust and coherent system of checks and balances and mutual support frameworks. Some national jurisdictions do include international Ramsar obligations in national law and/or policy, which are binding within those countries and enforceable in their court systems.

WORKING WITH PARTNERS TO IMPLEMENT THE CONVENTION

The benefits of coordination and collaboration among conventions and international organizations with related or overlapping missions have been widely recognized for many years. The Ramsar Convention has been a pioneer in developing collaborative relationships with global and regional conventions, beginning with its first Memorandum of Understanding (MOU) with the Convention on Biological Diversity in 1996 and the CBD/Ramsar Joint Work Plan, first formalized in 1998 and now in its fourth iteration, 2007–2010. These have become models for collaboration between multilateral environmental agreements.

Ramsar is unique in its relationships with its partner organizations. The Convention has long worked with its International Organization Partners (IOPs)—BirdLife International, IUCN, Wetlands International, the Asian Wetlands Bureau, Wetlands for the Americas, and WWF International. In 2005, the Parties judged that the International Water Management Institute (IWMI) met the qualifications for Ramsar IOP status and endorsed the addition of that organization as another official partner of the Convention. It is hoped that an increasing number of international conservation NGOs engaged in wetland conservation will become Ramsar IOPs in the near future.

The IOPs provide invaluable support for the work of the Convention at global, regional, national, and local levels, chiefly by providing expert technical advice, field-level implementation assistance, and financial support. They also adopt the philosophy of the Ramsar Convention (its wise-use concept) and endorse the use of the Ramsar guidelines in their work around the world. The IOPs also participate regularly as observers in all meetings of the Conference of the Contracting Parties and the Standing Committee, and are full members of the Convention's Scientific and Technical Review Panel (STRP).

The International Freshwater Program of WWF has been particularly active in advancing the Convention's work. The WWF International Manager for Wetlands Conservation was presented with the Ramsar Wetland Conservation Award at the Tenth Conference of the Parties in 2008, "for actions that have significantly contributed to long-term conservation and sustainable use of wetlands." WWF International's financial and technical assistance and the collaboration from WWF regional and national offices has helped designate more than 84 million

hectares of freshwater protected areas, mostly as Ramsar sites. That number has since increased to 100 million hectares as of May 2009. The Ramsar Strategic Plan aims to have 250 million hectares declared as Ramsar sites by 2015.

WWF has similarly assisted countries in joining the Convention and bringing their wetland resources under the Ramsar umbrella of commitments, advice, and assistance. It has also aided Parties in developing their National Wetland Policies, site management plans, and other instruments of Ramsar implementation. Ten new Contracting Parties have joined the Convention on Wetlands during the 2000–2010 decade as a result of WWF efforts. WWF has been instrumental in helping Parties to develop their cooperative agreements under the Convention's Regional Initiatives program. Notable examples include the High Andean Wetlands Conservation Strategy and the Himalayan Wetlands Conservation Initiative, Lake Chad (ChadWet), and the Niger River (NigerWet). The WWF International Freshwater Program and WWF regional or country offices have helped designate Ramsar sites and "Transboundary Ramsar Sites." Other organizations have pursued similar work in international river basins such as CongoWet, NileWet, and Plata Basin (Parana-Paraguay).

Field projects for sustainable management of Ramsar sites and other wetlands are implemented by the WWF freshwater network in all regions, with financial support from a wide range of donors, including government aid agencies, foundations, and private sector companies. Other activities include wetlands management plans, with the development and formal endorsement of National Wetlands Policies; setting up National Wetlands Committees; and supporting specific projects such as the creation of North Africa's first Wetland Information Centre in Algeria.

THE CONVENTION'S SUCCESS TO DATE

The 2011 anniversary year will be the occasion to take stock and assess the difficult and complex question of how successful the Ramsar Convention has been in achieving its mission. The Millennium Ecosystem Assessment recently found that inland and coastal wetlands are still being lost at a rate faster than that of any other ecosystem. The 2010 Biodiversity Indicators Partnership similarly reports accelerated rates of wetland loss in this decade and the last.

However, as the current Convention's deputy secretary general, Nick Davidson, has pointed out, we need to ask "if there is evidence as to how much worse the state of wetlands would have been without the many and inspirational efforts by people and organizations worldwide to implement the Convention." The Convention's Scientific and Technical Review Panel (STRP) is finding evidence that the national status of wetlands is affected positively where the Convention is being implemented, especially if the Party in question has put in place a National Wetland Policy and is undertaking other recommended implementation activities at national and local levels.

Ramsar guidance for the use of national wetland authorities and site managers has been instrumental in dealing with vital issues of water allocation and management, including "Guidelines for the allocation and management of water for maintaining the ecological functions of wetlands"; "An integrated framework for the Convention's water-related guidance"; "Managing groundwater to maintain ecological character"; and "Integrating wetland conservation and wise use into river basin management." All of these are available as part of the Ramsar Handbooks for the Wise Use of Wetlands toolkit (free download available at www. ramsar.org).

Recent surveys revealed a variety of environmental law/policy benefits related to Ramsar site designation, varying from site to site, but evident in the United

An African bullfrog (*Pyxicephalus adspersus*) in Chobe National Park, Botswana. In addition to hosting one of the greatest concentrations of wildlife in Africa, Chobe provides critical connectivity between the Okavango Delta and the Zambezi River. —Frans Lanting

Botswana

Spectacled caiman (*Caiman crocodilus*) in water lettuce (*Pistia stratiotes*), Hato Masaguaral working farm and biological station, Guárico Province, Venezuela.
—Pete Oxford

Venezuela, South America

States, Canada, and Africa. Ramsar designation was also found to contribute to the protection and management of the sites and the maintenance of their ecological character; to help demonstrate the sites' values to policy makers and the public (influencing land use and development activities); and to focus attention on long-term conservation objectives. A site's international status can also play an educational role about wetlands generally, and increase the surrounding community's pride in and support for its own wetland. Increased international recognition can also lead to increased ecotourism and scientific interest in particular areas.

Designation also helps to attract financial support for a site, through fundraising campaigns as well as in grant applications. In many cases, the Ramsar status of a wetland can create eligibility for international financial assistance, such as from the Global Environment Facility, and project assistance programs, such as Ramsar IOPs, Ramsar Small Grants Fund, Wetlands for the Future, and the Swiss Grant for Africa.

2011 AND THE FUTURE

The year 2011 will offer the Ramsar Convention many opportunities for celebration, for taking stock in progress made, and for establishing fresh ideas for the way forward. One of the clearest priorities for the Ramsar future is already known—finding innovative ways to increase the opportunities for collaboration between the Ramsar authorities in the Contracting Parties and the local, national, and regional representatives of the International Organization Partners. The Ramsar Secretariat is counting on the partner organizations to draw similar conclusions, so that we can continue this fruitful collaboration and ensure that the future availability of adequate water resources can meet biodiversity and human needs.

Fire salamander in Switzerland. —Thomas Marent

Switzerland

CONSERVATION INTERNATIONAL'S FRESHWATER STRATEGY

Tracy Farrell

In response to growing freshwater scarcity and ecosystem degradation, Conservation International (CI) is launching a freshwater strategy to catalyze a major paradigm shift in how we manage our fresh water. Global to local freshwater security will be enhanced through implementing this strategy by increasing knowledge of management alternatives, incorporating freshwater values into development decisions, strengthening markets for freshwater services, promoting enabling policies and governance, and scaling-up action for the conservation of entire natural freshwater systems, from headwaters to estuaries. This is the scale we believe is required for effective management of freshwater ecosystems, biodiversity, and land and water resources. Our program of work builds upon CI's twenty-plus years' worth of experience and expertise in biodiversity conservation and ecosystem management. Eight flagship projects represent threatened freshwater ecosystems and wilderness areas. These sites allow us to protect critical freshwater ecosystems, address threats to freshwater flows, and offer innovative and replicable solutions for sustainably managing freshwater ecosystems. They include Namaqualand, South Africa; the Upper Zambezi and Okavango Rivers, Southern Africa; Madagascar; the Atlantic Forest, Brazil; the Páramos, Colombia; the Qinghai province and Sichuan basin, China; the Lower Mekong in Cambodia; and Viti Levu, Fiji.

CI is well-positioned to catalyze an urgent transformation from global water depletion and pollution to freshwater security. Our approach is comprehensive and vertically integrated, from communities to global institutions and markets. Over two decades of practical conservation experience, core expertise, diverse partnerships, and a base of sound science position CI to be an immediate and influential agent of change in the freshwater sector. Our deep biodiversity conservation roots offer urgent input to freshwater ecosystem science and management—offering vital insight on the ecological ramifications of human actions and ecosystem-based alternatives. Our science and field knowledge will influence infrastructure and agriculture development agendas to better utilize natural ecosystems in water provision. Our ecology, spatial planning, and economics tools will provide decision-support for integrated water resource management tools across large-scale natural ecosystems. We will also be able to replicate and scale up our payment-for-ecosystem-services programs across critical freshwater landscapes. All of CI's efforts will be scaled up through partnership with governments, civil society, corporations, and communities. The expected results of strategy implementation include enhanced freshwater ecosystem function and service storage, and delivery for at least 20% of the areas with the highest freshwater service and biodiversity concentration on Earth—benefiting fresh water-dependent species and at least half a billion people.

Left: An aerial shot of the Okavango Delta, Botswana, where Cape Buffalo make a difficult trek across the river. —Beverly Joubert

Following spread: Wildebeest (*Connochaetes taurinus*) migrating in the rain on the Masai Mara, Kenya. —Stephen Maka

AUTHOR CONTACT INFORMATION

Russell A. Mittermeier

President

Conservation International

2011 Crystal Drive, Suite 500

Arlington, VA 22202

USA

r.mittermeier@conservation.org

Tracy A. Farrell

Senior Director of Freshwater

Conservation Program

Global Strategies Division

Conservation International

2011 Crystal Drive, Suite 500

Arlington, VA 22202

USA

t.farrell@conservation.org

Ian J. Harrison

Freshwater Species Assessment

and Program Fundraising Manager

Science and Knowledge Division

Conservation International

2011 Crystal Drive, Suite 500

Arlington, VA 22202

USA

i.harrison@conservation.org

Amy J. Upgren

Latin America Manager, Conservation

Outcomes

Science and Knowledge Division

Conservation International

2011 Crystal Drive, Suite 500

Arlington, VA 22202

USA

a.upgren@conservation.org

Thomas M. Brooks

Vice President for Science

and Chief Scientist

NatureServe

1101 Wilson Blvd., 15th Floor

Arlington VA 22209

USA

tbrooks@NatureServe.org

Luc Hoffmann

Vice President Emeritus

WWF International

Left: Adult male hooded merganser (*Lophodytes cucullatus*) in breeding plumage,
Montezuma National Wildlife Refuge, New York, USA.
—Gerrit Vyn

PREAMBLE

Cristina G. Mittermeier
President
International League of
Conservation Photographers
2011 Crystal Drive, Suite 500
Arlington, VA 22202
USA
cristina@ilcp.com

FOREWORD

Luc Hoffmann
Vice President Emeritus
WWF International

INTRODUCTION. FRESH WATER: THE ESSENCE OF LIFE

Russell A. Mittermeier
President
Conservation International
2011 Crystal Drive, Suite 500
Arlington, VA 22202
USA
r.mittermeier@conservation.org

Thomas M. Brooks
Vice President for Science and Chief
Scientist
NatureServe
1101 Wilson Blvd., 15th Floor
Arlington VA 22209
USA
tbrooks@NatureServe.org

Tracy A. Farrell
Senior Director of
Freshwater Conservation Program
Global Strategies Division
Conservation International
2011Crystal Drive, Suite 500
Arlington, VA 22202
USA
t.farrell@conservation.org

Amy J. Upgren
Latin America Manager,
Conservation Outcomes
Science and Knowledge
Conservation International
2011 Crystal Drive, Suite 500
Arlington, VA 22202
USA
a.upgren@conservation.org

Ian J. Harrison
Freshwater Species Assessment and
Program Fundraising Manager
Science and Knowledge
Conservation International
2011 Crystal Drive, Suite 500
Arlington, VA 22202
USA
i.harrison@conservation.org

Topiltzin Contreras-MacBeath
Chair, IUCN Freshwater Conservation
Sub-Committee
Centro de Investigaciones Biológicas
Universidad Autónoma del
Estado de Morelos
México
topis@uaem.mx

Richard Sneider
Unger Fabrik, Principal
LLC / Oneworld Apparel, LLC
Chairman's Council
Conservation International
1515 E. 15th Street
Los Angeles, CA 90021
USA

Fabian Oberfeld
Unger Fabrik, Principal
LLC / Oneworld Apparel, LLC
Chairman's Council
Conservation International
1515 E. 15th Street
Los Angeles, CA 90021
USA

Andrew A. Rosenberg
Senior Vice-President
Science and Knowledge
Conservation International
2011 Crystal Drive, Suite 500
Arlington, VA 22202
USA
a.rosenberg@conservation.org

Fredrick Boltz
Senior Vice-President
Global Strategies and Climate Change
Conservation International
2011 Crystal Drive, Suite 500
Arlington, VA 22202
USA
f.boltz@conservation.org

Claude Gascon
Executive Vice-President
Programs and Science
Conservation International
2011 Crystal Drive, Suite 500
Arlington, VA 22202
USA
c.gascon@conservation.org

Olivier Langrand
Executive Vice-President
Public Sector Engagement
Conservation International
2011 Crystal Drive, Suite 500
Arlington, VA 22202
USA
o.langrand@conservation.org

CHAPTER I. A WEALTH OF LIFE: SPECIES DIVERSITY IN FRESHWATER SYSTEMS

Estelle Balian
Science Officer – Belgian Biodiversity
Platform
Freshwater Laboratory, Royal Belgian
Institute of Natural Sciences
Rue Vautier 29
B - 1000 Brussels
Belgium

estelle.balian@naturalsciences.be

Ian J. Harrison
(see above)

Helen Barber-James
Assistant Curator
Department of Freshwater Invertebrates
Makana Biodiversity Centre
Albany Museum
Grahamstown 6139
and Department of Zoology
and Entomology
Rhodes University
Grahamstown 6139
South Africa
H.James@ru.ac.za

Stuart H.M. Butchart
Global Research and Indicators Coordinator,
BirdLife International,
Wellbrook Court,
Girton Road
Cambridge, CB3 0NA
UK
Stuart.Butchart@birdlife.org

Patricia Chambers
Section Head and Research Scientist,
  Biogeochemistry
Environment Canada
867 Lakeshore Road
PO Box 5050
Burlington, ON L7R 4A6
Canada
patricia.chambers@ec.gc.ca

Jay Cordeiro
Research Zoologist
NatureServe
11 Avenue de Lafayette, 5th Fl.
Boston, MA 02111
USA
jay_cordeiro@natureserve.org

Neil Cumberlidge
Professor
Department of Biology
Northern Michigan University
Marquette, MI 49855
USA
ncumberl@nmu.edu

Ferdinand (Ferdy) de Moor
Senior Specialist Scientist and Curator
Department of Freshwater Invertebrates
Makana Biodiversity Centre
Albany Museum
Somerset St,
Grahamstown, 6139
Department of Zoology
and Entomology
Rhodes University
Grahamstown 6139
South Africa
F.deMoor@ru.ac.za

Claude Gascon
(see above)

Vincent Kalkman
European Invertebrate Survey - Nederland
Nationaal Natuurhistorisch Museum -
naturalis
Postbus 9517
2300 RA Leiden
The Netherlands
vincent.kalkman@ncbnaturalis.nl

Peter Paul van Dijk
Director Tortoise and Freshwater Turtle
Conservation Program
President's Office
Conservation International
2011 Crystal Drive, Suite 500
Arlington, VA 22202
USA
p.vandijk@conservation.org

Darren Yeo
Assistant Professor
Department of Biological Sciences
National University of Singapore
14 Science Drive 4
Singapore 117543
Republic of Singapore
darrenyeo@nus.edu.sg

CHAPTER 2. AQUATIC ECOSYSTEMS: DIVERSITY AND DYNAMISM

Melanie L. J. Stiassny
Axelrod Research Curator
Department of Ichthyology
American Museum of Natural History
Central Park West at 79th Street
New York, NY 10024-5192
USA
mljs@amnh.org

Carmen Revenga
Senior Scientist – Fisheries
Global Marine Team
The Nature Conservancy
Worldwide Office
4245 N. Fairfax Drive,Suite 100
Arlington, VA 22203
USA
crevenga@tnc.org

Patrick Comer
Chief Terrestrial Ecologist
NatureServe
4001 Discovery Drive Suite 2110
Boulder, CO 80303
USA
Pat_Comer@natureserve.org

CHAPTER 3. FRESHWATER ECOSYSTEMS UNDER THREAT: THE ULTIMATE HOTSPOT

Michele L. Thieme
Freshwater Conservation Biologist
World Wildlife Fund
Conservation Science Program
1250 24th St, NW
Washington, DC 20037
USA
michele.thieme@WWFUS.ORG

Eren Turak
Senior Environmental Scientist
New South Wales Department of
Environment, Climate Change & Water
Level 18, 59-61 Goulburn St.
Sydney
South NSW 1232
Australia
Eren.Turak@environment.nsw.gov.au

Peter McIntyre
Center for Limnology
University of Wisconsin
680 North Park Street
Madison, WI 53706-1413
USA
pmcintyre@wisc.edu

William Darwall
Manager
Freshwater Biodiversity Unit
IUCN Species Programme
219c Huntingdon Road
Cambridge, CB3 0DL
UK
William.DARWALL@iucn.org

Klement Tockner
Director
Leibniz-Institute of Freshwater Ecology
and Inland Fisheries
IGB
12587 Berlin
Germany
tockner@igb-berlin.de

Jay Cordeiro
(see above)

Stuart H. M. Butchart
(see above)

CHAPTER 4.
PROTECTED AREAS FOR
FRESHWATER ECOSYSTEMS:
ESSENTIAL BUT
UNDERREPRESENTED

David Allan
Professor and Associate Dean for
    Academic Affairs
School of Natural Resources &
Environment
The University of Michigan
440 Church Street
Ann Arbor, MI 48109-1041
USA
dallan@umich.edu

Peter Esselman
Research Associate
Department of Fisheries and Wildlife
Michigan State University
East Lansing, MI 48824-1222
USA
pce@msu.edu

Robin Abell
Biologist
World Wildlife Fund
Conservation Science Program
1250 24th St, NW
Washington, DC 20037
USA
robin.ABELL@wwfus.org

Peter McIntyre
(see above)

Nicolas Tubbs
Technical Officer
Specialist Groups & Expert Network
    Coordinator
Biodiversity & Ecological Networks
    Programme
Wetlands International
PO Box 471
6700 AL Wageningen
The Netherlands
Nicolas.Tubbs@wetlands.org

Harry Biggs
Program Integrator: Adaptive Biodiversity
Outcomes
Conservation Services Division
Kruger National Park
Private Bag X402
Skukuza 1350
South Africa
biggs@sanparks.org

Leandro Castello
Postdoctoral Fellow
Woods Hole Research Center
149 Woods Hole Road
Falmouth, MA 02540 -1644
USA
lcastello@whrc.org

Aaron Jenkins
Senior Programme Officer
Wetlands International - Oceania
PO Box S6
Superfresh
Tamavua
Suva
Fiji
aaron.jenkins@wetlands-oceania.org

Richard Kingsford
Professor
Director of Australian Wetlands
and Rivers Centre
School of Biological, Earth, and
    Environmental Sciences
University of New South Wales
Sydney, NSW 2052
Australia
richard.kingsford@unsw.edu.au

CHAPTER 5.
FRESHWATER ECOSYSTEM
SERVICES: ESSENTIAL FOR
HUMAN WELL-BEING

Tracy A. Farrell
(see above)

David Batker
Executive Director
Earth Economics
1121 Tacoma Ave South
Tacoma, WA 98402
USA
dbatker@eartheconomics.org

Lucy Emerton
Chief Economist
Environment Management Group
15 Havelock Road
Colombo 5
Sri Lanka
lucy@environment-group.org

Will Turner
Senior Director
Conservation Priorities and Outreach
Conservation International
2011 Crystal Drive, Suite 500
Arlington, VA 22202
USA
w.turner@conservation.org

CHAPTER 6. FRESH WATER FOR THE FUTURE: POLICY TO SECURE AN ESSENTIAL SERVICE FOR ALL

D. Mark Smith
Head, Water Programme
Environment and Development Group
IUCN
28 rue Mauverney
CH-1196 Gland
Switzerland
Mark.Smith@iucn.org

APPENDIX. SOME EXAMPLES OF COMMON ENGAGEMENT FOR CONSERVING THE WORLD'S WETLANDS

Denis Landenbergue
Manager, Wetlands Conservation
WWF International
Avenue du Mont-Blanc
1196 Gland
Switzerland

Dwight Peck
Documentation Officer
Ramsar Secretariat
28 Rue Mauverney
CH-1196 Gland
Switzerland

Tracy A. Farrell
(see above)

Following spread: Alpenglow on Mt. Sefton, New Zealand. —Chris Linder

Left: Alaska Brown Bear (*Ursus arctos*), Katmai National Park. —Roy Toft

FRESH WATER

The San Rafael Glacier ends its journey in
Patagonia, Chile. —Daniel Beltra

Patagonia, Chile

A traditional owner at a sacred pool, Arnhem Land, Northern Territory, Australia. —Wade Davis

Australia

AUTHOR BIOS

Russell A. Mittermeier is President of Conservation International, a position he has occupied since 1989. His areas of expertise include primatology, herpetology, tropical biology, and biodiversity conservation. In addition to his work with Conservation International, he has a long association with IUCN/SSC, where he has served as chairman of the IUCN Species Survival Commission (SSC) Primate Specialist Group since 1977, as a member of the Steering Committee of the SSC since 1984, and as a regional councillor for North America and the Caribbean since 2004. Most recently, he was elected a vice president for IUCN for the period 2009–2012. Mittermeier's work has taken him to more than 130 countries on seven continents, and he has conducted fieldwork in more than twenty countries, with much of his work having focused on Amazonia (particularly Brazil and Suriname), the Atlantic Forest region of Brazil, and Madagascar. He received his PhD from Harvard University in 1977, and has published more than 570 scientific and popular papers and nineteen books. Among the honors he has received are the Order of the Golden Ark of the Netherlands (1995); Grand Sash and Order of the Yellow Star, Republic of Suriname (1998); the Order of the Southern Cross of the Brazilian Government (1998); the Aldo Leopold Award from the American Society of Mammalogists (2004); the Sir Peter Scott Award of IUCN's Species Survival Commission (2008); and Harvard University's Roger Tory Peterson Medal (2009).

Tracy A. Farrell is the Senior Director of the Freshwater Initiative at Conservation International (CI). She has spent the past five years developing and leading crosscutting initiatives in the areas of fresh water, ecosystem services, and wildlife trade. In this role, Farrell creates research agendas, strategic directions, and business plans to refine CI's niche and partnership approach to address these as well as other emerging institutional priorities. She has published broadly across these and other areas in both peer-reviewed and popular publications, and has ten years' experience aligning research and field activities to ensure solid program delivery, largely in North, Central, and South America. Before joining CI, Farrell served as dean of the School for Field Studies and was also a visiting professor/instructor for Virginia Tech's Department of Forestry.

Ian J. Harrison is part of Conservation International's Science and Knowledge Division and the International Union for Conservation of Nature (IUCN) Species Programme. Harrison coordinates fundraising for the Global Freshwater Biodiversity Assessment (GFBA), a joint program run by Conservation International (CI), IUCN's Species Programme, and NatureServe. The objective of the GFBA is to compile data on the distribution and conservation status of freshwater species in order to expand the taxonomic and geographic coverage of the IUCN Red List of Threatened Species. He is a member of the executive committee of the IUCN-Species Survival Commission/Wetlands International Freshwater Fish Specialist Group. Harrison also works with Dr. Tracy Farrell (see left) on CI's Freshwater Initiative, including projects on freshwater ecosystem services. Part of his time is spent at the American Museum of Natural History (AMNH), New York, where he is a research associate in the Department of Ichthyology. He has worked with Dr. Melanie Stiassny (AMNH) on studies of extinctions in freshwater fishes, over the last 500 years. He is an associate editor for the *Journal of Fish Biology* and assistant editor for the *Journal of Afrotropical Zoology*. Harrison's PhD thesis (University of Bristol, England) was an analysis of the implications of small body size on the biology of fishes. He has conducted fieldwork in Europe, Central and South America, West Africa and central West Africa, the Philippines, and the central Pacific.

Amy J.Upgren works with the Conservation Priorities and Outreach Team of the Science and Knowledge Division at Conservation International (CI). In conjunction with CI regional offices and partners in Latin America and the Caribbean, she identifies biodiversity conservation priorities and analyzes their contribution to human well-being in terms of ecosystem service provision. She received a Bachelor of Arts in History from Haverford College and a Master of Environmental Management from Duke University. Prior to CI, her freshwater experience included developing national regulations to protect freshwater systems with the Office of Water at the U.S. Environmental Protection Agency; restoring wetlands in Yellowstone National Park; working with The Nature Conservancy on river conservation initiatives in the Brazilian Cerrado; and assessing watersheds for restoration potential with North Carolina's Department of Environment and Natural Resources.

Thomas M.Brooks from Brighton, United Kingdom, holds a Bachelor of Arts (Hons) in Geography from the University of Cambridge (1993) and a PhD in Ecology and Evolutionary Biology from the University of Tennessee (1998). He is currently the vice president for science and chief scientist at NatureServe, a network of eighty-two Natural Heritage Programs and Conservation Data Centers dedicated to providing the scientific basis for effective biodiversity conservation action. Brooks is an ornithologist by training, with extensive field experience in tropical forests of Asia, South America, and Africa; his interests lie in threatened species conservation (especially of birds) and in biodiversity hotspots (especially in tropical forests). He holds visiting positions at ICRAF-the World Agroforestry Center in the University of the Philippines Los Baños, and in the Department of Geography of the University of Tasmania. He also has a longstanding involvement with the International Union for the Conservation of Nature, and has served on its Conserving Biodiversity Core Program Group since 2009, on the Steering Committee of its Species Survival Commission since 2004, and on its Red List Committee since 2001. Brooks has authored 171 scientific and popular articles, of which nineteen have been published in Nature or Science.

Luc Hoffmann since his earliest days in Basel, Switzerland, has devoted his life to the preservation of nature. As a child, he was intrigued with the natural world and recognized the fragility of life on Earth. At twenty-five, he founded the Tour du Valat (southern France) as a biological research institute that today is known and respected throughout the world.
After receiving his PhD in Zoology from the University of Basel, Dr. Hoffmann conducted—in the 1950s—the first-ever studies of waterbird populations and wetland ecology. He was instrumental in either creating or sustaining organizations such as the Ramsar Convention, the International Union for Conservation of Nature, the WWF, and Wetlands International. He has served as director, board member, vice president, and chairman of numerous conservation organizations, and has been honored by more than a dozen nations and continents for his service. Truly a pioneer of the ecology movement, Dr. Hoffmann continues to travel throughout the world, offering his expertise and support where needed.

REFERENCES

INTRODUCTION:
FRESH WATER
THE ESSENCE OF LIFE

Abell R., J. D. Allan and B. Lehner. 2007. Unlocking the Potential of Protected Areas for Freshwaters. *Biological Conservation*. 134: 48–63.

Abell, R., M. L. Thieme, C. Revenga, M. Bryer, M. Kottelat, N. Bogutskaya, B. Coad, N. Mandrak, S. Contreras Balderas, W. Bussing, M. L. J. Stiassny, P. Skelton, G. R. Allen, P. Unmack, A. Naseka, R. Ng, N. Sindorf, J. Robertson, E. Armijo, J. V. Higgins, T. J. Heibel, E. Wikramanayake, D. Olson, H. L. López, R. E. Reis, J. G. Lundberg, M. H. Sabaj Pérez and P. Petry. 2008. Freshwater Ecoregions of the World: A New Map of Biogeographic Units for Freshwater Biodiversity Conservation. *BioScience*. 58 (5):403-414.

Allan J. D., R. Abell, Z. Hogan, C. Revenga, B. W. Taylor, R. L. Welcomme and K. Winemiller. 2005. Overfishing of Inland Waters. *BioScience*. 55:1041-1051.

Baillie, J. E. M., Hilton-Taylor, C. and Stuart, S. N., eds. 2004. 2004 IUCN *Red List of Threatened Species. A Global Species Assessment*. IUCN, Gland, Switzerland and Cambridge, UK. xxiv + 191 pp.

Balian, E. V., H. Segers, C. Lévêque and K. Martens. 2008a. An Introduction to the Freshwater Animal Diversity Assessment (FADA) Project. *Hydrobiologia*. 595:3-8.

Balian, E. V., H. Segers, C. Lévêque and K. Martens. 2008b. The Freshwater Animal Diversity Assessment: An Overview of the Results. *Hydrobiologia*. 595:627-637.

Bates, B. C., Z. W. Kundzewicz, S. Wu and J. P. Palutikof, eds. 2008. Climate Change and Water. Technical Paper of the Intergovernmental Panel on Climate Change. Geneva, IPCC Secretariat.

BirdLife International. 2002. *Important Bird Areas and Potential Ramsar Sites in Africa*. Cambridge, UK: BirdLife International.

Birdlife International. 2008. *State of the World's Birds 2008: Indicators for Our Changing World*. Birdlife International, Cambridge, UK.

Bogan, A. E. 2008. Global Diversity of Freshwater Mussels (Mollusca, Bivalvia) in Freshwater. *Hydrobiologia*. 595:139-147.

Boyd, C., T. M. Brooks, S. H. M. Butchart, G. L. Edgar, G. A. B. da Fonseca, F. Hawkins, M. Hoffmann, W. Sechrest, S. N. Stuart and P. P. van Dijk. 2008. Spatial Scale and the Conservation of Threatened Species. *Conservation Letters*. 37-43.

Bradshaw, C. J. A., N. S. Sodhi, K. S. H. Peh and B. W. Brook. 2007. Global Evidence that Deforestation Amplifies Flood Risk and Severity in the Developing World. *Global Change Biology*. doi: 10.1111/j.1365-2486.2007.01446.x. Journal Compilation: Blackwell Publishing Ltd.

Brooks, T. M., R. A. Mittermeier, G. A. B. da Fonseca, J. Gerlach, M. Hoffmann, J. F. Lamoreux, C. G. Mittermeier, J. D. Pilgrim and A. S. L. Rodrigues. 2006. Gobal Biodiversity Conservation Priorities. *Science*. 313:58-61.

Chambers, P. A., P. Lacoul, K. J. Murphy and S. M. Thomaz. 2008. Global Diversity of Aquatic Macrophytes in Freshwater. *Hydrobiologia*. 595:9-26.

Chung Kim, K. and L. B. Byrne. 2006. Biodiversity Loss and the Taxonomic Bottleneck: Emerging Biodiversity Science. *Ecological research*. 21:6.

CNA Corporation. 2007. National Security and the Threat of Climate Change. Alexandria, VA. http://securityandclimate.cna.org/report/National%20Security%20and%20the%20Threat%20of%20Climate%20Change.pdf

Cumberlidge, N., P. K. L. Ng, D. C. J. Yeo, C. Magalhães, M. R. Campos, F. Alvarez, T. Naruse, S. R. Daniels, L. J. Esser, F. Y. K. Attipoe, F. -L. Clotilde-Ba, W. R. T. Darwall, A. McIvor, J. E. M. Baillie, B. Collen and M. Ram. 2009. Freshwater Crabs and the Biodiversity Crisis: Importance, Threats, Status, and Conservation Challenges. *Biological Conservation*. 142:1665-1673.

Darwall, W. R. T., K. G. Smith, D. Tweddle and P. Skelton. 2009. *The Status and Distribution of Freshwater Biodiversity in Southern Africa*. Gland, Switzerland and Grahamstown, South Africa: IUCN and SAIAB. http://data.iucn.org/dbtw-wpd/edocs/2009-003.pdf

Darwall, W. R. T., K. Smith, T. Lowe and J.C. Vié. 2005. The Status and Distribution of Freshwater Biodiversity in Eastern Africa. viii, 36. *Occasional Paper of the IUCN Species Survival Commission 31*. IUCN, Gland, Switzerland and Cambridge, UK: IUCN SSC Freshwater Biodiversity Assessment Programme.

Eken et al. 2004. Key Biodiversity Areas as Site Conservation Targets. *Bioscience*. (54)12: 1110–1118.

Falkenmark, M. 2003. Fresh Water as Shared between Society and Systems: From Divided Approaches to Integrated Challenges. *Philosophical Transactions of the Royal Society of London B*. 358:2037–2049.

Falkenmark, M. and D. Molden. 2008. Wake Up to Realities of River Basin Closure. *International Journal of Water Resources Development*. 24(2):201–215.

Fjeldså, J. 1993. The Decline and Probable Extinction of the Colombian Grebe Podiceps andinus. *Bird Conservation International*. 3: 221–234.

Food and Agricultural Organization of the United Nations (FAO). 1995. Chapter 10. *Planning for Sustainable use of Land Resources: Towards a New Approach*. —Background paper to FAO's Task Managership for of UNCED's Agenda 21. FAO, Rome.

Food and Agricultural Organization of the United Nations (FAO). 2007. The State of the World's Fisheries and Aquaculture 2006. Fisheries and Aquaculture Department, Rome, Italy.

Food and Agriculture Organization of the United Nations (FAO). 2008. Yearbook of Fisheries Statistics. Summary Tables. ftp://ftp.fao.org/fi/stat/summary/summ_05/a1a.pdf

Food and Agricultural Organization of the United Nations (FAO). 2009. Aquastat Database. www.fao.org/nr/aquastat/

Forslund, A., B. M Renofalt, S. Barchiesi, K. Cross, S. Davison, T. A. Farrell, L. Korsgaard, K. Krchnak, M. McClain, K. Meijer and M. Smith. 2009. Securing Water for Ecosystems and Human Well-Being. The Importance of Environmental Flows. Swedish Water House Report 24. SIWI.

Gleick, P. H., H. Cooley, M. J. Cohen, M. Morikawa, J. Morrison and M. Palaniappan. 2009. *The World's Water 2008-2009, The Biennial Report on Freshwater Resources.* Pacific Institute for Studies in Development, Environment and Security. Washington, DC: Island Press.

Hails, C. 2008. *Living Planet Report 2008. Apollo The International Magazine Of Art And Antiques.* WWF International. Gland, Switzerland.

Harrison, I. J. and M. L. J. Stiassny. 1999. The Quiet Crisis: A Preliminary Listing of the Freshwater Fishes of the World that are Extinct or "Missing in Action." *Extinctions in Near Time: Causes, Contexts, and Consequences.* R. MacPhee. eds. 271-332. New York: Kluwer Academic/Plenum Publishers.

Helfman, G. S. 2007. Fish Conservation: A Guide to Understanding and Restoring Global Aquatic Biodiversity and Fishery Resources. Washington, DC: Island Press

Hunter, L. A. 1988. Status of the Endemic Atitlan Grebe of Guatemala: Is It Extinct? *The Condor* 90: 906-912.

International Union for Conservation of Nature (IUCN). 2010. The *IUCN Red List of Threatened Species.* 2010.1. www.iucnredlist.org.

Jenkins, C. N. and L. Joppa. 2009. Expansion of the Global Terrestrial Protected Area System. *Biological Conservation.* 142(10):2166-2174.

Kottelat, M. and X.-L. Chu. 1988. Revision of *Yunnanilus* with Descriptions of a Miniature Species Flock and Six New Species from China. (Cypriniformes: Homalopteridae). *Environmental Biology of Fishes* 23: 65-93.

Kottelat, M., R. Britz, H. H. Tan and K.-E. Witte. 2006. Paedocypris, a New Genus of Southeast Asian Cyprinid Fish with a Remarkable Sexual Dimorphism, Comprises the World's Smallest Vertebrate. Proceedings of the Royal Society of London, Series B. 273: 895-899.

Kottelat, M and J. Freyhof. 2007. Handbook of European Freshwater Fishes. Kottelat, Cornol, Switzerland: Kottelat; and Berlin, Germany: Freyhof.

Langhammer, P. F., M. I. Bakarr, L. A. Bennun, T. M. Brooks, R. P. Clay, W. T. Darwall, N. De Silva, G. J. Edgar, G. Eken, L. D. C Fishpool, G. A. B. da Fonseca, M. N. Foster, D. H. Knox, P. Matiku, E.A. Radford, A.L.S. Rodrigues, P. Salaman, W. Sechres and A.W. Tordoff. 2007. Identification and Gap Analysis of Key Biodiversity Areas: Targets for Comprehensive Protected Area Systems. Gland, Switzerland: IUCN.

Li, L., C. Liu and H. Mou. 2000. River Conservation in Central and Eastern Asia. *Global Perspectives on River Conservation. Science, Policy and Practice.* 263-380. P. J. Boon, B. R. Davies and G. E. Petts, eds. Chichester, England: John Wiley and Sons.

Lundberg, J. G., M. Kottelat, G. R. Smith, M. L. J. Stiassny and A. C. Gill. 2000. So Many Fishes, So Little Time: An Overview of Recent Ichthyological Discoveries in Freshwaters. *Annals of the Missouri Botanical Gardens.* 87(1):26-62.

Margat, J., and V. Andréassian. 2008. L'Eau, les Idées Reçues. Paris: Editions le Cavalier Bleu.

Millennium Ecosystem Assessment (MEA) 2005. *Ecosystems and Human Well-Being: Wetlands and Water Synthesis.* Washington, DC.: Island Press. Finlayson, C. M., D'Cruz, R. and Davidson, N. et al. Washington DC, World Resources Institute

Miller, P. J. 1979. Adaptiveness and Implications of Small Size in Teleosts. *Symposia of the Zoological Society of London* 44: 263-306

Miller, P. J. 1996. The Functional Ecology of Small Fish: Some Opportunities and Consequences. *Symposia of the Zoological Society of London* 69: 175-199.

Mittermeier, R. A., N. Myers, P. Robles Gil and C. G. Mittermeier (eds.). 1999. *Hotspots: Earth's Biologically Richest and Most Endangered Terrestrial Ecosystems.* CEMEX, S. A., Monterrey, Mexico and Agrupación Sierra Madre, Mexico City, Mexico.

Mittermeier, R. A., P. Robles Gil, M. Hoffmann, J. Pilgrim, T. Brooks, C. G. Mittermeier, J. Lamoreux, and G. A. B. da Fonseca. 2004. *Hotspots Revisited: Earth's Biologically Richest and Most Endangered Ecoregions.* Mexico City, Mexico: CEMEX.

Mittermeier, R. A., M. B. Harris, C. G. Mittermeier, J. M. C. Da Silva, R. Lourival, G. A. B. da Fonseca and P. Seligmann. 2005a. Pantanal: South America's Wetland Jewel. Ontario, Canada: Firefly Books Ltd.

Myers, N. 1988. Threatened Biotas: "Hot spots" in Tropical Forests. *The Environmentalist.* 8(3):187-208.

Myers, N., R. A. Mittermeier, C. G. Mittermeier, G. A. B. da Fonseca, and J. Kent. 2000. Biodiversity Hotspots for Conservation Priorities. *Nature.* 403:853-858.

Nilsson, C., C. A. Reidy, M. Dynesius, C. Revenga. 2005. Fragmentation and Flow Regulation of the World's Large River Systems. *Science.* 308:405-408.

Organization for Economic Cooperation and Development (OECD). 2005. OECD SIDS Initial Assessment Report of LAS. In: 20th SIAM meeting; 19-21 April 2005; Paris, France Washington, DC Council for LAB/LAS Environmental Research. *The CLER Review*, 10, December 2005.

Penning, M., G. McG Reid, H. Koldewey, G. Dick, B. Andrews, K. Arai, P. Garratt, S. Gendron, J. Lange, K. Tanner, S. Tonge, P. Van Den Sande, D. Warmolts and C. Gibson. eds. 2009. Turning the Tide: A Global Aquarium Strategy for Conservation and Sustainability. World Association of Zoos and Aquariums, Bern, Switzerland.

Poff, N. L., B. D. Richter, A. Arthington, S. E. Bunn, R. J. Naiman, E. Kendy, M. Acreman, C. Apse, B. P. Bledsoe, M. C. Freeman, J. Henricksen, R. B. Jacobson, J. G. Kennen, D. M. Merritt, J. H. O'Keefe, J. D, Olden, K. Rogers, R. E. Tharme, and A. Warner. 2009. The Ecological Limits of Hydrologic Alteration (ELOHA): A New Framework for Developing Regional Environmental Flow Standards. *Freshwater Biology*.

Postel, S. L. 1995. Where Have All the Rivers Gone? *World Watch*. 8(3).

Postel, S. L., G. C. Daly, and P. R. Ehrlich. 1996. Human Appropriation of Renewable Fresh Water. *Science*. 271:785–788.

Revenga, C. and Y. Kura. 2003. Status and Trends of Biodiversity of Inland Water Ecosystems. Secretariat of the Convention on Biological Diversity, Montreal, Technical Series no. 11.

Revenga, C., I. Campbell, R. Abell, P. de Villiers and M. Bryer. 2005. Prospects for Monitoring Freshwater Ecosystems Towards the 2010 Targets. *Philosophical Transactions of the Royal Society Series B*. 360:397–413.

Ricketts, T. H., E. Dinerstein, T. Boucher, T. M. Brooks, S. H. M. Butchart, M. Hoffmann, J. F. Lamoreux, J, Morrison, M. Parr, J. D. Pilgrim, A. S. L. Rodrigues, W. Sechrest, G. E. Wallace, K. Berlin, J. Bielby, N. D. Burgess, D. R. Church, N. Cox, D. Knox, C. Loucks, G. W. Luck, L. L. Master, R. Moore, R. Naidoo, R. Ridgely, G. E. Schatz, G. Shire, H. Strand, W. Wettengel and E. Wikramanayake. 2005. Pinpointing and Preventing Imminent Extinctions. *PNAS*. 102(51): 18497–18501.

Shiklomanov, I. A. 2000. Appraisal and Assessment of World Water Resources. *Water International*. 25(1):11–32.

Strong, E. E., O. Gargominy, W. F. Ponder and P. Bouchet. 2008. Global Diversity of Gastropods (Gastropoda; Mollusca) in Freshwater. *Hydrobiologia*. 595:149–166.

United Nations Development Program (UNDP) - Human Development Report. 2006. UNEP. 2007.

Vintinner. E. C. 2009. Thirsty Metropolis: A Case Study of New York City's Drinking Water. Lessons in Conservation. 2. http://ncep.amnh.org/linc/

Wells, N. A. 2003. Geology and Soils: Some Hypotheses on the Mesozoic and Cenozoic Paleoenvironmental History of Madgascar. 16–34. *The Natural History of Madagascar*. Goodman, S. M. and J. P. Benstread. eds. Chicago, USA: University of Chicago Press.

Witte, F., M. Welten, M. Heemskerk, I. Van der Stap, L. Ham, H. Rutjes, and J. Wanink 2008. Major Morphological Changes in a Lake Victoria Cichlid Fish Within Two Decades. *Biological Journal of the Linnean Society*, 94, 41–52.

World Commission on Dams. 2000. *Dams and development: A new framework for decision-making*. Earthscan Publications Ltd., London, UK and Sterling, VA, USA.

World Health Organization (WHO) and United Nations Children's Fund (UNICEF). 2004. WHO/UNICEF Joint Monitoring Programme for Water Supply and Sanitation. Meeting the MDG Drinking Water and Sanitation Target: A Mid-Term Assessment of Progress. 33.

World Water Assessment Programme (WWAP). 2009. The United Nations World Water Development Report 3: Water in a Changing World. Paris and London: UNESCO Publishing and Earthscan.

World Water Council. 2004. E-Conference Synthesis: Virtual Water Trade - Conscious Choices, March 2004.

World Database on Protected Areas (WDPA). 2009. IUCN-WDPA & UNEP-WCMC. WDPA, Washington, DC.

CHAPTER ONE:
A WEALTH OF LIFE: SPECIES DIVERSITY IN FRESHWATER SYSTEMS

Abebe, E., W. Decraemer and P. De Ley. 2008. Global Diversity of Nematodes (Nematoda) in Freshwater. *Hydrobiologia*. 595:67–78.

Abell, R., M. L. Thieme, C. Revenga, M. Bryer, M. Kottelat, N. Bogutskaya, B. Coad, N. Mandrak, S. Contreras Balderas, W. Bussing, M. L. J. Stiassny, P. Skelton, G. R. Allen, P. Unmack, A. Naseka, R. Ng, N. Sindorf, J. Robertson, E. Armijo, J. V. Higgins, T. J. Heibel, E. Wikramanayake, D. Olson, H. L López, R. E. Reis, J. G. Lundberg, M. H. Sabaj Pérez and P. Petry. 2008. Freshwater Ecoregions of the World: A New Map of Biogeographic Units for Freshwater Biodiversity Conservation. *BioScience*. 58 (5):403–414.

Abramovitz, J. N. 1996. Imperiled waters, Impoverished Future: The Decline of Freshwater Ecosystems. Worldwatch Paper 128. Washington DC: Worldwatch Insitute. 80

Agostinho, A. A., S. M. Thomaz, and L. C. Gomes. 2005. Conservation of the Biodiversity of Brazil's Inland Waters. *Conservation Biology*. 19(3):646–652.

Alexander, D. E. and R. W. Fairbridge, eds. 1999. Encyclopedia of Environmental Science. 768. PO 322, 3300 AH Dordrecht, The Netherlands: Kluwer Academic Publishers.

Amedegnato, C. and H. Devriese. 2008. Global Diversity of Ture and Pygmy Grasshoppers (Acridomorpha, Ortheoptera) in Freshwater. *Hydrobiologia*. 595:535–543.

Armitage, P. D., P. S. Cranston and L. C. V. Pinder 1995. The Chironomidae: Biology and Ecology of Non-biting Midges. London: Chapman and Hall.

Bain, R. H., A. Lathrop, R. W. Murphy, N. L. Orlov and H. T. Cuc. 2003. Cryptic Species of a Cascade Frog from Southeast Asia: Taxonomic Revisions and Descriptions of Six New Species. *American Museum Novitates*. 3417:1–60.

Right: Day gecko (*Phelsuma madagascariensis*) drinking water, Ankarana Special Reserve, Madagascar.
—Pete Oxford

Balian, E. V., H. Segers, C. Lévêque and K. Martens. 2008a. An Introduction to the Freshwater Animal Diversity Assessment (FADA) Project. *Hydrobiologia*. 595:3–8.

Balian, E. V., H. Segers, C. Lévêque and K. Martens. 2008b. The Freshwater Animal Diversity Assessment: An Overview of the Results. *Hydrobiologia*. 595:627–637.

Baran, E., T. Jantunen and K. C. Chanton. 2008. Values of Inland Fisheries in the Mekong River Basin. *Tropical River Fisheries Valuation: Background Papers to a Global Synthesis.* WorldFish Center Studies and Reviews. 1836:227–290. Penang, Malaysia: WorldFish Center.

Barber-James, H. M., J-L. Gattolliat, M. Sartori and M. D. Hubbard. 2008. Global Diversity of Mayflies (Ephemeroptera: Insecta) in Freshwater. *Hydrobiologia*. 595:339–350.

Bartsch, I. 2008. Global Diversity of Halacarid Mites (Halacaridae: Acari: Arachnida) in Freshwater. *Hydrobiologia*. 595:1317–322.

Bauer, A. M. and T. Jackman. 2008. Global Diversity of Lizards in Freshwater (Reptilia: Lacertilia). *Hydrobiologia*. 595:581–586.

Belk, D. and J. Brtek. 1995. Checklist of the Anostraca. *Hydrobiologia*. 298:315–353.

Belk, D. and J. Brtek. 1997. Supplement to "Checklist of the Anostraca." *Hydrobiologia*. 359:243–245.

Bennett, A. M. R. 2008. Global Diversity of Hymenopterans (Hymenoptera; Insecta) in Freshwater. *Hydrobiologia*. 595:529–534.

BirdLife International. 2010. IUCN Red List of Threatened Birds. Available a www.birdlife.org/datazone.

Bogan, A. E. 2008. Global Diversity of Freshwater Mussels (Mollusca, Bivalvia) in Freshwater. *Hydrobiologia*. 595:139–147.

Bond-Buckup, G., C. G. Jara, M. Pérez-Losada, L. Buckup and K.A. Crandall. 2008. Global Diversity of Crabs (Aeglidae: Anomura: Decapoda) in Freshwater. *Hydrobiologia*. 595:267–273.

Boxshall, G. A. and D. Defaye. 2008. Global Diversity of Copepods (Crustacea: Copepoda) in Freshwater. *Hydrobiologia*. 595:195–207.

Brendonck, L., D. C. Rogers, J. Olesen, S. Weeks and W. R. Hoeh. 2008. Global Diversity of Large Branchiopods (Crustacea: Branchiopoda) in Freshwater. *Hydrobiologia*. 595:167–176.

Briggs J. 2003. The Biogeographic and Tectonic History of India. *Journal of Biogeography*. 30:381–388

Brittain, J. and M. Sartori. 2009. Ephemerotpera (Mayflies). *Encyclopedia of Insects*, 2nd Edition. V. H. Resh and R. T. Cardé, eds. 328–333. Amsterdam, The Netherlands: Academic Press.

Brown, K. M., B. Lang and K. E. Perez. 2008. The Conservation Ecology of North American Pleurocerid and Hydrobiid Gastropods. *Journal of the North American Benthological Society*. 27(2):484–495.

Buhlmann, K. A., T. S. B. Akre, J. B. Iverson, D. Karapatakis, R. A. Mittermeier, A. Georges, A. G. J. Rhodin, P. P. van Dijk, and J. W. Gibbons. 2009. A Global Analysis of Tortoise and Freshwater Turtle Distributions with Identification of Priority Conservation Areas. *Chelonian Conservation and Biology*. 8(2):116–149.

Burch, J. B. and J. L. Tottenham. 1980. North American Freshwater Snails. *Walkerana*. 1(3):81–215.

Camacho, A. I. and G. Valdecasas. 2008. Global Diversity of Syncarids (Syncarida; Crustacea) in Freshwater. *Hydrobiologia*. 595:257–266.

Carpenter, S. R. and D. M. Lodge. 1986. Effects of Submersed Macrophytes on Ecosystem Processes. *Aquatic Botany*. 26:341–370.

Chambers, P. A., P. Lacoul, K. J. Murphy and S. M. Thomaz. 2008. Global Diversity of Aquatic Macrophytes in Freshwater. *Hydrobiologia* 595:9–26.

Central Intelligence Agency (CIA). 2010. The World Factbook. https://www.cia.gov/library/publications/the-world-factbook/index.html

Clausnitzer, V., V. J. Kalkman, M. Ram, B. Collen, J. E. M. Baillie, M. Bedjanic, W. R. T. Darwall, K.-D. B. Dijkstra, R. Dow, J. Hawking, H. Karube, E. Malikova, D. Paulson, K. Schütte, F. Suhling, R. J. Villanueva, N. von Ellenrieder and K. Wilson. 2009. Odonata Enter the Biodiversity Crisis Debate: The First Global Assessment of an Insect Group. *Biological Conservation*. 142:1864–1869.

Colón-Gaud, C., S. Peterson, M. R. Whiles, S. S. Kilham, K. R. Lips and C. M. Pringle. 2008. Allochthonous Litter Inputs, Organic Matter Standing Stocks, and Organic Seston Dynamics in Upland Panamanian Streams: Potential Effects of Larval Amphibians on Organic Matter Dynamics. *Hydrobiologia* 603:301–312.

Cook C. D. K. 1970. Water Plants of the World. The Hague, Netherlands: Dr. W. Junk.

Cook, B. D., T. J. Page and J. M. Hughes. 2008. Importance of cryptic species for identifying "representative" units of biodiversity for freshwater conservation. *Biological Conservation*. 141:2821–2831.

Cover, M. R. and V. H. Resh. 2008. Global Diversity of Dobsonflies, Fishflies and Alderflies (Megaloptera; Insecta) and Spongillaflies, Nevrorthids and Osmylids (Neuroptera; Insecta) in Freshwater. *Hydrobiologia*. 595:409–417.

Crandall, K. A. and J. E. Buhay. 2008. Global Diversity of Crayfish (Astacidae, Cambaridae, and Parastacidae—Decapoda) in Freshwater. *Hydrobiologia*. 595:295–301.

Cumberlidge, N. 2008. Insular Species of Afrotropical Freshwater Crabs (Crustacea: Decapoda: Brachyura: Potamonautidae and Potamidae) with Special Reference to Madagascar and the Seychelles. *Contributions to Zoology.* 77(2): 71–81.

Left: Two Hindui men standing in Holy Water of the Ganges River at sunset, Varanasi, India.
—Art Wolfe

FRESH WATER

Guwahati fishmongers,
Northeastern Himalyas,
Assam, India.
—Sandesh Kadur

India

Cumberlidge, N., P. K. L. Ng, D. C. J. Yeo, C. Magalhães, M. R. Campos, F. Alvarez, T. Naruse, S. R. Daniels, L. J. Esser, F. Y. K. Attipoe, F.-L. Clotilde-Ba, W. R. T. Darwall, A. McIvor, J. E. M. Baillie, B. Collen and M. Ram. 2009. Freshwater Crabs and the Biodiversity Crisis: Importance, Threats, Status, and Conservation Challenges. *Biological Conservation.* 142:1665–1673.

Currie, D. C. and P. H. Adler. 2008. Global Diversity of Black Flies (Diptera: Simuliidae) in Freshwater. *Hydrobiologia.* 595:469–475.

Dai, A. Y. 1999. *Fauna Sinica (Arthropoda. Crustacea. Malacostraca. Decapoda. Parathelphusidae. Potamidae).* 501:238,30. Editorial Committee of Fauna Sinica, Academia Sinica. Beijing: Science Press.

Daniels, R. J. Ranjit. 2001. Endemic Fishes of the Western Ghats and the Satpura Hypothesis. *Current Science.* 81(3):240–244.

Darwall, W. R. T., K. Smith, T. Lowe and J. C. Vié. 2005. The Status and Distribution of Freshwater Biodiversity in Eastern Africa. viii, 36. *Occasional Paper of the IUCN Species Survival Commission 31.* IUCN, Gland, Switzerland and Cambridge, UK: IUCN SSC Freshwater Biodiversity Assessment Programme.

Darwall, W. R. T., K. G. Smith, D. Tweddle, D. and P. Skelton. 2009. *The Status and Distribution of Freshwater Biodiversity in Southern Africa.* Gland, Switzerland and Grahamstown, South Africa: IUCN and SAIAB. http://data.iucn.org/dbtw-wpd/edocs/2009-003.pdf

De Grave, S., Y. Cai and A. Anker. 2008. Global Diversity of Shrimps (Crustacea: Decapoda: Caridea) in Freshwater. *Hydrobiologia.* 595:287–293.

De Grave, S., N. D. Pentcheff, S. T. Ahyong, T.-Y. Chan, K. A. Crandall, P. C. Dworschak, D. L. Felder, R. M. Feldmann, C. H. J. M. Fransen, L. Y. D. Goulding, R. Lemaitre, M. E. Y. Low, J. W. Martin, P. K. L. Ng, C. E. Schweitzer, S. H. Tan, D. Tshudy and R. Wetzer. 2009. A Classification of Living and Fossil Genera of Decapod Crustaceans. *Raffles Bulletin of Zoology.* Supplement 21:1–109.

de Jong, H., P. Oosterbroek, J. Gelhaus, H. Reusch and C. Young. 2008. Global Diversity of Craneflies (Insecta, Diptera: Tipulidea or Tipulidae sensu lato) in Freshwater. *Hydrobiologia.* 595:457–467.

de Moor, F. C. and V. D. Ivanov. 2008. Global Diversity of Caddisflies (Trichoptera: Insecta) in Freshwater. *Hydrobiologia.* 595:393–407.

Denny, P. 1985. The Ecology and Management of African Wetland Vegetation. The Hague: W. Junk.

Dijkstra, K.-D. B. 2007. Demise and Rise: the Biogeography and Taxonomy of the Odonata of Tropical Africa. *PhD Thesis.* Leiden University, The Netherlands.

Dijkstra, K.-D. B. and V. Clausnitzer. 2006. Thoughts from Africa: How Can Forest Influence Species Composition, Diversity and Speciation in Tropical Odonata? *Forest and Dragonflies.* A. Cordero Rivera, ed.; Sofia, Bulgaria: Pensoft Publishers.

Dillon, R. T. 2000. *The Ecology of Freshwater Molluscs.* Cambridge, United Kingdom: Cambridge University Press.

Dingle R. V., W. G., Siesser and A. R. Newton 1983. *Mesozoic and Tertiary Geology of Southern Africa.* Rotterdam: Balkema.

Di Sabatino, A. H. Smit, R. Gerecke, T. Goldschmidt, N. Matsumoto and B. Cicolani. 2008. Global Diversity of Water Mites (Acari, Hydrachinida; Arachnida) in Freshwater. *Hydrobiologia.* 595:303–315.

Dudgeon, D. 2000. Large-Scale Hydrological Changes in Tropical Asia: Prospects for Riverine Biodiversity. *BioScience.* 50(9):793–806.

Dudgeon, D., A. H. Arthington, M. O. Gessner, Z-I. Kawabata, D. J. Knowler, C. Lévêque, R. J. Naiman, A.-H. Prieur-Richard, D. Soto, M. L. J. Stiassny and C. A. Sullivan. 2006. Freshwater Biodiversity: Importance, Threats, Status and Conservation Challenges. *Biological Reviews.* 81:163–182.

Eschmeyer, W. N. and R. Fricke, eds. 2010. Catalog of Fishes. http://research.calacademy.org/ichthyology/catalog/fishcatmain.asp

Ferrington, L. C. 2008a. Global Diversity of Scorpionflies and Hangingflies (Mecoptera) in Freshwater. *Hydrobiologia.* 595:443–445.

Ferrington, L. C. 2008b. Global Diversity of Non-biting Midges (Chironomidae; Insecta-Diptera) in Freshwater. *Hydrobiologia.* 595:447–455.

Finlay, B. J. and G. F. Esteban. 1998. Freshwater Protozoa: Biodiversity and Ecological Function. *Biodiversity and Conservation.* 7:1163–1186.

Fochetti, R. and J. M. Tierno de Figueroa. 2008. Global Diversity of Stoneflies (Plecoptera; Insecta) in Freshwater. *Hydrobiologia.* 595:365–377.

Forro, L., N. M. Korovchinsky, A. A. Kotov and A. Petrusek. 2008. Global Diversity of Cladocerans (Cladocera; Crustacea) in Freshwater. *Hydrobiologia.* 595:177–184.

Froese, R. and D. Pauly. 2010. FishBase. Version (01/2020). http://www.fishbase.org.

Frost, D. R., T. Grant., J. Faivovich, R. H. Bain, A. Haas, C. F. B. Haddad, R. O. De Sá, A. Channing, M. Wilinson, S. J. Donnellan, C. J. Raxworthy, J. A. Campbell, B. L. Blotto, P. Moler, R. C. Drewes, R. A. Nussbaum, J. D. Lynch, D. M. Green and W. C. Wheeler. 2006. The Amphibian Tree of Life. *Bulletin of the American Museum of Natural History.* 297:1–370.

Fu, C., J. Wu, J. Chen, Q. Wu and G. Lei. 2003. Freshwater Fish Biodiversity in the Yangtze River Basin of China: Patterns, Threats and Conservation. *Biodiversity and Conservation.* 12: 1649–1685.

Garey, J. R., S. J. McInnes and P. B. Nichols. 2008. Global Diversity of Tardigrades (Tardigrada) in Freshwater. *Hydrobiologia.* 595:101–106.

Gaston, K. J. and P. H. Williams. 1996. Spatial Patterns in Taxonomic Diversity. *Biodiversity: A Biology of Numbers and Difference.* K. J. Gaston, ed. 202–229. Oxford, UK: Blackwell Science Limited.

Gattolliat, J-L. and C. Nieto. 2009. The Family Baetidae (Insecta: Ephemeroptera): Synthesis and Future Challenges. *Aquatic Insects*. 31. Supplement 1:41–62.

Glasby, C. J. and T. Timm. 2008. Global Diversity of Polychaetes (Polychaeta; Annelida) in Freshwater. *Hydrobiologia*. 595:107–115

Goodman, S. M. and J. P. Benstead, eds. 2003. *The Natural History of Madagascar*. Chicago, Illinois: The University of Chicago Press.

Goodman, S. M., and J. P. Benstead. 2005. Updated Estimates of Biotic Diversity and Endemism for Madagascar. *Oryx*. 39 (1):73–77.

Graf, D. L. and K. S. Cummings. 2007. Review of the Systematics and Global Diversity of Freshwater Mussel Species (Bivalvia: Unionoida). *Journal of Molluscan Studies*. 73:291–314.

Groombridge, B. and M. B. Jenkins. 2002. *World Atlas of Biodiversity: Earth's Living Resources in the 21st Century*. Berkeley, California: University of California Press.

Guiry, M. D. and G. M. Guiry. 2010. AlgaeBase. National University of Ireland, Galway. http://www.algaebase.org

Harris, M. B., W. Tomas, G. Mourão, C. J. Da Silva, E. Guimarães, F. Sonoda, and E. Fachim. Safeguarding the Pantanal Wetlands: Threats and Conservation Initiatives. *Conservation Biology* 19 (3):714–720.

Harrison, I. J. and M. L. J. Stiassny. 1999. The Quiet Crisis: A Preliminary Listing of the Freshwater Fishes of the World that are Extinct or "Missing in Action." *Extinctions in Near Time: Causes, Contexts, and Consequences*. R. MacPhee, ed. 271–332. New York: Kluwer Academic/ Plenum Publishers.

Hayes, T. B., V. Khoury, A. Narayan, M. Nazir, A. Park, T. Brown, L. Adame, E. Chan, D. Buchholz, T. Stueve, and S. Gallipeau. 2010. Atrazine Induces

Complete Feminization and Chemical Castration in Male African Clawed Frogs (*Xenopus laevis*). *Proceedings of the National Academy of Sciences*. 107 (10):4612–4617.

Heino, J., R. Virkkala and H.Toivonen. 2009. Climate Change and Freshwater Biodiversity: Detected Patterns, Future Trends and Adaptations in Northern Regions. *Biological Reviews*. 84:39–54.

Herder, F., J. Schwarzer, J. Pfaender, R. K. Hadiaty and U. K. Schliewen. 2006. Preliminary Checklist of Sailfin Silversides (Teleostei: Telmatherinidae) in the Malili Lakes of Sulawesi (Indonesia), with a Synopsis of Systematics and Threats. *Verhandlungen der Gesellschaft für Ichthyologie*. 5:139–163.

Hershler, R. 1998. A Systematic Review of the Hydrobiid Snails (Gastropoda: Rissooidea) of the Great Basin, Western United States. Part I. Genus *Pyrgulopsis*. *The Veliger*. 41(1):1–132.

Hershler, R. 1999. A Systematic Review of the Hydrobiid Snails (Gastropoda: Rissooidea) of the Great Basin, Western United States. Part II. Genera *Colligyrus*, *Eremopyrgus*, *Fluminicola*, *Pristinicola*, and *Tryonia*. *The Veliger*. 42(4):306–337.

Hilton-Taylor, C., C. Pollock, J. Chanson, S. H. M. Butchart, T. Oldfield and V. Katariya. 2009. States of the World's Species. *Wildlife in a Changing World. An Analysis of the 2008 IUCN Red List of Threatened Species*. J.-C. Vié, C. Hilton-Taylor and S. N. Stuart, eds. 15–42. Gland, Switzerland: IUCN.

Hughes, J. L. and M. E. Siddall. 2007. A new species of leech from the New York Metropolitan Area. *American Museum Novitates*. 3578:1–6.

IUCN (2010). The *IUCN Red List of Threatened Species*. 2010.1. http://www.iucnredlist.org

Jach, M. A. and M. Balke. 2008. Global Diversity of Water Beetles (Coleoptera) in Freshwater. *Hydrobiologia*. 595:419–442.

Jankowski, T., A. G. Collins and R. Campbell. 2008. Global Diversity of Inland Water Cnidarians. *Hydrobiologia*. 595:35–40.

Jaume, D. 2008. Global Diversity of Spelaeogriphaceans & Thermosbaenaceans (Crustacea; Spelaeogriphacea & Thermosbaenacea) in Freshwater. *Hydrobiologia*. 595:219–224.

Junk, W. J., M. G. Mota Soares and P. B. Bayley. 2007. Freshwater Fishes of the Amazon River Basin: Their Biodiversity, Fisheries, and Habitats. *Aquatic Ecosystem Health & Management*. 10(2):153–173.

Kalkman, V. J., V. Clausnitzer, K.-D. B. Dijkstra, A. G. Orr, D. R. Paulson and J. van Tol. 2008. Global Diversity of Dragonflies (Odonata) in Freshwater. *Hydrobiologia*. 595:351–363.

Kalkman, V. J., J.-P. Boudot, R. Bernard, K.-J. Conze, G. De Knijf, E. Dyatlova, S. Ferreira, J. Jovi , M. Ott, E. Riservato and G. Sahlén. 2010. European Red List of Dragonflies. Luxembourg: Publications Office of the European Union.

Köhler, J., F. Glaw, M. Vences. 2008. Essay 1.1. Trends in Rates of Amphibian Species Descriptions. *Threatened Amphibians of the World*. Stuart, S., M. Hoffmann, J. S. Chanson, N. A. Cox, R. J. Berridge, P. Ramani and B. E. Young, eds. 18. Barcelona, Spain: Lynx Edicions; Gland Switzerland: IUCN; and Arlington, Virginia, USA: Conservation International.

Kosten, S, G. Lacerot, E. Jeppesen, D. da Motta Marques, E. H. van Nes, N. Mazzeo and M. Scheffer. 2009. Effects of Submerged Vegetation on Water Clarity Across Climates. *Ecosystems*. 12:1117–1129.

Kottelat, M and J. Freyhof. 2007. *Handbook of European Freshwater Fishes*. Kottelat, Cornol, Switzerland: Kottelat; and Berlin, Germany: Freyhof.

Kottelat, M. and T. Whitten. 1996. Freshwater Biodiversity in Asia with Special Reference to Fish. ix,59. *World Bank Technical Paper* 343.

Following spread: Berenty Reserve in the Southern Spiny Desert, Madagascar.
—Cristina G. Mittermeier

Kristensen, R. M. and P. Funch. 2000. A New Class With Complicated Jaws Like Those of Rotifera and Gnathostomulida. *Journal of Morphology* 246:1–49.

Leclerf, A., P. Usseglio-Polatera, J.-Y. Charcosset, D. Lambrigot, B. Bracht, and E. Chauvet. 2006. Assessment of Functional Integrity of Eutrophic Streams Using Litter Breakdown and Benthic Macroinvertebrates. *Archiv f r Hydrobiologie.* 165:105–126.

Lévêque, C. 1997. *Biodiversity Dynamics and Conservation: The Freshwater of Tropical Africa.* Cambridge, UK: Cambridge University Press.

Lévêque, C., E. V. Balian and K. Martens. 2005. An Assessment of Animal Species Diversity in Continental Waters. *Hydrobiologia.* 542:39–67.

Lévêque, C., T. Oberdorff, D. Paugy, M. L. J. Stiassny and P. A. Tedesco. 2008. Global Diversity of Fish (Pisces) in Freshwater. *Hydrobiologia.* 595:545–567.

Lundberg, J. G., M. Kottelat, G. R. Smith, M. L. J. Stiassny and A. C. Gill. 2000. So Many Fishes, So Little Time: An Overview of Recent Ichthyological Discoveries in Freshwaters. *Annals of the Missouri Botanical Gardens.* 87(1):26–62.

Lydeard, C., R. H. Cowie, W. F. Ponder, A. E. Bogan, P. Bouchet, S. A. Clark, K. S. Cummings, T. J. Frest, O. Gargominy, D. G. Herbert, R. Hershler, K. E. Perez, B. Roth, M. Seddon, E.E. Strong and F.G. Thompson. 2004. The Global Decline of Nonmarine Mollusks. *BioScience.* 54(4):321–330.

Manconi, R. and R. Pronzato. 2008. Global Diversity of Sponges (Poreifera: Spongillina) in Freshwater. *Hydrobiologia.* 595:27–33.

Martens, K. 2010. The International Year of Biodiversity. *Hydrobiologia.* 637:1–2.

Martens, K., I. Schon, C. Meisch and D. J. Horne.2008. Global Diversity of Ostracods (Ostracoda, Crustacea) in Freshwater. *Hydrobiologia.* 595:185–193.

Martin, S. 2008. Global Diversity of Crocodiles (Crocodilia, Reptilia) in Freshwater.

Hydrobiologia. 595:587–591.

Martin, P., E. Martinez-Ansemil, A. Pinder, T. Timm and M. J. Wetzel. 2008. Global Diversity of Oligochaetous Clitellates ("Oligochaeta"; Clitellata) in Freshwater. *Hydrobiologia.* 595:117–127.

Massard, J. A. and G. Geimer. 2008. Global Diversity of Bryozoans (Bryozoa or Ectoprocta) in Freshwater. *Hydrobiologia.* 595:93–99.

McAllister, D. E., A. L. Hamilton and B. Harvey. 1997. Global Freshwater Biodiversity: Striving for the Integrity of Freshwater Ecosystems. *Sea Wind—Bulletin of Ocean Voice International.* 11(3):1–140.

Mey, W. and W. Speidel. 2008. Global Diversity of Butterflies (Lepidotera) in Freshwater. *Hydrobiologia.* 595:521–528.

Mittermeier, R. A., M. B. Harris, C. G. Mittermeier, J. M. C. Da Silva, R. Lourival, G. A. B. da Fonseca and P. Seligmann. 2005a. *Pantanal: South America's Wetland Jewel.* Ontario, Canada: Firefly Books Ltd.

Mittermeier, R. A., P. R. Gil, M. Hoffmann, J. Pilgrim, T. Brooks, C. G. Mittermeier, J. Lamoreux and G. A. B. da Fonseca 2005b. *Hotspots Revisited: Earth's Biologically Richest and Most Endangered Terrestrial Ecoregions.* Mexico: CEMEX, Conservation International and Agrupación Sierra Madre.

Morse, J. C. 2010. Trichoptera World Checklist. http://entweb.clemson.edu/database/trichopt/index.htm.

Motomura, H., S. Tsukawaki and T. Kamiya. 2002. A Preliminary Survey of the Fishes of Lake Tonle Sap Near Siem Reap, Cambodia. *Bulletin of the National Science Museum, Tokyo.* Series A28(4):233–246.

Myers, G. S. 1951. Freshwater Fishes and East Indian Zoogeography. *Stanford Ichthyological Bulletin.* 4:11–21.

Myers, N., R. A. Mittermeier, C. G. Mittermeier, G. A. B. da Fonseca, and J. Kent. 2000. Biodiversity Hotspots for Conservation Priorities. *Nature.* 403:853–858.

NatureServe. 2010. NatureServe Explorere. An Online Encyclopedia of Life. http://www.natureserve.org/explorer/

Neves R. J., A. E. Bogan, J. D. Williams, S. A. Ahlstedt and P. W. Hartfield. 1997. Status of Aquatic Mollusks in the Southeastern United States: A Downward Spiral of Diversity. *Aquatic Fauna in Peril: The Southeastern Perspective.* G. W. Benz and D. E. Collins, eds. 43–85. Decatur, Georgia, USA: Lenz Design and Communications.

Ng, P. K. L. 1994. Peat Swamp Fishes of Southeast Asia – Diversity Under Threat. *Wallaceana* 73: 1–5.

Ortega, H., B. Rengrifo, I. Samanez and C. Palma. 2007. Diversidad y el Estado de Conservación de Cuerpos de Agua Amazónicos en el Nororiente del Perú. *Rev. peru. biol. número especial 13.* (3):189–193.

Palmer, M. A., A. P. Covich, B. J. Finlay, J. Gilbert, K. D. Hyde, R. K. Johnson, T. Kairesalo, S. Lake, C. R. Lovell, R. J. Naiman, C. Ricci, F. Sabater and D. Strayer. 1997. Biodiversity and Ecosystem Processes in Freshwater Sediments. *Ambio.* 26 (8):571–577.

Pauwels, O. S. G., V. Walllach and P. David. 2008. Global Diversity of Snakes (Serpentes; Reptilia) in Freshwater. *Hydrobiologia.* 595:599–605.

Peck, L. S. 2005. Prospects for Surviving Climate Change in Antarctic Aquatic Species. *Frontiers in Zoology.* 2(9):1–8.

Penning W. E., M. Mjelde, B. Dudley, S. Hellsten, J. Hanganu, A. Kolada, M. van den Berg, S. Poikane, G. Phillips, N. Willby and F. Ecke. 2008. Classifying Aquatic Macrophytes as Indicators of Eutrophication in European Lakes. *Aquatic Ecology.* 42:237–251.

Petr, T. 2000. Interactions Between Fish and Aquatic Macrophytes in Inland Waters. A Review.

Food and Agriculture Organization of the United Nations (FAO) Fisheries Technical Paper 396. 185. Rome, Italy: FAO.

Pieterse, A. H. 1990. Introduction (Chapter 1). *Aquatic Weeds.* A. H. Pieterse and K. J. Murphy, eds. 3–16. Oxford, UK: Oxford University.

Poinar, G. 2008. Global Diversity of Hairworms (Nematomorpha: Gordiaceae) in Freshwater. *Hydrobiologia.* 595:79–83.

Polhemus, D. A., 1997. Phylogenetic Analysis of the Hawaiian Damselfly Genus Megalagrion (Odonata: Coenagrionidae): Implications for Biogeophy, Ecology and Conservation Biology. *Pacific Science.* 51:395–412.

Polhemus, J. T. and D. A. Polhemus. 2008. Global Diversity of True Bugs (Heteroptera; Insecta) in Freshwater. *Hydrobiologia.* 595:379–391.

Poly, W. J. 2008. Global Diversity of Fishlice (Crustacea: Braandchiura: Argulidae) in Freshwater. *Hydrobiologia.* 595:1209–212.

Ponder, W. F. 1997. Conservation Status, Threats and Habitat Requirements of Australian Terrestrial and Freshwater Mollusca. *Memoirs of the Museum of Victoria.* 56(2):421–430.

Ponder, W. F. and K. F. Walker. 2003. From Mound Springs to Mighty Rivers: The Conservation Status of Freshwater Molluscs in Australia. *Aquatic Ecosystem Health and Management.* 6(1):19–28.

Porter, M. L., K. Meland and W. Price. 2008. Global Diversity of Mysids (Crustacea-Mysida) in Freshwater. *Hydrobiologia.* 595:213–218.

Quirós, R., J. A. Bechara and E. K. de Resende. 2007. Fish Diversity and Ecology, Habitats and Fisheries for the Un-Dammed Riverine Axis Paraguay-Parana-Rio de la Plata (Southern South America). *Aquatic Ecosystem Health & Management.* 10(2):187–200.

Rainboth, W.I. 1996. Fishes of the Cambodian Mekong. 265. Rome, Italy: Food and Agriculture Organization of the United Nations (FAO).

Reaka-Kudla, M. L., D. E. Wilson and E. O. Wilson, eds. 1997. *Biodiversity II, Understanding and Protecting Our Biological Resources.* 549. Washington, DC: Joseph Henry Press.
Reis, R. E., S. O. Kullander and C. J. Ferraris. 2003. *Checklist of the Freshwater Fishes of South and Central America.* Porto Alegre: EDIPUCRS.

Revenga, C. and Y. Kura. 2003. *Status and Trends of Biodiversity of Inland Water Ecosystems.* Secretariat of the Convention on Biological Diversity, Montreal. Technical Series no. 11.

Revenga, C., I. Campbell, R. Abell, P. de Villiers and M. Bryer. 2005. Prospects for Monitoring Freshwater Ecosystems Towards the 2010 Targets. *Philosophical Transactions of the Royal Society Series B.* 360:397–413.

Roberts, T. R. 1995. Mekong Mainstream Hydropower Projects: Run-of-the River or Ruin-of-the-River? *Natural History Bulletin of the Siam Society.* 43:9–19.

Roberts, T. R. 2001. Killing the Mekong: China's Fluvicidal Hydropower-Cum-Navigation Development Scheme. *Natural History Bulletin of the Siam Society.* 49:143–159.

Rodriguez, M. A., K. O. Winemiller, W. M. Lewis, Jr. and D. C. Taphorn Baechle. 2007. The Freshwater Habitats, Fishes, and Fisheries of the Orinoco River Basin. *Aquatic Ecosystem Health & Management.* 10(2):140–152.

Rueda, L. M. 2008. Global Diversity of Mosquitoes (Insecta: Diptera: Culicidae) in Freshwater. *Hydrobiologia.* 595:477–487.

Rutishauser, R. 1997. Structural and Developmental Diversity in Podostemaceae (River-Weeds). *Aquatic Botany* 57:29–70.

Saltonstall, K. 2002. Cryptic Invasion by a Non-native Genotype of the Common Reed, *Phragmites australis,* into North America. *Proceedings of the National Academy of Sciences of the United States of America* 99:2445–2449.

Schatz, H. and V. Behan-Pelletier. 2008. Global Diversity of Oribatids (Oribatida: Acari: Arachnida). *Hydrobiologia.* 595:323–328.

Scheffer M., S. H. Hosper, M. L. Meijer, B. Moss and E. Jeppesen. 1993. Alternative Equilibria in Shallow Lakes. *Trends in Ecology and Evolution.* 8:275–279.

Schockaert, E. R., M. Hooge, R. Sluys, S. Schilling, S. Tyler and T. Artois. 2008. Global Diversity of Free Living Flatworms (Platyhelminthes, "Turbellaria") in Freshwater. *Hydrobiologia.* 595:41–48.

Segers, H. 2008. Global Divesity of Rotifers (Rotifera) in Freshwater. *Hydrobiologia.* 595:49–59.

Shearer, C. A., E. Descals, B. Kohlmeyer, J. Kohlmeyer, L. Marvanova, D. Padgett, D. Porter, H. A. Raja, J. P. Schmit, H. A. Thorton and H. Voglymayr. 2007. Fungal Biodiversity in Aquatic Habitats. *Biodiversity and Conservation.* 16:49–67.
Sket, B. 1999. The Nature of Biodiversity in Hypogean Waters and How it Is Endangered. *Biodiversity and Conservation.* 8:1319–1338.

Sket, B. and P. Trontelj. 2008. Global Diversity of Leeches (Hirudinea) in Freshwater. *Hydrobiologia.* 595:129–137.

Smith, K. G. and W. R. T. Darwall. 2006. The Status and Distribution of Freshwater Fish Endemic to the Mediterranean Basin. vi , 34. Gland, Switzerland and Cambridge, UK: IUCN.

Spillings, B. L., B. D. Brooke, L. L. Koekemoer , J. Chiphwanya, M. Coetzee and R. H. Hunt. 2009. A New Species Concealed by *Anopheles funestus* Giles, a Major Malaria Vector in Africa. *American Journal of Tropical Medicine and Hygiene.* 81(3):510–515.

Sterling, E. J., M. M. Hurley and L. D. Minh. 2006. *Vietnam: A Natural History.* New Haven, Connecticut, USA: Yale University Press

Stiassny, M. L. J. 1999. The Medium Is the Message: Freshwater Biodiversity in Peril. *The*

Living Planet in Crisis: Biodiversity Science and Policy. 53–71. J. Cracraft. and F. T. Grifo, eds. 53–71. USA: Columbia University Press.

Stiassny, M. L. J. 2002. Conservation of Freshwater Fish Biodiversity: The Knowledge Impediment. *Verhandlungen der Gesellschaft f r Ichthyolgie.* 3:7–18.

Stiassny, M. L. J., G. G. Teugels and C. D. Hopkins. 2007. Poissons d'eaux douces et saumâtres de basse Guinée, ouest de l'Afrique centrale. Paris, France: IRD and Muséum National d'Histoire Naturelle; Tervuren, Belgium: Musée Royal de l'Afrique Central.

Strayer, D. L., J. A. Downing, W. R. Haag, T. L. King, J. B. Layzer, T. J. Newton and S. J. Nichols. 2004. Pearly Mussels, North America's Most Imperiled Animals. *BioScience.* 54(5):429–439.

Strong, E. E., O. Gargominy, W. F. Ponder, and P. Bouchet. 2008. Global Diversity of Gastropods (Gastropoda; Mollusca) in Freshwater. *Hydrobiologia.* 595:149–166.

Stuart, S., M. Hoffmann, J. S. Chanson, N. A. Cox, R. J. Berridge, P. Ramani and B. E. Young, eds. 2008. *Threatened Amphibians of the World.* Barcelona: Lynx Edicions; Gland, Switzerland: IUCN; and Arlington, Virgina, USA: Conservation International.

Sundberg, P. and R. Gibson. 2008. Global Diversity of Nemerteans (Nemertea) in Freshwater. *Hydrobiologia.* 595:61–66.

Thieme, M. L., R. Abell, M. L. J. Stiassny, P. Skelton, B. Lehner, G. G. Teugels, E. Dinerstein, A. K. Toham, N. Burgess, and D. Olson. 2005. *Freshwater Ecoregions of Africa and Madagascar: A Conservation Assessment.* Washington DC: Island Press.

Tudge, C. 2000. *The Variety of Life: A Survey and a Celebration of All the Creatures that Have Ever Lived.* xii, 684.New York: Oxford University Press.

Turtle Taxonomy Working Group [A. G. J. Rhodon, J. F. Parham, P. P. van Dijk, and J. B. Iverson]. 2009. Turtles of the World: Annotated Checklist of taxonomy and Synonymy, 2009 Update,

with Conservation Status Summary. *Chelonian Research Monographs.* 5: 39–84

Vainola, R., J. D. S. Witt, M. Grabowski, J. H. Bradbury, K. Jazdzewski and B. Sket. 2008. Global Diversity of Amphipods (Amphipoda; Crustacea) in Freshwater. *Hydrobiologia.* 595:241–255.

Vieites, D. R., K. C. Wollenbergb, F. Andreonec, J. Köhlerd, F. Glawe and M. Vences. 2009. Vast Underestimation of Madagascar's Biodiversity Evidenced by an Integrative Amphibian Inventory. *Proceedings of the National Academy of Sciences.* 106 (20): 8267–8272.

Wagner, R., M. Bartak, A. Borkent, G. Courtney, B. Goddeeris, J.-P. Haenni, L. Knutson, A. Pont, G. E. Rotheray, R. Rozkosny, B. Sinclair, N. Woodley, T. Zatwarnicki and P. Zwick. 2008. Global Diversity of Dipteran Families (Insecta Diptera) in Freshwater (Excluding Simulidae, Culicidae, Chironomidae, Tipulidae and Tabanidae). *Hydrobiologia.* 595:489–519.

Wallace, A. R. 1876. *The Geographical Distribution of Animals.* New York: Harper.

Whiles, M. R., K. R. Lips, C. M. Pringle, S. S. Kilham, R. J. Bixby, R. Brenes, S. Connelly, J. C. Colon-Gaud, M. Hunte-Brown, A. D. Huryn, C. Montgomery and S. Peterso. 2006. The Effects of Amphibian Population Declines on the Structure and Function of Neotropical Stream Ecosystems. *Frontiers in Ecology and the Environment.* 4(1):27–34.

Wilson, G. D. F. 2008. Global Diversity of Isopod Crustaceans (Crustacea; Isopoda) in Freshwater. *Hydrobiologia.* 595:231–240.

Yeo, D. C. J., P. K. L. Ng, N. Cumberlidge, C. Magalhães, S. R. Daniels and M. R. Campos. 2008. Global Diversity of Crabs (Crustacea: Decapoda: Brachyura) in Freshwater. *Hydrobiologia.* 595:275–286.

Yoder, A. D. and M. D. Nowak 2006. Has Vicariance or Dispersal Been the Predominant Biogeographic Force in Madagascar? Only Time Will Tell. *Annual Review of Ecology, Evolution and Systematics.* 37:405–431.

Yuma, M., K. Hosoya and Y. Nagata. 1998. Distribution of the Freshwater Fishes of Japan: An Historical Overview. *Environmental Biology of Fishes.* 52:97–124.

Zhang, X. J., T. D. Yao, X. L. Ma, and N. L. Wang. 2002. Microorganisms in a High Altitude Glacier Ice in Tibet. *Folia Microbiologica.* 47(3):241–245.

CHAPTER TWO:
AQUATIC ECOSYSTEMS: DIVERSITY AND DYNAMISM

AmphibiaWeb. 2010. http://amphibiaweb.org/

Brunke, M. and T. Gonser. 1997. The ecologic significance of exchange processes between rivers and groundwater. *Freshwater Biology* 37(1): 1–33.

Cohen, A., Bills, R., et al. (1993). «The impact of sediment pollution on biodiversity in Lake Tanganyika.» *Conservation Biology* 7(3):667–677.

Costanza, R., R. d'Arge, R. deGroot et al. 1997. The value of the world's ecosystem services and natural capital. *Nature* 387: 253–260.

Coulter, G. W. (1991) Lake Tanganyika and its life. Oxford, UK: Oxford Univ. Press.

Danielopol D. L., P. Pospisil and R. Rouch. 2000. Biodiversity in Groundwater: A Largescale View. *Trends in Ecology and Evolution* 15(6): 223–224.

Danielopol, D. L., C. Griebler, A. Gunatilaka and J. Notenboom. 2003. Present State and Future Prospects for Groundwater Ecosystems. *Environmental Conservation.* 30 (2): 104–130.

Dodd Jr., C. K. 1992. Biological diversity of a temporary pond herpetofauna in north Florida sandhills. *Biodiversity Conservation.* 1:125–142.

Dudgeon, D. 1992. Endangered ecosystems: a review of the conservation status of tropical Asian rivers. *Hydrobiologia* 248: 167–191.

Dudgeon, D., A. H. Arthington, M. O. Gessner, Z.-I. Kawabata, A.-H. Prieur-Richard, D. Soto, M. L. J. Stiassny and C. A. Sullivan. 2006. Freshwater biodiversity: importance, threats, status and conservation challenges. *Biological Reviews.* 81:163–182.

Edwards, R. T. 1998. The Hyporheic Zone In River Ecology and Management: Lessons from the Pacific Coastal Ecoregion, eds. Robert J. Naiman and Robert E. Bilby. New York: Springer-Verlag.

Fraser, L. H. and P. A. Keddy. 2005. The world's largest wetlands: ecology and conservation. Cambridge: Cambridge University Press.

Gende, S. M. and T. P. Quinn. 2006. "The Fish and the Forest: Salmon-catching bears fertilize forests with the partially eaten carcasses of their favorite food." Scientific American, online edition (http://www.sciam.com/sciammag/?contents=2006-08), August 2006.

Gibert, J. and L. Deharveng. 2002. Subterranean Ecosystems: A Truncated Functional Biodiversity. *BioScience.* 52(6):473–481.

Gleick, P. H. 1996. Water Resources. *Encyclopedia of Climate and Weather.* 2:817–823. S. H. Schneider, ed. New York: Oxford University Press.

Gopal, B., B. Bose, and A. B. Goswani. 2000. River Conservation in the Indian Sub-continent. *Global Perspectives on River Conservation: Science, Policy, and Practice.* P. J. Boon, B. R. Davies and G. E. Petts. eds. 233–261. Chichester, UK: John Wiley and Sons Ltd.

Harris, M., W. Tomas, G. Mourão, C. J. Da Silva, E. Guimarães, F. Sonoda and E. Fachim. 2005. Safeguarding the Pantanal Wetlands: Threats and Conservation Initiatives. *Conservation Biology* 19(3):714–720.

Herbst, D. 1988. Comparative population ecology of Ephydra hians at Mono Lake and Albert Lake. *Hydrobiologia* 158:145–166
.

Hoekstra, J., J. L. Molnar, M. Jennings, C. Revenga, M. D. Spalding, T. M. Boucher, J. C. Robertson, and T. J. Heibel, with Katherine Ellison. 2010. *The Atlas of Global Conservation: Changes, Challenges, and Opportunities to Make a Difference.* U.C. Press, Berkeley, CA.

Holsinger J. R. 1993. Biodiversity of Subterranean Amphipod Crustaceans: Global Patterns and Zoogeographical Implications. *Journal of Natural History* 27: 821–835.

Isom, B. G. and P. Yokley. Mussels of Bear Creek Watershed, Alabama and Mississippi, with a discussion of the area geology. *American Midland Naturalist* 79(1): 189–196.

Jauhiainen, J., H. Takahashi, J. E. P. Heikkinen, P. J. Martikainen and ,H. Vasander. 2005. Carbon fluxes from a tropical peat swamp forest floor. Global Change Biology 11(10), 1788–1797.

Junk, W., ed. 1997. *The Central Amazon Floodplain: Ecology of a Pulsing System.* 1997. Germany: Springer-Verlag.

Kottelat, M., R. Britz, H. H. Tan and K.-E. Witte. 2006. Paedocypris, a new genus of southeast Asian cyprinid fish with a remarkable sexual dimorphism, comprises the world's smallest vertebrate. *Proceedings of the Royal Society of London, Series B*, 273: 895–899.

Lascu, C. 2004. Movile Cave, Romania from *Encyclopedia of Caves and Karst Science.* Online: Taylor and Francis. http://www.bookrags.com/tandf/movile-cave-romania-tf/.

Lascu, C., R. Popa, S. M. Sarbu, L. Vlasceanu and S. Prodan. 1993. La grotte de Movile: une faune hors du temps. *La Recherche* 24:1092–1098.

Leopold, L. B. and K. S. Davis. 1966. Water. Life Science Library, Time Inc., New York.

Lévêque, C., E. V. Balian and K. Martens. 2005. An assessment of animal species diversity in continental waters. *Hydrobiologia.* 542:39–67.

Lytle, D. A. and N. L. R. Poff. 2004. "Adaptation to natural flow regimes." *TRENDS in Ecology and Evolution*, Vol. 19, No. 2: 94–100.

Lundberg, J. G., M. Kottelat, G. R. Smith, M. L. J. Stiassny and A. C. Gill. 2000. So Many Fishes, So Little Time: An Overview of Recent Ichthyological Discovery in Continental Waters. *Annals of the Missouri Botanical Gardens.* 87(1):26–62.

Mackay, A. W., R. J. Flower and L. Z. Granina. (2002) Lake Baikal. In: *The Physical Geography of Northern Eurasia: Russia and Neighbouring States.* M. Shahgedanova and A. Goudie, eds. OUP, Oxford. (Chapter 17) pp 403–421. Arthington, A. H., ed. 2010. Environmental Flows: Science and Management. Freshwater Biology, Special Issue. 55(1): 1–260.

McAllister, D. E., A. L. Hamilton and B. Harvey. 1997. Global freshwater biodiversity: striking for the integrity of freshwater systems. *Sea Wind.* 11:1–140.

Mitsch, W. J., J. G. Gosselink. 2000. The value of wetlands: importance of scale and landscape setting. *Ecological Economics* 35: 25–33.

Mittermeier, R. A., M. B. Harris, C. G. Mittermeier, J. M. C. Da Silva, R. Lourival, G.A.B. da Fonseca and P. Seligmann. 2005a. Pantanal: South America's Wetland Jewel. Firefly Books Ltd., Ontario, Canada.

Moser, M., C. Prentice and S. Frazier. 1996. A global overview of wetland loss and degradation. Proceedings to the 6th Meeting of the Contracting Parties of the Ramsar Convention. Volume 10.

Nilsson, C. 1992. Conservation management of riparian communities. In: *Ecological Principles of Nature Conservation. Applications in Temperate and Boreal Environments.* L. Hansson, ed. Elsevier, London.

Postel, S. and B. Richter. 2003. *Rivers for Life: Managing Water for People and Nature.* Island Press, Washington, DC.

Pringle, L. 1987. Planet Earth. Rivers and Lakes. Time Life Books, Alexandria, VA.

Proudlove, G. 2006. Subterranean fishes of the world. An account of the subterranean (hypogean) fishes described up to 2003 with a bibliography 1541–2004. Moulis: International Society for Subterranean Biology

Pusey, B. J. and A. H. Arthington. 2003. Importance of the riparian zone to the conservation and management of freshwater fish: a review. *Marine and Freshwater Research.* 54:1–16.

Revenga, C., J. Brunner, N. Henninger, K. Kassem and R. Payne. 2000. *Pilot analysis of global ecosystems: Freshwater systems.* Washington, DC: World Resources Institute.

Rossiter, A. and H. Kawanabe. 2000. Ancient Lakes: Biodiversity, Ecology and Evolution. Advances in Ecological Research. 31. Academic Press.

Russian Ministry of Natural Resources, 2007. "Lake Baikal Protection fact sheet" administered by Rosprirodnadzor (Russian Nature Protection and Oversight Inspectorate). Information available in Russian, on-line at: http://www.geol. irk.ru/baikal/baikal.htm

Rzóska, J. (1974). "The upper Nile swamps, a tropical wetland study" *Freshwater Biology* 4:1–30.

Schmitter-Soto, J. J., F. A. Comín, E. Escobar-Briones, J. Herrera-Silveira, J. Alcocer, E. Suárez-Morales, M. ElEias-Gutiérrez, V. Díaz-Arce, L. E. Marín and B. Steinich. 2002. Hydrogeochemical and biological characteristics of cenotes in the Yucatán Peninsula (SE Mexico). *Hydrobiologia.* 467: 215–228.

Sebastian, A. 2002. Globally threatened mammal and bird species in Malaysian peat swamp forests. Peatlands for people: natural resources function and sustainable management. J. Rieley and S. Page, eds. 22–28. BPPT and Indonesian Peat Association, Jakarta.

Sket, B. 1997. Distribution of *Proteus* (Amphibia: Urodela: Proteidae) and its Possible Explanation. *Journal of Biogeography.* 24:263–280.

Sket, B. 1999. The Nature of Biodiversity in Hypogean Waters and How it is Endangered. *Biodiversity and Conservation*. 8:1319–1338.

Stoch F. 1995. The Ecological and Historical Determinants of Crustacean Diversity in Groundwaters, or: Why Are There So Many Species? *Mémoires de Biospéologie* 22:139–160.

Strong, E. E., O. Gargominy, Ponder, and P. Bouchet. 2008. Global Diversity of Gastropods (Gastropoda; Mollusca) in Freshwater. *Hydrobiologia.* 595:149–166.

Trajano, E. 2001. Ecology of subterranean fishes: an overview. *Environmental Biology of Fishes.* 62:133–160.

Turak, E. and K. Koop. 2008. Multi-attribute ecological river topology for assessing ecological conditions and conservation planning, Hydrobiologia. 603:83–104. UNDP, 2006. Malaysia's Peat Swamp Forests. Conservation and Sustainable Use. UNDP, Kuala Lumpur, Malaysia, 33pp.

Vannote R. L., G.W. Minshall, K. W. Cummins, J. R. Sedell and C. E. Cushing. 1980. The river continuum concept. *Canadian Journal of Fisheries and Aquatic Sciences.* 37:130–137.

Vicentini, B. 2008. As diferentes faces do igapó. Mini-Curso *in Ecologia da Floresta Amazônica. Projeto Dinâmica Biológica de Fragmentos Florestais.* Instituto Nacional de Pesquisas da Amazônia and Smithsonian Institution.

White, W. B., D. C. culver, J. S. Herman, T. C. Kane and J. E. Mylroie. 1995. Karst lands. *American Scientist* 83(5):450–459.

Yule, C. M. 2010. Loss of biodiversity and ecosystem functioning in Indo-Malayan peat swamp forests. *Biodiversity Conservation.* 19: 393–409.

CHAPTER THREE:

FRESHWATER ECOSYSTEMS UNDER THREAT: THE ULTIMATE HOTSPOT

Abell, R., M. Thieme, C. Revenga, M. Bryer, M. Kottelat, N. Bogutskaya, B. Coad, N. Mandrak, S. Contreras Balderas, W. Bussing, M. L. J. Stiassny, P. Skelton, G. R. Allen, P. Unmack, A. Naseka, R. Ng, N. Sindorf, J. Robertson, E. Armijo, J. Higgins, T. J. Heibel, E. Wikramanayake, D. Olson, H. L. Lopez, R. E. Reis, J. G. Lundberg, M. H. Sabaj Perez and P. Petry. 2008. Freshwater Ecoregions of the World: A New Map of Biogeographic Units for Freshwater Biodiversity Conservation *BioScience* 58:403–414.

Alemayehu, T., W. Furi and D. Legesse. 2007. Impact of Water Overexploitation on Highland Lakes of Eastern Ethiopia. *Environmental Geology* 52:147–154.

Allan, J. D. 2004. Landscapes and Riverscapes: The Influence of Land Use on Stream Ecosystems. *Annual Review of Ecology Evolution and Systematics* 35:257–284.

Allan, J. D., R. Abell, Z. Hogan, C. Revenga, B. W. Taylor, R. L. Welcomme and K. Winemiller. 2005. Overfishing of Inland Waters. *Bioscience* 55:1041–1051.

Allan, J. D. and A. S. Flecker. 1993. Biodiversity Conservation in Running Waters. *BioScience* 43:32–42.

Balian, E., H. Segers, C. Lévéque and K. Martens. 2008. Freshwater Animal Diversity Assessment: An Overview of the Results. *Hydrobiologia* 595:627–637.

Benstead, J. P., P. H. De Rham, J.-L. Gattolliat, F.-M. Gibon, P. V. Loiselle, M. Sartori, J.P. Sparks, and M. L. J. Stiassny. 2003. Conserving Madagascar's Freshwater Biodiversity. *BioScience* 53(11):1101–1111.

BirdLife International. 2010. IUCN Red List of Threatened Birds. Available at www.birdlife.org/ datazone.

Bohanak, A. J. and D. G. Jenkins. 2003. Ecological and Evolutionary Significance of Dispersal by Freshwater Invertebrates. *Ecology Letters* 6:783–796.

Brinson, M. M. and A. I. Malvárez. 2002. Temperate Freshwater Wetlands: Types, Status, and Threats. *Environmental Conservation* 29:115–133.

Brown, K. M., B. Lang and K. E. Perez. 2008. The Conservation Ecology of North American Pleurocerid and Hydrobiid Gastropods. *Journal of the North American Benthological Society.* 27(2):484–495.

Buhlmann, K. A., T. S. B. Akre, J. B. Iverson, D. Karapatakis, R. A. Mittermeier, A. Georges, A. G. J. Rhodin, P. P. van Dijk and J. W. Gibbons. 2009. A Global Analysis of Tortoise and Freshwater Turtle Distributions with Identification of Priority Conservation Areas. *Chelonian Conservation and Biology.* 8(2):116–149.

Butchart, S. H. M., A. J. Stattersfield, L. A. Bennun, H. R. Akçakaya, J. E. M. Baillie, S. N. Stuart, C. Hilton-Taylor. and G. M. Mace. 2005. Using Red List Indices to Measure Progress Towards the 2010 Target and Beyond. *Phiosophical Transations of the Royal Society.* 1454:255–268.

Carpenter, S. R. 2003. *Regime Shifts in Lake Ecosystems: Pattern and Variation. Volume 15 in the Excellence in Ecology Series.* Ecology Institute, Oldendorf/Luhe, Germany.

Castello, L., J. P. Viana, G. Watkins, M. Pinedo-Vasquez, and V. A. Luzadis. 2009. Lessons from Integrating Fishers of Arapaima in Small-Scale Fisheries Management at the Mamiraua Reserve, Amazon. *Environmental Management* 43:197–209.

Chapman, L. J., C. A. Chapman, L. Kaufman, F. Witte, and J. Balirwa. 2008. Biodiversity Conservation in African Inland Waters: Lessons of the Lake Victoria Region. *Verhandlungen des Internationalen Verein Limnologie* 30:16–34.

Christensen, D.L., B.J. Herwig, D.E. Schindler, and S.R. Carpenter. 1996. Impacts of Lakeshore Residential Development on Coarse Woody Debris in North Temperate Lakes. *Ecological Applications* 6:1143–1149.

Claassen, C. 1994. Washboards, Pigtoes, and Muckets: Historic Musseling in the Mississippi Watershed. *Historical Archaeology* 28:1–145.

Clausnitzer, V., V. J. Kalkman, M. Ram, B. Collen, J. E. M. Baillie, M. Bedjanic, W. R. T. Darwall, K.-D. B. Dijkstra, R. Dow, J. Hawking, H. Karube, E. Malikova, D. Paulson, K. Schütte, F. Suhling, R. J. Villanueva, N. von Ellenrieder and K. Wilson. 2009. Odonata Enter the Biodiversity Crisis Debate: The First Global Assessment of an Insect Group. *Biological Conservation.* 142:1864–1869

Cumberlidge, N., P. K. Ng, D. C. J. Yeo, C. Magalhães, M. R. Campos, F. Alvarez, T. Naruse, S. R. Daniel, L. J. Esser, F. Y. K. Attipoe, F.-L. Clotilde-Ba, W. Darwall, A. McIvor, J. E. M. Baillie, B. Collen and M. Ram. 2009. Freshwater Crabs and the Biodiversity Crisis: Importance, Threats, Status, and Conservation Challenges. *Biological Conservation* 142:1665–1673.

Darwall, W. R. T., K. G. Smith, T. Lowe, and J.-C. Vié. 2005. The Status and Distribution of Freshwater Biodiversity in Eastern Africa. IUCN SSC Freshwater Biodiversity Assessment Programme, Gland, Switzerland and Cambridge, UK.

Darwall, W. R. T., K. G. Smith, D. Tweddle and P. Skelton. 2009. The Status and Distribution of Freshwater Biodiversity in Southern Africa. IUCN and SAIAB, Gland, Switzerland and Grahamstown, South Africa.

Davies, P. M. 2010. Climate Change Implications for River Restoration in Global Biodiversity Hotspots. *Restoration Ecology* 18(3):261–268.

Dent, C. L., G. S. Cumming and S.R. Carpenter. 2002. Multiple States in River and Lake Ecosystems. *Philosophical Transactions of the Royal Society of London Series B-Biological Sciences* 357: 635–645.

Donnelly, T. H., M. R. Grace and B.T. Hart. 1997. Algal Blooms in the Darling-Barwon River, Australia. *Water Air and Soil Pollution* 99:487–496.

Dudgeon, D., A. H. Arthington, M. O. Gessner, Z. I. Kawabata, D. J. Knowler, C. Leveque, R. J. Naiman, A. H. Prieur-Richard, D. Soto, M. L. J. Stiassny and C. A. Sullivan. 2005. Freshwater Biodiversity: Importance, Threats, Status and Conservation Challenges. *Biological Reviews* 81:163–182.

Dugan, P., M. M. Dey and V. V. Sugunan. 2006. Fisheries and Water Productivity in Tropical River Basins: Enhancing Food Security and Livelihoods by Managing Water for Fish. *Agricultural Water Management* 80:262–275.

Dugan, P., V. V. Sugunan, R. L. Welcomme, C. Bene, R. Brummett, E. M. C. M. Beveridge, A. Kofi, U. Amerasinghe, A. Arthington, S. Blixt, S. Chimatiro, P. Katiha, J. King, J. Kolding, S. Nguyen Khoa, and J. Turpie. 2007. Inland Fisheries and Aquaculture. *Water for Food, Water for Life: A Comprehensive Assessment of Water Management in Agriculture.* D. Molden, ed. 459–483. London, UK., Earthscan and Colombo, Sri Lanka, IWMI.

FAO. 2009. Aquastat database. www.fao.org/nr/aquastat/.

Finlayson, C. M., and R. D'Cruz. 2005. Inland Water Systems. Pages 551–583 in *Ecosystems and Human Well-being: Current State and Trends, Volume I, Millenium Ecosystem Assessment.* R. Costanza, P. Jacobi and F. Rijsberman, eds. 551–583. Washington DC, Island Press.

Geddes, M. C. and C. M. Jones. 1997. Australian Freshwater Crayfish: Exploitation by Fishing and Aquaculture. *Australian Biologist* 10:70–75.

Glantz, M. H. 2007. Aral Sea basin: a sea dies, a sea also rises. *Ambio* 36: 323–327. Gozlan, R. E, J. R. Britton, I. Cowx and G. H. Copp. 2010. Current Knowledge on Non-native Freshwater Fish Introductions. *Journal of Fish Biology* 76:751–786.

Graf, W. L. 1999. Damnation: A Geographic Census of American Dams and Their Large-Scale Hydrologic Impacts. *Water Resources Research* 35:1305–1311.

Graf, D. L. and K. S. Cummings. 2007. Review of the Systematics and Global Diversity of Freshwater Mussel Species (Bivalvia: Unionoida). *Journal of Molluscan Studies* 73:291–314.

Hecky, R. E., R. Mugidde, P. S. Ramlal, M. R. Talbot and G. W. Kling. 2010. Multiple Stressors Cause Rapid Ecosystem Change in Lake Victoria. *Freshwater Biology* 55:19–42.

Heino, J., R. Virkkala and H. Toivonen. 2009. Climate Change and Freshwater Biodiversity: Detected Patterns, Future Trends and Adaptations in Northern Regions. *Biological Reviews* 84:39–54.

Hering, D., A. Schmidt-Kloiber, J. Murphy, S. Lücke, C. Zamora-Muñoz, M. J. López Rodríguez, T. Huber, and W. Graf. 2009. Potential Impact of Climate Change on Aquatic Insects: A Sensitivity Analysis for European Caddisflies (Trichoptera) Based on Distribution Patterns and Ecological Preferences. *Aquatic Sciences* 71:3–14.

Hilton-Taylor, C., C. Pollock, J. Chanson, S. H. M. Butchart, T. Oldfield and V. Katariya. 2009. States of the World's Species. *Wildlife in a Changing World. An Analysis of the 2008 IUCN Red List of Threatened Species.* J.-C. Vié, C. Hilton-Taylor and S. N. Stuart, eds. 15–42. Gland, Switzerland: IUCN.

Hinck, J. E., V. S. Blazer, C. J. Schmitt, D. M. Papoulias and D. E. Tillitt. 2009. Widespread Occurrence of Intersex in Black Basses (*Micropterus* spp.) from U.S. Rivers, 1995–2004. *Aquatic Toxicology* 95:6070.

Hoekstra, J. M., T. M. Boucher, T. H. Ricketts, and C. Roberts. 2005. Confronting a Biome Crisis: Global Disparities of Habitat Loss and Protection. *Ecology Letters* 8:23–29.

Horwitz, P. 1994. Distribution and Conservation of the Tasmanian Giant Freshwater Lobster *Astacopsis gouldi* (Decapoda: Parastacidae). *Biological Conservation* 69:199–206.

IUCN 2010. The *IUCN Red List of Threatened Species.* 2010.1 www.iucnredlist.org

IUCN/SSC. 2004. Red List Assessments of Madagascar's Freshwater Fish. http://intranet.iucn.org/webfiles/doc/SpeciesProg/FBU/IUCN_Madagascar_freshwater_fish_2004.pdf

Jackson, C. R. 2006. Wetland Hydrology. *Ecology of freshwater and estuarine wetlands.* D. P. Batzer and R. R. Sharitz, eds. 43–81. Berkeley, CA, University of California Press.

Jackson, R. B., S. R. Carpenter, C. N. Dahm, D. M. McKnight, R. J. Naiman, S. L. Postel and S.W. Running. 2001. Water in a Changing World. *Ecological Applications* 11:1027–1045.

Jelks, H. L., S. J. Walsh, N. M. Burkhead, S. Contreras Balderas, E. Díaz-Pardo, D. A. Hendrickson, J. Lyons, N. E. Mandrak, F. McCormick, J. S. Nelson, S. P. Platania, B. A. Porter, C. B. Renaud, J. J. Schmitter-Soto, E. B. Taylor and M. L. Warren. 2008. Conservation Status of Imperiled North American Freshwater and Diadromous Fishes. *Fisheries* 33:372–407.

Jobling, S., M. Nolan, C. R. Tyler, G. Brighty, and J. P. Sumpter. 1998. Widespread Sexual Disruption in Wild Fish. *Environmental Science & Technology* 32:2498–2506.

Kalkman, V., V. Clausnitzer, B. Klaas-Douwe, A. G. Dijkstra, D.R. Orr, and J. v. T. Paulson. 2008. Global Diversity of Dragonflies (Odonata) in Freshwater. *Hydrobiologia* 595:351–363.

Karr, J. R., and D. R. Dudley. 1981. Ecological Perspective on Water Quality Goals. *Environmental Management* 5:55–68.

Kottelat, M., and J. Freyhof. 2007. *Handbook of European Freshwater Fishes.* Cornal, Switzerland, Publications Kottelat.

Kundzewicz, Z. W., L. J. Mata, N. Arnell, P. Döll, B. Jiménez, K. Miller, T. Oki, Z. en and I. Shiklomanov. 2008. The Implications of Projected Climate Change for Freshwater Resources and Their Management. *Hydrological Sciences Journal/Journal des sciences hydrologiques* 53:3–10.

Kura, Y., C. Revenga, E. Hocino, and G. Mock. 2004. Fishing for Answers: Making Sense of the Global Fish Crisis. Washington DC, World Resources Institute.

Lake, P. S., M. A. Palmer, P. Biro, J. Cole, A. P. Covich, C. Dahm, J. Gibert, W. Goedkoop, K. Martens and J. Verhoeven. 2000. Global Change and the Biodiversity of Freshwater Ecosystems: Impacts on Linkages Between Above-sediment and Sediment Biota. *Bioscience* 50:1099–1107.

Larned, S. T., T. Daltry, D. B. Arscott and K. Tockner. 2010. Emerging Concepts in Temporary River Ecology. *Freshwater Biology* 55:717–738.

Lévêque, C., T. Oberdorff, D. Paugy, M. L. J. Stiassny and P. A. Tedesco. 2008. Global Diversity of Fish (Pisces) in Freshwater. *Hydrobiologia* 595:545–567.

Levshina, S. I., N. N. Efimov and V.N. Bazarkin. 2009. Assessment of the Amur River Ecosystem Pollution with Benzene and Its Derivatives Caused by an Accident at the Chemical Plant in Jilin City, China. *Bulletin of Environmental Contamination and Toxicology* 83:776–779.

Lydeard, C., R. H. Cowie, W. F. Ponder, A. E. Bogan, P. Bouchet, S. A. Clark, K. S. Cummings, T. J. Frest, O. Gargominy, D. G. Herbert, R. Hershler, K. E. Perez, B. Roth, M. Seddon, E. E. Strong and F. G. Thompson. 2004. The Global Decline of Non-marine Mollusks. *BioScience.* 54(4):321–330.

Lysne, S. J., K. E. Perez, K. M. Brown, R. L. Minton and J. D. Sides. 2008. A Review of Freshwater Gastropod Conservation: Challenges and Opportunities. *Journal of the North American Benthological Society* 27(2):463–470.

Malmqvist, B. and S. Rundle. 2002. Threats to the Running Water Ecosystems of the World. *Environmental Conservation* 29:134–153.

Malone, T. C., D. J. Conley, T. R. Fisher, P. M. Glibert, L. W. Harding and K. G. Sellner. 1996. Scales of Nutrient-limited Phytoplankton Productivity in Chesapeake Bay. *Estuaries* 19:371–385.

Maser, C. and J. R. Sedell. 1994. *From the Forest to the Sea: The Ecology of Wood in Streams, Rivers, Estuaries, and Oceans.* Delray Beach, Florida, St. Lucie Press.

Master, L. L., B. A. Stein, L. S. Kutner and G. A. Hammerson. 2000. Vanishing Assets: Conservation Status of U.S. Species. *Precious Heritage: The Status of Biodiversity in the United States.* Stein, B. A., L. S. Kutner and J.S. Adams, eds. 93–118. New York: Oxford University Press.

Matthews, J. H., T. Le Quesne, R. Wilby, G. Pegram, C. Von der Heyden, A. J. Wickel, J. Hartmann, C. McSweeney, C. Guthrie, G. Blate, G. Kimura de Frietas and E. Levine. 2009. *Flowing Forward: Informing Climate-resilient Biodiversity Conservation and Integrated Water Resources Management Decisions*. Washington, DC, The World Bank.

Matthews, J. H., and A. J. Wickel. 2009. Embracing Uncertainty in Freshwater Climate Change Adaptation: A Natural History Approach. *Climate and Development* 1:269–279.

Mills, L. J. and C. Chichester. 2005. Review of Evidence: Are Endocrine-disrupting Chemicals in the Aquatic Environment Impacting Fish Populations? *Science of the Total Environment* 343:1–34.

Milly, P. C. D., J. Betancourt, M. Falkenmark, R. M. Hirsch, Z. W. Kundzewicz, D. P. Lettenmaier and R. J. Stouffer. 2008. Stationarity Is Dead: Whither Water Management? *Science* 319:573–574.

Mohseni, O., H. G. Stefan and J. G. Eaton. 2003. Global Warming and Potential Changes in Fish Habitat in US Streams. *Climatic Change* 59:389–409.

NatureServe. 2010. NatureServe Explorere. An Online Encyclopedia of Life. http://www.natureserve.org/explorer/.

Neill, C., L. A. Deegan, S. M. Thomas, C. L. Haupert, A. V. Krusche, V. M. Ballester and R. L. Victoria. 2006. Deforestation Alters the Hydraulic and Biogeochemical Characteristics of Small Lowland Amazonian Streams. *Hydrological Processes* 20:2563–2580.

Nel, J. L., D. J. Roux, R. Abell, P. J. Ashton, R. M. Cowling, J. V. Higgins, M. Thieme and J.H. Viers. 2009. Progress and Challenges in Freshwater Conservation Planning. *Aquatic Conservation: Marine and Freshwater Ecosystems* 19:474–485.

Neves, R. J., A. E. Bogan, J. D. Williams, S. A. Ahlstedt and P. W. Hartfield. 1997. Status of Aquatic Mollusks in the Southeastern United States: A Downward Spiral of Diversity. *Aquatic*

Fauna in Peril: The Southeastern Perspective. G. W. Benz and D. E. Collins, eds. 43–85. Southeast Aquatic Research Institute Special Publication 1, Decatur, Georgia, Lenz Design and Communications.

Nilsson, C., C. A. Reidy, M. Dynesius and C. Revenga. 2005. Fragmentation and Flow Regulation of the World's Large River Systems. *Science* 308:405–408.

Olden, J. D., M. J. Kennard and B. J. Pusey. 2008. Species Invasions and the Changing Biogeography of Australian Freshwater Fishes. *Global Ecology and Biogeography* 17:25–37.

Olden, J. D. and N. L. Poff. 2005. Long-term Trends in Native and Non-native Fish Faunas of the American Southwest. *Animal Biodiversity and Conservation* 28:75–89.

Ormerod, S. J., M. Dobson, A. G. Hildrew and C. R. Townsend. 2010. Multiple Stressors in Freshwater Ecosystems. *Freshwater Biology* 55:1–4.

Palmer, M. A., E. S. Bernhardt, W. H. Schlesinger, K. N. Eshleman, E. Foufoula-Georgiou, M. S. Hendryx, A. D. Lemly, G. E. Likens, O. L. Loucks, M. E. Power, P. S. White and P. R. Wilcock. 2010. Mountaintop Mining Consequences. *Science* 327:148–149.

Perez, K. E. and R. L. Minton. 2008. Practical Implications for Systematics and Taxonomy in North American Freshwater Gastropod Conservation. *Journal of the North American Benthological Society* 27(2):471–483.

Pikitch, E. K., P. Doukakis, L. Lauck, P. Chakrabarty,and D. L. Erickson. 2005. Status, Trends and Management of Sturgeon and Paddlefish Fisheries. *Fish and Fisheries* 6:233–265.

Pimentel, D., S. McNair, J. Janecka, J. Wightman, C. Simmonds, C. O'Connell, E. Wong, L. Russel, J. Zern, T. Aquino and T. Tsomondo. 2001. Economic and Environmental Threats of Alien Plant, Animal, and Microbe Invasions. *Agriculture, Ecosystems and Environment* 84:1–20.

Pimentel, D., R. Zuniga and D. Morrison. 2005. Update on the Environmental and Economic Costs

Associated with Alien-invasive Species in the United States. *Ecological Economics* 52:273–288.

Poff, N. L., J. D. Allan, M. B. Bain, J. R. Karr, K. L. Prestegaard, B. D. Richter, R. E. Sparks and J. C. Stromberg. 1997. The Natural Flow Regime: A Paradigm for River Conservation and Restoration. *BioScience* 47:769–784.

Postel, S. L. 2003. Securing Water for People, Crops, and Ecosystems: New Mindset and New Priorities. *Natural Resources Forum* 27:89–98.

Pringle, C. M., M. C. Freeman and B. J. Freeman. 2000. Regional Effects of Hydrologic Alterations on Riverine Microbiota in the New World: Tropical-Temperate Comparisons. *BioScience* 50:807–823.

Rahel, F. J. 2000. Homogenization of Fish Faunas Across the United States. *Science* 288:854–856.

Ricciardi, A. and J. B. Rasmussen. 1999. Extinction Rates of North American Freshwater Fauna. *Conservation Biology* 13:1220–1222.

Riservato, E., J.-P. Boudot, S. Ferreira, M. Jovi , V. J. Kalkman, W. Schneider, B. Samraoui, and A. Cuttelod, eds. 2009. *The Status and Distribution of Dragonflies in the Mediterranean*. Gland, Switzerland and Malaga, Spain: IUCN.

Rosenzweig, C., G. Casassa, D.J. Karoly, A. Imeson, C. Liu, A. Menzel, S. Rawlins, T.L. Root, B. Seguin, P. Tryjanowski and C. E. Hanson. 2007. Assessment of Observed Changes and Responses in Natural and Managed Systems. *Climate Change 2007: Impacts, Adaptation and Vulnerability. Contribution of Working Group II to the Fourth Assessment Report of the Intergovernmental Panel on Climate Change*. M. L. Parry, O. F. Canziani, J. P. Palutikof and P. J. van der Linden, eds. 79–131. Cambridge, UK: Cambridge University Press.

Schindler, D. W. and J. P. Smol. 2006. Cumulative Effects of Climate Warming and Other Human Activities on Freshwaters of Arctic and Subarctic North America. *Ambio* 35:160–168.

Schipper, J., J. S.Chanson, F. Chiozza, N. A. Cox, M. Hoffmann, V. Katariya, J. Lamoreux, A. S. L.

Rodrigues, S. N. Stuart, H. J. Temple, J. Baillie, L. Boitani, T. E. Lacher, R. A. Mittermeier, A. T. Smith, D. Absolon, J. M. Aguiar, G. Amori, N. Bakkour, R. Baldi, R. J. Berridge, J. Bielby, P. A. Black, J. Blanc, T. M. Brooks, J. A. Burton, T. M. Butynski, G. Catullo, R. Chapman, Z. Cokeliss, B. Collen, J. Conroy, J. G. Cooke, G. A. B. da Fonseca, A. E. Derocher, H. T. Dublin, J. W. Duckworth, L. Emmons, R. H. Emslie, M. Festa-Bianchet, M. Foster, S. Foster, D. L. Garshelis, C. Gates, M. Gimenez-Dixon, S. Gonzalez, J. F. Gonzalez-Maya, T. C. Good, G. Hammerson, P. S. Hammond, D. Happold, M. Happold, J. Hare, R. B. Harris, C. E. Hawkins, M. Haywood, L. R. Heaney, S. Hedges, K. M. Helgen, C. Hilton-Taylor, S. A. Ainul Hussain, N. Ishii, T. A. Jefferson, R. K. B. Jenkins, C. H. Johnston, M. Keith, J. Kingdon, D. H. Knox, K. M. Kovacs, P. Langhammer, K. Leus, R. Lewison, G. Lichtenstein, L. F. Lowry, Z. Macavoy, G. M. Mace, D. P. Mallon, M. Masi, M. W. McKnight, R. A. Medellín, P. Medici, G. Mills, P.D. Moehlman, S. Molur, A. Mora, K. Nowell, J. F. Oates, W. Olech, W. R. L. Oliver, M. Oprea, B. D. Patterson, W. F. Perrin, B. A. Polidoro, C. Pollock, A. Powel, Y. Protas, P. Racey, J. Ragle, P. Ramani, G. Rathbun, R. R Reeves, S. B Reilly, J. E. Reynolds, C. Rondinini, R. G.Rosell-Ambal, M. Rulli, A. B. Rylands, S. Savini, C. J. Schank, W. Sechrest, C. Self-Sullivan, A. Shoemaker, C. Sillero-Zubiri, N. De Silva, D. E. Smith, C. Srinivasulu, P. J. Stephenson, P. van Strien, B. K. Talukdar, B. L. Taylor, R. Timmins, D. G. Tirira, M. F. Tognelli, K. Tsytsulina, L. M. Veiga, J.-C. Vié, E. A. Williamson, S. A. Wyatt, Y. Xie and B. E. Young. 2008. The Status of the World's Terrestial and Aquatic Mammals. *Science* 322 (5899) 225-230

Scholes, R. J., G. M. Mace, W. Turner, G. N. Geller, N. Jürgens, A. Larigauderie, D. Muchoney, B. A. Walther and H.A. Mooney. 2008. Toward a Global Biodiversity Observing System. *Science* 321:1044-1045.

Shiklomanov, I. A. 2000. Appraisal and Assessment of World Water Resources. *Water International* 25:11-32. Smith, K. G., and W. R. T. Darwall, eds. 2006. *The Status and Distribution of Freshwater Fish Endemic to the Mediterranean Basin.* Gland, Switzerland and Cambridge, UK: IUCN.

Smith, S. V., W. H. Renwick, J. D. Bartley, and R. D. Buddemeir. 2002. Distribution and Significance of Small, Artificial Water Bodies Across the United States Landscape. *Science of the Total Environment* 299:21-36.

Stein, B. A., L. S. Kutner and J. S. Adams, eds. 2000. *Precious Heritage: The Status of Biodiversity in the United States.* New York: Oxford University Press.

Stiassny, M. L. J. 1999. The Medium is the Message: Freshwater Biodiversity in Peril. *The Living Planet in Crisis: Biodiversity Science and Policy.* Cracraft, J. and F. T. Grifo, eds. 53-71 USA : Columbia University Press.

Strayer, D. L. 2006. Challenges For Freshwater Invertebrate Conservation. *Journal of the North American Benthological Society* 25(2):271-287.

Strayer, D. L. 2009. Twenty Years of Zebra Mussels: Lessons From the Mollusk That Made Headlines. *Frontiers in Ecology and the Environment* 7:135-141.

Strayer, D. L. 2010. Alien Species in Fresh Waters: Ecological Effects, Interactions With Other Stressors, and Prospects for the Future. *Freshwater Biology* 55:152-174.

Strayer, D. L., J.A. Downing, W. R. Haag, T. L. King, J. B. Layzer, T. J. Newton and S. J. Nichols. 2004. Pearly Mussels, North America's Most Imperiled Animals. *BioScience.* 54(5):429-439.

Stuart, S. N., J. S. Chanson, N. A. Cox, B. Young, A. S. L. Rodrigues, D. L. Fischman and R. W. Waller. 2004. Status and Trends of Amphibian Declines and Extinctions Worldwide. *Science* 306:1783-1786.

Stuart, S., M.Hoffmann, J. S.Chanson, N. A. Cox, R. J. Berridge, P. Ramani and B. E. Young, eds. 2008. *Threatened Amphibians of the World.* Barcelona: Lynx Edicions; Gland, Switzerland: IUCN and Arlington, Virgina, USA: Conservation International.

Taylor, B. W., A. S. Flecker and R. O. J. Hall. 2006. Loss of a Harvested Fish Species Disrupts

Carbon Flow in a Diverse Tropical River. *Science* 313:833-836.

Tockner, K., S. E. Bunn, C. Gordon, R. J. Naiman, G. P. Quinn and J. A. Stanford. 2008. Flood Plains: Critically Threatened Ecosystems. *Aquatic Ecosystems.* N. Polunin, ed. 45-61. Cambridge, UK: Cambridge University Press.

Tockner, K., U. Uehlinger and C. T. Robinson, eds. 2009. *Rivers of Europe.* Elsevier/Academic Press, San Diego, USA.

Tognelli, M. F., K. Tsytsulina, L. M. Veiga, J.-C. Vié, E. A. Williamson, S. A. Wyatt, Y. Xie and B.E. Young. 2008. The Status of the World's Terrestrial and Aquatic Mammals. *Science.* 322(5899):225-230.

Totten, M. 2008. Global Hydropower and Hydrodams (unpublished).

Turtle Taxonomy Working Group [A. G. J. Rhodon, J. F. Parham, P. P. van Dijk and J. B. Iverson]. 2009. Turtles of the World: Annotated Checklist of Taxonomy and Synonymy, 2009 Update, with Conservation Status Summary. *Chelonian Research Monographs* 5:39-84.

Vié, J.-C., C. Hilton-Taylor and S. N. Stuart, eds. 2009. *Wildlife in a changing world: an analysis of the 2008 Red List of Threatened Species.* Gland, Switzerland: IUCN.

Vörösmarty , C. J., M. Meybeck, B. Fekete, K. Sharma, P. Green and J. P. M. Syvitski. 2003. Anthropogenic Sediment Retention: Major Global Impact From Registered River Impoundments. *Global and Planetary Change* 39:169-190.

Vörösmarty, C. J., D. Lettenmaier, C. Lévêque, M. Meybeck, C. Pahl-Wostl, J. Alcamo, W. Cosgrove, H. Grassl, H. Hoff, P. Kabat, F. Lansigan, R. Lawford and R. Naiman. 2004. Humans Transforming the Global Water System. *Eos AGU Transactions* 85:513-514

Walsh, C. J., A. H. Roy, J. W. Feminella, P. D. Cottingham, P. M. Groffman and R. P. Morgan. 2005. The Urban Stream Syndrome: Current Knowledge and the Search for a Cure. *Journal of the North American Benthological Society,* 24:706–723.

Wang, H. J. and J. Q. Sun. 2009. Variability of Northeast China River Break-up Date. *Advances in Atmospheric Sciences* 26:701–706.

Williams, J. D., M. L.Warren Jr., K. S. Cummings, J. L. Harris and R. J. Neves. 1993. Conservation Status of Freshwater Mussels of the United States and Canada. *Fisheries.* 18(9):6–22.

Williamson, M. and A. Fitter. 1996. The Varying Success of Invaders. *Ecology* 77:1661–1666.

Witte, F., J. H. Wanink and M. Kishe-Machumu. 2007. Species Distinction and the Biodiversity Crisis in Lake Victoria. *Transactions of the American Fisheries Society* 136:1146–1159.

Wondzell, S. M., and P. A. Bisson. 2003. Influence of Wood and Aquatic Biodiversity. *The Ecology and Management of Wood in World Rivers.* S. Gregory, K. Boyer and A. Gurnell, eds. 249–264. Bethesda, Maryland, USA: American Fisheries Society.

World Commission on Dams. 2000. *Dams and Development: A New Framework for Decision-Making.* London, UK and Sterling, VA, USA: Earthscan Publications Ltd.

Xenopouloś, M. A., D. M. Lodge, J. Alcamo, M. Marker, K. Schulze and D. P. van Vuuren. 2005. Scenarios of Freshwater Fish Extinctions From Climate Change and Water Withdrawal. *Global Change Biology* 11:1557–1564.

Young, W. J., F. M. Marston and J. R. Davis. 1996. Nutrient Exports and Land Use in Australian Catchments. *Journal of Environmental Management* 47:165–183.

CHAPTER FOUR:

PROTECTED AREAS FOR
FRESHWATER ECOSYSTEMS:
ESSENTIAL BUT
UNDERREPRESENTED

Abell R. A., J. D. Allan and B. Lehner. 2007. Unlocking the potential of protected areas for freshwaters. *Biological Conservation* 134: 48–63.

Abell R. A., M. Thieme, C. Revenga, et al. 2008. Freshwater ecoregions of the world: a new map of biogeographic units for freshwater biodiversity conservation. *BioScience* 58: 403–414.

Allan, J. D., R. A. Abell, Z. Hogan, et al. 2005. Overfishing of inland waters. *BioScience* 55:1041–1051.

Amis, M. A. M. Rouget, M. Lotter and J. Day. 2009. Integrating freshwater and terrestrial priorities in conservation planning. *Biological Conservation* 142:2217– 2226.

Balian, E. V., H. Segers, C. Lévêque and K. Martens. 2008. The freshwater animal diversity assessment: an overview of the results. 595:627–637.

Beintema, A. J., J. van der Kamp and B. Kone (éds.). 2007. Les forêts inondées: trésors du Delta Intérieur du Niger au Mali. A&W-report 964. Altenburg &Wymenga conseillers écologiques, Veenwouden. Wetlands International, Sévaré. Pays-Bas/Mali .

Canadian Heritage Rivers Board. 2009. The Canadian Heritage Rivers System. Annual Report 2008-2009. Minister of Public Works and Government Services Canada, Ottawa.

Crivelli, A. J., 2002. The role of protected areas in freshwater fish conservation. *Conservation of Freshwater Fishes: Options for the Future* 373–388. M. J. Collares-Pereira, I. G. Cowx, M. M. Coelho, eds.. Fishing News Books, Oxford, UK.

Dudgeon D, A. H. Arthington, M. O. Gessner, et al. 2006. Freshwater biodiversity: importance, threats, status and conservation challenges. *Biological Reviews* 81: 163–182.

Dudley, N., ed. (2008). Guidelines for Applying Protected Area Management Categories. Gland, Switzerland: IUCN. x + 86pp. http://www.iucn.org/about/union/commissions/wcpa/wcpa_puball/wcpa_pubsubj ect/wcpa_categoriespub/?1662/Guidelines-for-applying-protected-area-management-categories

Esselman, P. C. and J. D. Allan. 2010. Application of species distribution models and conservation planning software to the design of a reserve network for the riverine fishes of northeastern Mesoamerica. *Freshwater Biology* (in press).

Finlayson, C. M. and R. D'Cruz. 2005. A conceptual framework for the wise use of wetlands and the maintenance of their ecological character. Chapter 20 (Inland Water Systems, current state and trends).

Gilman, R. T., R. A. Abell and C. E. Williams. 2004. How can conservation biology inform the practice of Integrated River Basin Management? *Journal of River Basin Management* 2:135–148.

Herbert M. E., P. B. McIntyre, P. Doran, J. D. Allan and R. Abell. 2010. How well do Terrestrial Reserve Networks Represent Aquatic Ecosystems? *Conservation Biology* DOI: 10.1111/j.1523-1739.2010.01460.x

IUCN-WCPA. WCPA Freshwater and Protected Areas Task Force. 2008. Online document: http://www.iucn.org/about/union/commissions/wcpa/wcpa_what/wcpa_conservin gsd/wcpa_freshwalert/. Accessed 10 March 2010.

Jenkins A. P., S. D. Jupiter, I. Qauqau and J. Atherton. 2010. The importance of ecosystem-based management for conserving aquatic migratory pathways on tropical high islands: a case study from Fiji. *Aquatic Conservation: Marine and Freshwater Ecosystems* 20:224–238.

Jenkins, C. N. and L. Joppa (2009). Expansion of the global terrestrial protected area system. *Biological Conservation* 142(10):2166–2174.

Joosten H. and Wetlands International (www.wetlands.org). 2009. The Global Peatland CO2 Picture: Peatland status and drainage related emissions in all countries of the world.

Kingsford, R. T. and R. F. Thomas. 1995. The Macquarie Marshes in Arid Australia and their waterbirds: A 50-year history of decline. *Environmental Management* 19(6): 867–878.

Kingsford, R. T. 2000. Review: Ecological impacts of dams, water diversions and river management on floodplain wetlands in Australia. *Austral Ecology* 25:109–127.

Linke S., R. L. Pressey, R. C. Bailey and R. H. Norris. 2007. Management options for river conservation planning: condition and conservation re-visited. *Freshwater Biology* 52: 918–938.

Margules C. R. and R. L. Pressey. 2000. Systematic conservation planning. *Nature* 405(6783):243–253.

Moilanen, A., J. Leathwick and J. Elith. 2008. A method for spatial freshwater conservation prioritization. *Freshwater Biology* 53:577–592.

National Wild and Scenic Rivers. Online document: http://www.rivers.gov/publications/rivers-table.pdf. Accessed 10 March 2010.

Nel J. L., D. J. Roux, G. Maree, et al. 2007. Rivers in peril inside and outside protected areas: A systematic approach to conservation assessment of river ecosystems. *Diversity and Distributions* 13: 341–352.

Nel, J. L., D. J. Roux, R. A. Abell, et al. 2009. Progress and challenges in freshwater conservation planning. *Aquatic Conservation: Marine and Freshwater Ecosystems* 19: 474–485.

Nilsson, C., C. A. Reidy, M. Dynesius and C. Revenga. 2005. Fragmentation and flow regulation of the world's large river systems. *Science* 308:405–408.

Pace, M. L., J. J. Cole, S. R.Carpenter, et al. 2004. Whole-lake carbon: 13 additions reveal terrestrial support of aquatic food webs. *Nature* 427: 240–243.

Parish, F., A. Sirin, D. Charman, et al., eds. 2008. Assessment on Peatlands, Biodiversity and Climate Change: Main Report. Global Environment Centre, Kuala Lumpur and Wetlands International, Wageningen.

Reinthal, P. 1993. Evaluating biodiversity and conserving Lake Malawi's cichlid fish fauna. *Conservation Biology* 7:712–718.

Roux D. J., J. L. Nel, P. J. Ashton, et al. 2008. Designing protected areas to conserve riverine biodiversity: Lessons from a hypothetical redesign of the Kruger National Park. *Biological Conservation* 141:100 –117.

Ricciardi, A. and J. B. Rasmussen.1999. Extinction rates of North American freshwater fauna. *Conservation Biology* 13:1220–1222.

Sarkar S., R. L. Pressey, D. P.Faith, et al. 2006. Biodiversity conservation planning tools: Present status and challenges for the future. *Annual Review of Environment and Resources* 31:123–159.

Sowa S. P., G. Annis, M. E. Morey and D. D. Diamond. 2007. A GAP analysis and comprehensive conservation strategy for riverine ecosystems of Missouri. *Ecological Monographs* 77: 301–334.

Thieme, M., B. Lehner, R. Abell, et al. 2007. Freshwater conservation planning in data-poor areas: An example from a remote Amazonian basin (Madre de Dios River, Peru and Bolivia). *Biological Conservation* 135:484–501.

Tochner, K and J. A. Stanford. 2002. Riverine flood plains: present state and future trends. *Environmental Conservation* 29:308–330.

van Eijk, P. and R. Kumar. 2009. Bio-rights in theory and practice. A financing mechanism for linking poverty alleviation and environmental conservation. Wetlands International, Wageningen, The Netherlands.

Wetlands International, 2009. Planting trees to eat fish: Field experiences in wetlands and poverty reduction (pp55–63). Wetlands International, Wageningen, The Netherlands.

Wetlands International. 2006. Waterbird Population Estimates: Fourth Edition. Wetlands International, Wageningen, The Netherlands.

CHAPTER FIVE:
FRESHWATER ECOSYSTEM SERVICES: ESSENTIAL FOR HUMAN WELL-BEING

Allan, J. D., R. Abell, Z. Hogan, C. Revenga, B. W. Taylor, R. L. Welcomme and K. Winemiller. 2005. Overfishing of Inland Waters. *BioScience.* 55:1041–1051.

Baran, E. 2005. Cambodian inland fisheries: Facts, figures, and context. Worldfish Center and Inland Fisheries Research and Development Institute. Phnom Penh, Cambodia.

Baron, J. S., N. L. R. Poff, P. L. Angermeier, C. N. Dahm, P. H. Gleick, N. G. Hairston, Jr., R. B. Jackson, C. A. Johnston, B. D. Richter and A.D. Steinman. 2002. Meeting Ecological and Societal Needs for Freshwater. *Ecological Applications.* 12(5):247–1260.

Bates, B. C., Z. W. Kundzewicz, S. Wu and J. P. Palutikof, eds. 2008. Climate Change and Water. Technical Paper of the Intergovernmental Panel on Climate Change. Geneva, IPCC Secretariat.

Barbier, E. 1994. Valuing Environmental Functions: Tropical Wetlands. *Land Economics.* 70(2):155–73.

Batker, D. 2010. Discussion on the Review of Ecosystem Service Valuation Studies in the Ecosystem Service Database. Earth Economics, Seattle, Washington, March 31, 2010.

Bogan, A. E. 2008. Global Diversity of Freshwater Mussels (Mollusca, Bivalvia) in Freshwater. *Hydrobiologia.* 595:139–147.

Bradshaw, C. J. A., B. W. Brook, K. S.-H. Peh and N.S. Sodhi. 2009. Flooding Policy Makers with Evidence to Save Forests. *Ambio.* 38(2):125–126.

Braga, M. I. J. 1999. Integrating Freshwater Ecosystem Function and Services with Water Development Projects. Environment Division, Sustainable Development Department. Inter-American Development Bank, Washington, DC.

Right: Thunderstorm forming over farmhouse along Thunder Basin National Grasslands, Powder River Basin, Northeastern Wyoming, USA.—Morgan Heim

Bunn, S. E. and A. H. Arthington. 2002. Basic Principles and Ecological Consequences of Altered Flow Regimes for Aquatic Biodiversity. *Environmental Management.* 30:492–507.

Cassman, K. G. and S. Wood. 2005. Cultivated Systems. *Ecosystems and Human Well-Being.* 1:745–794. *Current State and Trends, Millennium Ecosystem Assessment.* R. Hassan, R. Scholes and N. Ash, eds. Washington, DC: Island Press.

Chambers, P. A., P. Lacoul, K. J. Murphy and S. M. Thomaz. 2008. Global diversity of aquatic macrophytes in freshwater. *Hydrobiologia* 59(5): 9–26.

Comprehensive Assessment of Water Management in Agriculture (CAoWMiA). 2007. *Water for Food, Water for Life: A Comprehensive Assessment of Water Management in Agriculture.* London: Earthscan and Colombo: International Water Management Institute.

Costanza, R., O. Perez-Maqueo, M. L. Martinez, P. Sutton, S. J. Anderson and K. Mulder. 2008. The Value of Coastal Wetlands for Hurricane Protection. *Ambio 37.* 9:241–248.

Daily, G. C. 1997. *Nature's Services: Societal Dependence on Natural Ecosystems.* Washington, DC: Island Press.

Dugan, P., V. V. Sugunan, R. L. Welcomme, C. Bene, R. E. Brummett, M. C. M. K. Beveridge, A. Amerasinghe, U. Arthington, A. Blixt, M. Chimatiro, S. Katiha, P. King, J. Kolding, J. Khoa, S. Nguyen and J.Turpie. 2007. Inland fisheries and Aquaculture. 459–483. *Water for Food, Water for Life: A Comprehensive Assessment of Water Management in Agriculture.* Molden, D., ed. London, UK and Colombo, Sri Lanka: Earthscan.

Emerton, L., N. Erdenesaikhan, B. de Veen, D. Tsogoo, L. Janchivdorj, P. Suvd, B. Enkhtsetseg, G. Gandolgor, Ch. Dorjsuren, D. Sainbayar and A. Enkhbaatar. 2009. The Economic Value of the Upper Tuul Ecosystem in Mongolia. The World Bank, Washington, DC.

Emerton, L. 2005. Values and Rewards: Counting and Capturing Ecosystem Water Services for Sustainable Development. IUCN Water, Nature and Economics Technical Paper No. 1, IUCN-The World Conservation Union, Ecosystems and Livelihoods Group Asia. http://cmsdata.iucn.org/downloads/2005_047.pdf.

Emerton, L. and E. Bos. 2004. VALUE: Counting Ecosystems as Water Infrastructure. IUCN-The World Conservation Union. Gland, Switzerland. http://data.iucn.org/dbtw-wpd/edocs/2004-046.pdf.

Espinosa, C. 2005. Payment for Water-Based Environmental Services: Ecuador's Experiences, Lessons Learned and Ways Forward. IUCN Water, Nature and Economics Technical Paper No. 2. IUCN-The World Conservation Union, Ecosystems and Livelihoods Group Asia. Colombo.

Finlayson, M., R. D'Cruz, N. Aladin, D.R. Barker, G. Beltram, J. Brouwer, N. Davidson, L. Duker, W. Junk, M. D. Kaplowitz, H. Ketelaars, E. Kreuzberg-Mukhina, G. de la Lanza Espino, C. Lévêque, A. Lopez, R. G. Milton, P. Mirabzadeh, D. Pritchard, C. Revenga, M. Rivera, A. S. Hussainy, M. Silvius and M. Steinkamp. 2006. Inland Water Systems. Ecosystems and human well-being. Vol.1 Current State and Trends. Scholes R., H. R. and N. Ash, eds. 551–583. Millennium Ecosystem Assessment. Washington, DC: Island Press.

Froese, R. and D. Pauly. 2010. FishBase. Version 01/2020. www.fishbase.org.

Food and Agriculture Organization of the United Nations (FAO). 2004. The State of World Fisheries and Aquaculture. Rome, Italy: FAO.

Food and Agriculture Organization of the United Nations (FAO). 2006. Global Forest Resources Assessment 2005. Rome, Italy.

Gallai, N., J-M Salles, J. Settele and B. E. Vaissière. 2007. Economic valuation of the vulnerability of world agriculture confronted to pollinator decline. Institut National de la Recherche Agronomique, Paris, France.

Helfman, G. S. 2007. Fish Conservation: A Guide to Understanding and Restoring Global Aquatic Biodiversity and Fishery Resources. Washington, DC Island Press.

Hirji, R. and R. Davis, eds. 2009. Environmental Flows in Water Resources Policies, Plans, and Projects. Case studies. The World Bank, Washington, DC.

Howard, J. K. and K. M. Cuffey. 2006. The Functional Role of Native Freshwater Mussels in the Fluvial Benthic Environment. *Freshwater Biology* 51: 460–474.

Inamdar, N., T. A. Farrell, R. A. Mittermeier, C. Hutchinson, J. R. Barborak, S. Matus, A. Aggens, E. Williamson. 2009. Into the Wild: Ecotourism and Recreational Values. *The Wealth of Nature: Ecosystem Services, Biodiversity and Human Well-Being.* J. A. McNeely, R. A. Mittermeier, T. M. Brooks, F. Boltz and N. Ash, eds. 2:63–74. Arlington, VA: CEMEX Conservation Book Series; ILCP.

International Institute for Environment and Development (IIED). 2007. Issues Paper for Discussion in Developing a DFID Research Programme on Water Ecosystem Services and Poverty Reduction Under Climate Change. March 2007.

Jones, J. P. J. R. Rasamy, A. Harvey, A. Toon B. Oidtmann, M. E. Randrianarison N. Raminosoa, O. R. Ravoahangimalala. 2009. The Perfect Invader: A Parthenogenic Crayfish Poses a New Threat to Madagascar's Freshwater Biodiversity. *Biological Invasions.* 11:1475–1482.

LePrieur, F., O. Beauchard, S. Blanchet, T. Oberdorff and S. Brosse. 2008. Fish Invasions in the World's River Systems: When Natural Processes Are Blurred by Human Activities. *PLoS Biology.* 6:404–410.

Li, L., C. Liu and H. Mou. 2000. River Conservation in Central and Eastern Asia 263–280. *Global Perspectives on River Conservation: Science, Policy and Practice.* P. J. Boon, B. R. Davies and G. E. Petts, eds. Chichester, England: John Wiley and Sons.

Loh, J., ed. 2008. 2010 and Beyond. *Rising to the Biodiversity Challenge.* WWF, Gland, Switzerland.

Left: A great egret hunts fish from a small gravel bar in the middle of a former excavated gravel pit. Though great egrets are widely distributed, they are extremely rare visitors to Colorado. This manmade wetland has created habitat inviting enough for the bird. Sawhill Ponds Boulder, Colorado, USA.
—Morgan Heim

Margat, J. and V. Andréassian. 2008. L'eau, les idées reçues. Paris: Editions le Cavalier Bleu.

Millennium Ecosystem Assessment (MEA). 2005a. *Ecosystems and Human Well-Being: Wetlands and Water Synthesis.* Washington, DC: Island Press. Finlayson, C. M., R. D'Cruz and N. Davidson, et al. Washington DC, World Resources Institute.

Millennium Ecosystem Assessment (MEA) 2005b. *Ecosystems and Human Well-Being: Wetlands and Water Synthesis.* World Resources Institute, Washington, DC.

Meybeck, M., P. Green and C. J. Vörösmarty. 2001. A New Typology for Mountains and Other Relief Classes: An Application to Global Continental Water Resources and Population Distribution. *Mountain Research and Development.* 21:34–45.

Mitsch, W. J. and J. G. Gosselink (2000). *Wetlands.* Third edition. New York, John Wiley and Sons, Inc.

Mittermeier, R. A., C. G. Mittermeier, T. M. Brooks, J. D. Pilgrim, W. R. Konstant, G. A. B. da Fonseca and C. Kormos. 2003. Wilderness and Biodiversity Conservation. *Proceedings of the National Academy of Science.* 100:10309– 10313.

Mittermeier, R. A., P. Robles Gil, M. Hoffmann, J. Pilgrim, T. Brooks, C. G. Mittermeier, J. Lamoreux and G. A. B. da Fonseca. 2004. *Hotspots Revisited: Earth's Biologically Richest and Most Endangered Ecoregions.* Mexico City, Mexico: CEMEX.

Myers, N., R. A. Mittermeier, C. G. Mittermeier, G. A. B. da Fonseca and J. Kent. 2000. Biodiversity Hotspots for Conservation Priorities. *Nature.* 403:853–858.

Neiland, A. E., S. Jaffry, B. M. B. Laduc, M. Sarcha and S. P. Madakand. 2000. Inland Fisheries of North East Nigeria Including the Upper River Benue, Lake Chad and the Nguru–Gashua Wetlands: I. Characterisation and Analysis of Planning Suppositions. *Fisheries Research.* 48(3):229–243.

Pearce, D. 1992. Economic Valuation and the Natural World. Centre for Social and Economic Research on the Global Environment. London.

Phillips, M. J., M. B. Reantaso and P. N. Bueno. 2002. Environment, Livelihoods and Indigenous Cold Water Fishes. Cold Water Fisheries in the Trans-Himalayan Countries. Petr, T. and S. B. Swar, eds. 37–46. Food and Agriculture Organization of the United Nations (FAO) Fisheries Technical Paper 431. Rome, Italy: FAO.

Poff, N. L., J. D. Allan, M. B. Bain, J. R. Karr, K. L. Prestegaard, B. D. Richter, R. E. Sparks and J. C. Stromberg. 1997. The natural flow regime: a paradigm for river conservation and restoration. *BioScience* 47: 769–784.

Perrot-Maître, D. and P. Davis. 2001. Case Studies of Markets and Innovative Financial Mechanisms for Water Services from Forests. Forest Trends and World Resources Institute (WRI). Washington, DC.

Postel, S. L. and B. Richter 2003. Rivers for Life: Managing Water for People and Nature. Washington, DC: Island Press.

Ramsar Convention on Wetlands (RAMSAR). 2001. Wetland Values and Functions. The Ramsar Bureau, Gland, Switzerland. http://ramsar.org.

Resource, Environment and Economics Center for Studies (REECS). 2008. Marketing the Environment Through PES. Policy Brief 2008-04. Quezon City: REECS Inc.

Revenga, C. and Y. Kura. 2003. Status and Trends of Biodiversity of Inland Water Ecosystems. Secretariat of the Convention on Biological Diversity, Montreal, Technical Series no. 11.

Richter, B. 2009. Re-thinking Environmental Flows; from Allocations and Reserves to Sustainability Boundaries. *River Research and Applications.* Published online: www.interscience.wiley.com. DOI: 10.1002/rra.1320.
Rojas, M. and B. Aylward. 2002. *Cooperation Between a Small Private Hydropower Producer and a Conservation NGO for Forest Protection: The Case of La Esperanza, Costa Rica.* Land-Water

Linkages in Rural Watersheds Case Study Series. Food and Agriculture Organisation of the United Nations (FAO), Rome.

Sheil, Douglas and Murkiyarso, Daniel. 2009. How Forests Attract Rain: An Examination of a New Hypothesis. *BioScience.* 59(4):341–347.

Shields, F. D. Jr., A. Simon and L. J. Steffen. 2000. Reservoir Effects on Downstream River Channel Migration. *Environmental Conservation.* 27(1):54–66.

Silverman, H., J. Nichols, J. Cherry, E. Archberger, J. Lynn and T. Dietz. 1997. Clearance of Laboratory-Cultured Bacteria by Freshwater Bivalves: Differences Between Lentic and Lotic Unionids. *Canadian Journal of Zoology.* 75:1857–1866.

Strong, E. E., O. Gargominy, W. Ponder and P. Bouchet. 2008. Global Diversity of Gastropods (Gastropoda; Mollusca) in Freshwater. *Hydrobiologia.* 595:149–166.

Syvitski, J. P. M., C. J. Vörösmarty, A. J. Kettner and P. Green. 2005. Impact of Humans on the Flux of Terrestrial Sediment to the Global Coastal Ocean. *Science.* 308(5720):376–380.

The Economics of Ecosystems and Biodiversity (TEEB). 2008. Interim Report on the Economics of Ecosystems and Biodiversity. Ec.europa.eu/environment/nature/biodiversity/economics/.

Vörösmarty, C. J. C. Lévêque and C. Revenga. 2005. Freshwater. *Millennium Ecosystem Assessment (MA), eds.* 165–207. Washington, DC: Island Press

Wallace, J. S., M. C. Acreman and C. A. Sullivan. 2003. The Sharing of Water Between Society and Ecosystems: from Conflict to Catchment-Based Co-Management. *Philosophical Transactions of the Royal Society of London.* B358:2011–2026.

Whittington, R. J. and R. Chong. 2007. Global Trade in Ornamental Fish from an Australian Perspective: The Case for Revised Import Risk Analysis and Management Strategies. *Preventive Veterinary Medicine.* 81(1–3):92–116.

World Meteorological Organization (WMO). 1997. Comprehensive Assessment of the Freshwater Resources of the World. Stockholm, Sweden: WMO and Stockholm Environment Institute.

WWF. 2009. 2010 and Beyond, Rising to the Biodiversity Challenge. *Living Planet Index*. Gland, Switzerland: WWF International.
Wowor, D. and P. K. L. Ng. 2007. The Giant Freshwater Prawns of the *Macrobrachium rosenbergii* Species Group (Crustacea: Decapoda: Caridea: Palaemonidae). *Raffles Bulletin of Zoology*. 55(2): 321–336.

CHAPTER SIX:
FRESH WATER FOR THE FUTURE: POLICY TO SECURE AN ESSENTIAL SERVICE FOR ALL

Bates, B. C., Z. W. Kundzewicz, S. Wu, and J.P. Palutikof, eds. 2008. *Climate Change and Water*. Technical Paper of the Intergovernmental Panel on Climate Change. Geneva: IPCC Secretariat.

Dyson, M., G. Bergkamp and J. Scanlon, eds. 2008. *FLOW – The Essentials of Environmental Flows*, 2nd Edition. Gland, Switzerland: IUCN.

Emerton, L. and E. Bos. 2004. *VALUE – Counting Ecosystems as Water Infrastructure*. Gland, Switzerland. IUCN.

Global Water Partnership and International Network of Basin Organizations (GWP/INBO). 2009. *A Handbook for Integrated Water Resources Management in Basins*. (http://www.oieau.org/IMG/pdf/GWP-INBOHandbookForIWRMinBasins-3.pdf.

International Conference on Water and the Environment (ICWE). 1992. Development Issues for the 21st Century. The Dublin Statement and Report of the Conference. Dublin, Ireland, 26–31 January 1992. Geneva: World Meteorological Organization.

Intergovernmental Panel on Climate Change (IPCC). 2007 *Contribution of Working Group II to the Fourth Assessment Report of the Intergovernmental Panel on Climate Change*. Cambridge and New York: Cambridge University Press.

Iza, A. and R. Stein, eds. 2009. *RULE – Reforming Water Governance*. Gland, Switzerland: IUCN.

Millennium Ecosystem Assessment (MEA). 2005. *Ecosystems and Human Well-Being: Wetlands and Water – Synthesis*. Washington, DC: World Resources Institute.

National Geographic. 2010. Groundwater – Important Underground Sources Are Shrinking. http://environment.nationalgeographic.com/environment/freshwater/grou ndwater/.

Rodell, M., I. Velicogna and J. S. Famiglietti. 2009. Satellite-based estimates of groundwater depletion in India. *Nature*. 460: 999–1002.

Sadoff, C., T. Greiber, M. Smith and G. Bergkamp. 2008. *SHARE – Managing Water Across Boundaries*. Gland, Switzerland: IUCN.

We would also like to thank the photographers who provided images for this book, and to those who devote their lives to documenting the history of conservation on our planet.

ACKNOWLEDGMENTS

Mike Hoffmann (International Union for Conservation of Nature; IUCN-SSC) provided helpful advice on defining the initial scope of the book. Mary Seddon (IUCN Mollusc Specialist Group) provided some helpful initial comments for chapter 1 (A Wealth of Life). Peter Paul van Dijk (Tortoise and Freshwater Turtle Conservation Program, Conservation International) and Claude Gascon (Programs and Science, Conservation International) provided some useful background information that was included in chapter 2 (Aquatic Ecosystems) and chapter 3 (Freshwater Ecosystems under Threat). For chapter 4 (Protected Areas for Freshwater Ecosystems). Bakary Kone (Wetlands International Mali) and Pieter van Eijk (Wetlands International; lead developer of the Bio-rights Approach referenced in that chapter) provided valuable information and input. Work conducted by Leandro Castello and included in chapter 4 was kindly supported by the Gordon and Betty Moore Foundation. Stuart Blanch (coordinator, The Environment Centre Northern Territory) provided the figure showing a visualization of place-based protection for fresh water (fig. 4.1). Frank Larsen (Science and Knowledge, Conservation International) prepared the global maps (fig. 5.1.) for chapter 5 (Freshwater Ecosystem Services). The editors are especially grateful to Colleen M. Vollberg (Freshwater Initiative, Conservation International) for considerable assistance in collating and checking references, figures, tables, and text in early versions of the manuscript, and to Stephen Nash (scientific illustrator, Conservation International) for creating or editing several tables and figures. Ian Harrison is grateful to the American Museum of Natural History, New York, for making its reference library and other resources available to him as a research associate of the Department of Ichthyology.

Opposite Page: Five Wai Wai boys having fun in a boat, Masekenari, Guyana.—Cristina G. Mittermeier

Above: Saut d'Eau is a site of spiritual significance to both Catholic and Vodou worshipers in Haiti. For both religions, the falls are the focus of large pilgrimages, with each including the devotional rite of bathing in the waters. Fresh water features play a critical role in spiritual observances around the globe. —Wade Davis